Warning!

Violence and the Supernatural

A supplement for the Rifts RPG.
Compatible with the entire Palladium Books® Megaverse®!

Dedicated to all our fans who have helped to make **Rifts**® one of the most popular role-playing games of all time! Thank you. We plan on providing many more years of epic adventure and excitement.

The cover painting is Kevin Long's incredible depiction of the laboratories at Mindwerks™. **It is here that the infamous and evil Angel of Death conducts her mind and body altering experiments.**

Other titles in the Rifts® series include:
Rifts® RPG
Rifts® Sourcebook One
Rifts® Sourcebook Two: Mechanoids®
Rifts® Conversion Book One
Rifts® Conversion Book Two: Pantheons of the Megaverse®
Rifts® World Book One: Vampire Kingdoms™
Rifts® World Book Two: Atlantis
Rifts® World Book Three: England
Rifts® World Book Four: Africa
Rifts® World Book Five: Triax™ and the NGR
Rifts® World Book Six: South America
Rifts®: Mercenaries™
Rifts® Dimension Book One: Wormwood™
Rifts® Dimension Book Two: Phaseworld™

Coming in 1995!
Rifts® World Book Seven: Rifts® Undersea
Rifts® Phase World® Sourcebook
Rifts®: The Juicer Uprisings™
Rifts®: Chi-Town World Book
Rifts®: The New West World Book
Rifts®: Lone Star World Book
Rifts® Novels

Other Palladium RPG titles include:
The Compendium of Weapons, Armor, and Castles™
The Compendium of Contemporary Weapons™
The Palladium® RPG
Revised Heroes Unlimited™
Villains Unlimited™
Aliens Unlimited™
Teenage Mutant Ninja Turtles® and Other Strangeness
After the Bomb®
Ninjas and Superspies™
Robotech® RPG
Macross II™ RPG
Beyond the Supernatural™

Second Printing - Febuary 1995

Copyright © 1994 Palladium Books® Inc.
Copyright © 1994 by Kevin Siembieda

Palladium Books, Rifts®, and Megaverse® are registered trademarks owned and licensed by Kevin Siembieda. Triax™, Mindwerks™ and Wormwood™ are trademarks owned by Kevin Siembieda and Palladium Books Inc.

Rifts® Sourcebook Three: Mindwerks is published by Palladium Books Inc., 12455 Universal Drive, Taylor, MI 48180. Printed in the USA.

Palladium Books® Presents:
Rifts® Sourcebook Three ™

Mindwerks

Written By: **Kevin Siembieda**

Senior Editor: **Alex Marciniszyn**

Editors: **Thomas Bartold**
James A. Osten

Cover Painting: **Kevin Long**

Interior Art: **Roger Petersen**
Vince Martin
Kevin Long
Newton Ewell
Kevin Siembieda
Scott Szczesniak
John Livesay

Art Direction & Keylining: **Kevin Siembieda**

Typography: **Maryann Siembieda**

Special Thanks to Roger Petersen and Vince Martin for knocking out some great artwork on a tight deadline. Kevin Long for another dynamic cover. To jet-lag Thom, back from Germany (how about that for irony), Maryann, Jim, Al, Steve, Julius, Dad and the usual gang for all their hard work and dedication.

Table of Contents

Quick Find Table

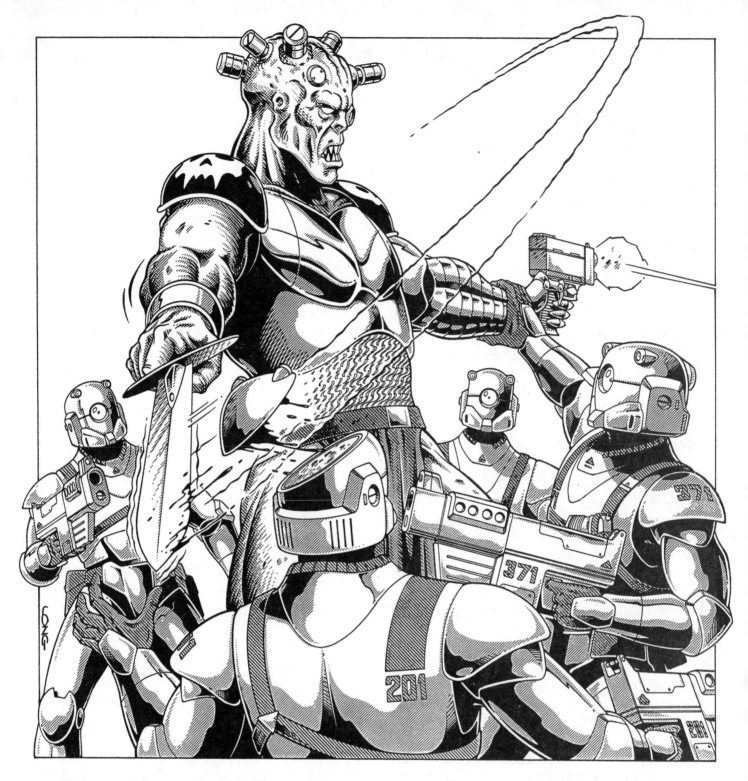

A Few Opening Words

Rifts Mindwerks is specifically a sourcebook for, or more accurately, an extension of **Rifts World Book Five: Triax & The NGR**. In many respects **Mindwerks** is what didn't make it into World Book Five.

Now, that may suggest that the ideas for **Mindwerks** are an after thought. That's the farthest thing from the truth! In fact, the ideas for the Mindwerks complex, The Angel of Death, new M.O.M. implants, psynetics, gene-splicers and the evil Millennium Tree were the source of my original inspiration for doing **Triax and The NGR** in the first place. It was just that I had too many fun and exciting ideas to squeeze into any one book. Add Mister Long's designs for bots, borgs and vehicles and it was a hopeless situation. So, at the very onset of writing **Rifts Triax & The NGR**, I decided to do two or three books dealing

with the technology, conflicts, people and places of Germany and Poland. I simply divided the ideas and combined the material that seemed to be most closely related to each other for inclusion in each respective book.

In **Mindwerks** we see the more sinister and chaotic elements afoot in this part of Europe. What awaits you in the pages to follow are new ideas, technology, magic, mystery, D-bees, villains, transmutation, chaos and insanity. There are enough adventure ideas, sub-plots, intrigue and danger to keep a campaign running for a year (heck, maybe a decade!). Enjoy.

Publication Note: After exploring parts of Europe, Africa and England we're back to the Americas with **Rifts Mercenaries**. This is a big, **Rifts Triax** style book with more bots, borgs, power armor, tanks, aircraft, boats, weapons, transdimensional arms dealers — rivals of the

Splugorth, mercenary characters, Coalition activity, campaign ideas, and more! Believe it or not, **Rifts Mercenaries** is finished and at the printers!! You will find it on store shelves in just a few weeks, the middle of August. Don't miss it!

Rifts South America, Rifts Undersea, Rifts Dimension Book Two: Phase World and even a few **Rifts Novels** (you demanded them) are currently nearing completion and will see publication by the end of 1994. Plus we already have some exciting things planned for 1995. The Palladium Megaverse just keeps expanding with infinite possibilities!

Mindwerks

M.O.M Technology

The origin of **Mindwerks** goes back to the time before the Great Cataclysm, during humankind's technological golden age and man's quest for human augmentation. Companies like Triax, KLS and the Cyberworks Network focused on advancements in robotics, cybernetics and weapon technologies. Others turned their attentions to nano-technology, medicine, chemical/Juicer augmentation, genetic engineering and other avenues of advancement.

The German based company known as **Mindwerks** was building a reputation for itself in the area of robotics and cybernetics. However, it was just one of a thousand corporations trying to carve their niche in the global robotics market. Prior to this, Mindwerks was a small high-tech firm who had pioneered the development of special optics, cameras and sensory equipment for use in aerospace and the science of parapsychology. The owners had an intense interest in psychic phenomena and established a respected research branch dedicated to the study of the paranormal. This operation had loose connections and affiliations with organizations such as the Lazlo Agency and various universities around the world. The corporation's name, Mindwerks, was indicative of its founders' interest in the potential of the human mind.

Consequently, it was not surprising that the Mindwerks people were the first to investigate claims by **Psytronics**, a small South American company, that they had developed brain implants and neuro stimulants that could tap the powers of the human mind. Psytronics called the radical new science *Mind Over Matter technology* or M.O.M. technology. The tiny upstart company and its incredible discoveries might have gone unrecognized and dissolved into bankruptcy without the timely intervention of Mindwerks.

The Germany corporation quickly confirmed Psytronics' claims and struck up a partnership with them. The infusion of Mindwerks' resources enabled Psytronics to continue its revolutionary research and development in South America. Meanwhile, in a bold and financially risky move, Mindwerks put their cybernetic and robotics development on the backburners and immersed themselves in the development of Mind Over Matter technology. They believed that while other companies developed cumbersome mechanical augmentation devices, they would unlock the secrets of the mind and reap financial rewards that would dwarf the competitive cybernetic and robot markets! They dreamed of a new world where many traditional technologies would become obsolete. A world where people would communicate via telepathy, the human body could be molded into physical perfection, disease eradicated, and everybody would possess incredible mental powers. Bionics and robot exo-skeletons would become second-rate alternatives to the natural, liberating powers of the mind unleashed! The possibilities seemed endless.

The early breakthroughs were impressive. Together with their South American partner, Mindwerks seemed to have hit upon the ultimate method of human augmentation. Physical augmentation was made possible through M.O.M. implants that stimulated parts of the brain on command to respond with natural chemical, neurological and electromagnetic energy to make the body stronger and faster. The M.O.M. enhanced individual was given superhuman strength, speed, prowess, endurance, heightened senses, increased healing ability, and resistance to pain and fatigue. The abilities were similar to the popular, chemically enhanced "Juicer," but without the problems of drug dependence, addiction, and eventual death. Mindwerks proudly declared that this was just the beginning! In time, they vowed their brain implants would give mankind control over psychic powers, including total recall, telepathy and telekinesis.

The mass media grabbed the story like a hungry dog with a bone. Overnight, Mindwerks was transformed from a little known cybernetics research and development firm into an innovative giant on the cutting edge of technology. Several governments were knocking down their door with funding for research into the military applications of M.O.M. technology. Rumors about the creation of the ultimate "super spy" were abundant.

For the next decade, Mind Over Matter technology seemed to be the greatest achievement in human augmentation. Brain implants were astonishingly easy to install and there was very little risk of physical injury or rejection. The initial emphasis was on physical augmentation to compete with cyborgs, Juicers and other forms of physical enhancements in humankind's quest for the supreme super-soldier. Psionic enhancements were under development (but would never be perfected). The value of stocks for both Mindwerks and Psytronics skyrocketed! Mindwerks was at the top and they made billions! However, their experiments, even with animals, soon came under fire as dangerous and inhumane. Then disaster struck.

After four or five years of perfect physical and mental health, the recipients of M.O.M. implants began to show aggressive, erratic and anti-social behavior. Mindwerks and Psytronics had successfully pushed for government approval and marketing of the implants without sufficient long-term studies. The initial results were so impressive, seemingly safe, and without any apparent (immediate) side effects, that the two corporations were able to get the patented procedure on the market in only six years. An exhaustive three year study showed no evidence of personality disorders or any dangerous abnormalities. They ignored indications of unusual brain activity and the fact that 20% of the control group (ten volunteers) randomly developed minor psionic abilities as a result of the implants. They had no idea what caused the psychic abilities to manifest themselves nor could they erase them, control or restrict the types of psi-powers that would appear. However, most military interest groups saw these "unexpected" abilities as a bonus, not a detractor, and encouraged the companies to move forward and for the world governments to approve the process.

It was a year after the initial study period and after the process had been approved for military and corporate application, that serious mental aberrations began to appear in the control group. At first, Mindwerks decided that they were random incidents. The several thousand new M.O.M. recipients were as mentally sound as could be. However, over the next five years *all* ten test subjects developed mental and/or emotional problems; some more extreme than others. Worse, many of the thousands who received M.O.M. implants after them also began to show signs of mental instability. The Psytronics Company reported the same findings and had concluded that long-term mental instability was an inevitable side effect of the M.O.M. process. The problem was that most subjects did not show any obvious evidence of mental deterioration until two to four years after the initial implant operation.

All recipients of M.O.M. brain implants suffered from hyper-activity, sleep disorders, and increased aggression or a sense of power that enticed them to be violent or to take unnecessary risks. The worst cases suffered from paranoia, multiple personalities, delusions, obsessions and phobias, among other maladies. The insanities were irreversible, even when the implants were removed. Furthermore, a full 50% of the subjects became suicidal when they were deprived of their implants and the super powers they had grown dependent upon. Equally alarming was the fact that 15% did not survive the removal of the implants. This mortality rate was inexplicable because the actual surgical process was no more dangerous than the initial implanting, which had less than a one percent fatality rate. Some doctors suggested that these patients simply did not want to live without the M.O.M. augmentation and willed themselves to die.

Of course, not all M.O.M. recipients were raving lunatics. In fact, an estimated 65% could lead reasonably normal lives for decades and did not represent an immediate danger to those around them. However, all continued to deteriorate with the passage of time and most would become dangerous. Mindwerks insisted that as many as 50% might never need to be institutionalized (Psytronics figures showed only 15% would escape such a fate). It was the 25% to 50% who would become homicidal maniacs whose lives were destroyed and represented a danger to society. One murderous rampage by a "Crazy" caused 34 million credits' worth of property damage, killed 17 and injured 220 people. Even those who lived comparatively normal and quiet lives were plagued with mental problems and had to be considered living time bombs that could explode at any moment.

Lawsuits flooded the two corporations. Psytronics went bankrupt within five years. Mindwerks lasted another ten but was teetering on the brink of ruin. Nothing they tried could reverse the insanity factor. Nor could they find a way to stop or even slow the mental and emotional deterioration caused by the M.O.M. implants. The corporation's credibility completely shattered, it hardly mattered that they were never able to tap or control the psychic powers of the mind.

One bleak day, a small nuclear exchange in distant South America triggered the eruption of the ley lines and the end of the world as modern man knew it. Dimensional Rifts tore open the fabric of space and time and the world shuddered. With that shudder billions perished and Mindwerks with them. Or so it was believed.

The Dawn of a New Era

As humankind began to claw its way out of the dark ages of devastation that rocked the planet, the secrets of M.O.M. conversion were rediscovered, along with Juicer chemical augmentation, cybernetics and other high-tech secrets from the lost age of human achievement. No one had ever been able to devise brain implants that did not cause mental deterioration, and the rediscovered science seems a bit cruder and insanity a more certain and immediate symptom than ever. Consequently, the warriors of Rifts Earth who submit to *M.O.M. conversion* have come to be known as "Crazies" (see the O.C.C. in the **Rifts RPG**, page 56). Ironically, the process that was co-developed in Germany is banned in the New German Republic. Some German villages and cities won't even allow a crazy within city limits. In and around Germany and Poland, only foolish wilderness folk, adventurers, street punks, D-bees and monsters undergo the mind altering process — most illegal body-chop-shops offer conventional Crazy Conversions. Today, M.O.M. conversions are more available to people in North America than Europe — with two notable and dangerous exceptions, some body-chop-shops in the Brodkil Empire and legendary Mindwerks.

There have been rumors of a mysterious underground laboratory called **Mindwerks** since before the NGR came into power. The stories are reminiscent of 20th Century reports of flying saucers and alien abductions. Many people have claimed to have witnessed or experienced strange events and experiments connected to Mindwerks, but none can prove them. Many of the abductions are explained away by simple solutions, like children and teens running away from home, kidnappings by gypsies or Splugorth slavers, homicide and attacks by D-bees, demons and monsters.

Many of the incredible tales surrounding Mindwerks tell of a vast underground complex located somewhere in southern Poland; the heart of the Brodkil Empire. It is said to have survived the Coming of the Rifts and is populated by insane scientists, borgs and bots from that era. Stories persist about madmen who have conducted mind and body altering experiments on the local inhabitants for centuries. Others insist the legendary technological shop of horrors is located in an alien dimension and that victims are "Rifted" back and forth by sadistic D-bees. Most tales tell of horrible experimentation performed on the abducted victims. Experiments that may be as simple as a physical examination and the taking of tissue or blood samples, to exercises in torture, bionic reconstruction, and operations on the brain! Some rumors even suggest that the monsters of legendary Mindwerks eat brains! Inevitably, the experience drives most people insane, if they survive at all! The unfortunates who do survive are transformed into murderous fiends or inhuman monsters, often unleashed back into the world to reap havoc or suffer persecution from those who fear them!

The stories consistently tell of a woman who calls herself an angel. This unlikely "angel" has become known as the Angel of Death (or Death Witch as she is known by the Brodkil). The stories are varied. In some she is a beguiling, beautiful human woman with the soul of a demon. Other stories suggest she is a human witch, an inhuman shape-changing monster who can make herself look human, or a demonic cyborg from another world. The most popular story among the gypsies and wilderness peasants says that The Angel of Death is an inhuman monster with the face of a beautiful woman but a body of living metal. She is said to speak in a commanding yet soft, gentle, sexy voice. Many report that she caresses and touches her victims in a loving manner, even as she cracks open their skull or performs some terrible act of torture. She tries to comfort those she experiments upon by telling them she's going to give them a great "gift" and/or make them "more powerful" than they could ever imagine. Of course, she ignores people who decline her "gift" or who plead for mercy and freedom. No captive is released until Death Witch has her way with them.

The exact types of torture and experiments conducted by The Angel of Death and her unholy legion include every atrocity one can imagine — but the vast majority have to do with experiments on the brain or disfiguring operations, creating hideous cyborgs. Legend warns that the Angel of Death is evil incarnate and that her "gifts of power," whether accepted willingly or forced upon helpless victims, brings only madness, sorrow and death!

Over the last hundred years, the legends surrounding Mindwerks have taken on the same mystique and superstitious air of a fantasy world. The NGR dismisses its existence as pure fiction. They attribute the appearance of strange new M.O.M. implants in and around the NGR and Poland as the handiwork of body-chop-shops operating in the Brodkil Empire — probably the product of monstrous D-bees since most of these items are found in brodkil and D-bees specimens.

The Truth Behind Mindwerks

As is so often the case, the legends behind Mindwerks are rooted in reality more than most civilized people would like to believe. Although clouded in superstition and masked in fantasy and wild supposition, Mindwerks and the Angel of Death are _real_ and represent a genuine danger to people in the area.

The woman who rules Mindwerks does not pretend to be "an angel," although she does nothing to dispel any of the rumors about her and relishes being an enigma. Her name is Angel Herrenisel and she is originally from Germany — Pre-Rifts Germany!

Angel Herrenisel was one of the owners and the chief M.O.M. researcher and developer at the Mindwerks Corporation. She was supervising the completion of a massive new cybernetic and M.O.M. technologies facility sponsored by the Polish government and two Polish industrialists. Since Mindwerks was teetering on the brink of bankruptcy, the corporation was quick to accept an offer from any organization that seemed to have faith in them. The fact that their sponsors were willing to prove their faith by constructing a new billion dollar mega-complex was all the more encouraging.

Angel Herrenisel was one of the 450 people (mostly workers and technicians) present at the site when the ley lines erupted and the world was plunged into chaos. The other Mindwerks locations were destroyed, as were their Polish sponsors and much of the world. The new complex survived because it was built entirely underground and was not subjected to any natural disasters or dimensional eruptions. Thus, while all around them fell and civilization was plunged into a second Dark Age, they survived without casualties. The Mindwerks complex was scheduled to open within the month, so 95% of the construction was completed and operational. Had the Great Cataclysm occurred a week later, some 3500 people would have been present. The Poland Mindwerks complex was divided equally into four main areas, a robot and cybernetic factory, internal operations (including an independent nuclear power plant, security and environmental control/life support) and research and development (primarily in the areas of cybernetics and M.O.M. technology).

Surviving the destruction of an entire world is a traumatic experience. Over the next month, 75 of the survivors committed suicide or died braving the carnage on the surface in foolhardy quests to find loved ones or to help other survivors. Angel, a natural leader, pulled herself together and took command. She decreed that the surface was off limits until the spatial anomalies causing unnatural storms, earthquakes and destruction had significantly subsided. Angel convinced her cohorts to seal the underground complex from the surface, until things settled down. During this time, they would fire up the factory to create robots that could be sent to explore the hostile environment on the surface rather than lose more valuable lives. Bionics were also suggested as a means to create a more durable explorer, but initially rejected in favor of robot drones. For the next two years the survivors dedicated themselves to the execution of this plan.

The robots found a world torn asunder. Even Poland and Germany, which had survived comparatively unscathed, laid mostly in ruin. Government and order were gone. Civilization was shattered and pandemonium reigned.

Angel convinced her companions that making the Mindwerks complex known would only lead to their own destruction. They agreed that Mindwerks could best serve their people by keeping quiet and developing the means to protect and help the survivors when the right moment arose. Although the Mindwerks complex had fabulous robot and bionic manufacturing facilities, it had very limited resources in the way of raw building materials. Robot production was slowed to a minimum and focus was switched to developing bionic and M.O.M. systems. Secret raiding squads composed of bots and borgs would scrounge through the ruins of toppled cities to collect the supplies and materials they needed. Sometimes they would even raid surface communities, but were always careful to avoid unnecessary violence and murder.

The next 50 years passed surprisingly quickly. Angel became the matriarch of the community and led (ruled) her people wisely. They were never in danger from the surface dwellers and lived productive and happy lives in the technological safety of the underground facility. Somehow, the "right time" to rise to the surface and help had not yet happened. The Mindwerks survivors and their progeny, whose numbers were now around 2700 strong, were divided over the issue of returning to the surface. Half wanted to remain secluded from the world. The other half desperately longed to join humanity and aid in their struggle to rebuild. Angel had mixed feelings herself. Although she leaned toward isolation and secrecy, she also felt a responsibility to her fellow man. The resources of the Mindwerks complex could be a tremendous asset to the new Polish and/or German nations.

Responding to growing pressure from her people, Angel finally agreed to lead the way to the surface for the first time in 55 years. Early on, she had subjected herself to experimental M.O.M. implants designed to keep the brain from aging and, to a more limited degree, slowed the aging and physical deterioration of the body as well. Thus, at the age of 83, Angel's mind was as sharp and alert as ever and she looked to be an attractive woman in her early forties.

Decades of research and surveillance had warned Angel and the people of Mindwerks about the dramatic transformation of the world, but none were quite prepared for the reality of it all. Walking through the rubble where once great cities stood, brought memories of the time before the Rifts. Memories that hung around Angel like tortured ghosts. There was no doubt that a new era in Earth's history had unfolded. After the initial shock, Angel and her cohorts enjoyed the pleasures of being out-of-doors among the flowers and trees. They enjoyed the wind running through their hair and the warmth of the sun nuzzling their cheeks.

The expeditionary squad approached one of the new kingdoms in the southwest, less than a hundred miles (160 km) from the Mindwerks complex. Research had indicated this government would be open to opportunity and had the greatest potential for growth. The following days were filled with celebration, hours of discussion and ended with an alliance. Over the next several months, two-thirds of the people from Mindwerks made new homes on the surface. The fledgling nation traded raw materials to Mindwerks, especially metals and ores, for robots and cybernetics. All of the apprehension drained from Angel with each successive achievement. She took solace in the notion that she had done the right thing and would be party to the rebirth of civilization. That dream soon turned into a nightmare.

A considerably larger, more aggressive and less civilized kingdom to the north saw their neighbor's growth and achievements as a threat to their sovereignty and launched a surprise attack. An attack designed to destroy the perceived enemy; not conquer. The city was leveled! 80% of the population was slaughtered; 17,000 were killed and thousands of others were injured! The fortunate escaped into the wilderness, but most perished. Among the dead, 1956 people from Mindwerks.

Angel herself suffered life threatening injuries trying to save a dozen children from a hospital that had become a blazing inferno. The exit was within reach when the ceiling collapsed, killing all but one of the children and Angel. She and the four year old child were pulled from the fire but both suffered third degree burns over 80% of their bodies and Angel's spine was shattered. With the assistance of some Mindwerks bots and her cyborg savior, the pair were taken back to Mindwerks. After 33 hours of surgery, Angel sat up. Reborn as a full conversion borg. The child also still lived hooked to a medical life support system, but the fire had transformed the beautiful girl into a hideous bag of charred and blistered flesh. The doctors wanted to pull the plug and let her die, but Angel demanded otherwise. "The girl must live," a cold, synthesized voice chimed menacingly. For the first time ever, the Angel who had been their strength, their light, and their leader, seemed frightening. The child would survive.

In the conqueror's zeal to destroy its enemy, they made no effort to capture anybody who might know the location of Mindwerks. Nor did they have any real idea what Mindwerks was or where it might exist. They had no inkling of the power the facility represented or the enemy they had just created. Thus, when the carnage was over, the invaders left, leaving Mindwerks safe and soon forgotten. Unfortunately for them, they were not so easily forgotten by Angel.

At the moment before his murder, one long-time friend of Angel Herrenisel would be remembered saying the experience not only destroyed Angel's body, but her soul as well. Angel, like the world around her, was transformed into something alien. The strong but compassionate leader became cold, twisted and evil. She craved revenge and chastised those who rebuffed her wishes. She had her cyborg body (and several spare bodies locked away in storage) improved with weapons and special features. One such feature was the recreation of her human face covered in synthetic flesh. Another was a voice box that simulated her once human voice, but even though it was duplicated to perfection, there was a cold and dangerous edge to it.

She doted on the child who had also been give an artificial body. The two became like mother and child and began to refer to each other as such. They'd take long walks and spend their every waking moment together working, talking and planning the future. Angel took the child's pain and molded her into a kindred spirit. A spirit driven by pain and who fed on hatred and dreams of revenge. Together they plotted horrible schemes of vengeance. Both had become monsters every bit as inhuman as the monsters who crawled out of the Rifts.

The change in Angel was so dramatic and frightening that scores of supporters left her side and abandoned Mindwerks forever. One man tried to politically usurp her reign. He and 21 of his closest followers were found brutally murdered. Angel denied any involvement and seemed to have an iron-clad alibi. Still, most believed she or her hellspawn adopted daughter were responsible. The last of the Mindwerks supporters left in droves. When the exodus ended, less than 90 remained. Among those faithful were others who craved revenge or coveted the power and/or safety Mindwerks had to offer — even if staying meant being in league with a devil.

The Legend Begins ...

Shortly after the exodus, the atmosphere at Mindwerks became dark and sinister. Talk of revenge and dark conspiracies were commonplace. It is at this point in time that Angel began to develop new types of M.O.M. implants and installed them in human subjects kidnapped from the surface. She would send her drones or lackeys to capture helpless victims, bring them back to Mindwerks, be subjected to experiments, released and monitored. Their mental, emotional and physical pain was of no concern to Angel, only her experiments mattered. With the passage of time, her minions became equally heartless and inhumane.

As more non-humans began to inhabit the area, she would capture D-bees to experiment upon. She became fascinated with their alien physiology and the potential it offered in regard to her work with M.O.M. technology. Every year, hundreds of people, human and non-human, were slaughtered under her blade or direction. Countless others would be transformed by her experiments with cybernetics or empowered but tormented by her M.O.M. implants. Angel didn't care, and her daughter followed happily in her blood drenched footsteps. Soon Angel became known as **The Angel of Death** and her adopted daughter, **The Angel of Vengeance**.

With time the madness escalated; perhaps magnified by the age negating implants in both women's brains. Mother and daughter, Death and Vengeance, engaged in horrible experiments and acts of cruelty and revenge. The Angel of Death had discovered many of the monster races

welcomed her M.O.M. implants even if they brought insanity or an early death. One brodkil chief openly sought her aid, pledging his and his tribe's eternal allegiance in exchange for her "magic." They wanted bionic limbs and brain implants to give them the power to vanquish their enemies. The chief completely dismissed the dangers of insanity saying he welcomed madness if it made each warrior fight like ten! The Angel of Death hesitated but finally complied when she learned that the monster's target was the kingdom that had destroyed her body and dreams so many years earlier.

The brodkil destroyed that nation and went on a rampage of murder and pillaging with their gargoyle allies. Although unknown at the time, this would be the beginning of the Brodkil Empire and an association with Mindwerks that has lasted over 220 years! The brodkil chief, and his sons after him, have kept their word with Angel, whom they call the "Death Witch." They show her their utmost respect and reverence. To the brodkil (and to a lesser degree, their gargoyle and D-bee allies) The Angel of Death and Angel of Vengeance are immortal demi-gods to be honored and feared.

Note: Mindwerks is a pre-Rifts, underground bionic and robotics factory that specializes in M.O.M. technology. It is located in southwest Poland near the Czechoslovakian border. Even among the brodkil, only a tiny handful know its exact location.

The Angel of Death

Among the inhabitants of Poland, Czechoslovakia, and Romania, The Angel of Death is known by many names, including Death's Angel, The Dark Angel, and Death Witch. Most peasants and gypsies believe the legends and see her and her daughter as supernatural forces of evil come to Earth to torment all lesser beings. Most common folk will flee in terror if forced to face either one of these monsters! Most local inhabitants and gypsies know a wealth of stories and superstitions about The Dark Angel, the Angel of Vengeance and Mindwerks (only half have any bearing in reality).

Over the last 20 years, The Angel of Death has worked more closely with the Brodkil Empire than ever. She and her minions have equipped tens of thousands with bionic limbs, weapons and psynetic M.O.M. brain implants.

Although The Angel of Death and her daughter may seem calculating and rational, they both have a psychotic hatred for most human life and little regard for life in general, including the brodkil with whom they are so closely associated. The two women are obsessed with death, vengeance and their own evil machinations. Both have come to think of themselves as powerful demi-gods rather than human beings.

The Angel of Death is extremely sadistic and loves to torture other beings. This torture usually takes the form of mind altering brain implants or bionic reconstruction. However, she has also been known to engage in pointless experiments and acts of torture to test a character's physical and mental endurance and to study the effects of her M.O.M. implants. She also enjoys cat and mouse games that test her cunning. However, she seldom takes foolish risks and NEVER jeopardizes the safety of Mindwerks (**Note:** Less than a dozen people outside of Mindwerks knows of its location).

The Angel of Death has continued her revolutionary work in the area of M.O.M. technology. In addition to the standard *crazies* physical augmentation process, she has developed a number of implants that provide limited physical augmentation without the entire range of insanities that accompanies the more powerful crazy process. Even more impressive, The Angel of Death has developed M.O.M. implants that instil psionic powers! She calls these brain implants **psynetic** devices. Unfortunately, psynetic implants also cause mental aberrations and insanity. One such creation is a M.O.M. microchip of her own design that keeps the human brain from deteriorating with age. The process is a complete success, but only she knows the secret of its construction

The Angel of Death in a more feminine (though still threatening) guise.

and surgical placement (those who worked on the project died centuries ago and computer records have vanished). Only the Angel of Death, Angel of Vengeance and a few experimental subjects have these implants. This psynetic implant may also be responsible, at least in part, for her insanities.

German Name: der Engel der Vernichtung (meaning Angel of Death or Annihilation — pronounced eng el der fair neek tung)

True Name: Angel Herrenisel

Alignment: Miscreant

Attributes: I.Q.: 21, M.E.: 18, M.A.: 13 (was 22 when she was human), P.S.: 24, P.P.: 24, P.E.: not applicable, P.B.: 12, Spd.: 134 (105 mph/168 km). All physical attributes are bionic.

Hit Points: See M.D.C.; full conversion borg, The Angel of Death is more machine than human.

M.D.C.: 280 M.D.C. of the main bionic body, plus Angel wears light infantry armor into combat which provides an additional 270 M.D.C.

P.P.E.: 4

O.C.C.: Cyber-Doc with special training in M.O.M. technology.

Level of Experience: 15th level cyber-doc in a cyborg body.

Natural Abilities & Disposition: Highly intelligent (+7% I.Q. skill bonus), with a curious and analytical mind, a strong will and relentless drive. Angel is a cold, calculating machine who tends to become obsessed with her goals. However, she can be incredibly patient and reserved.

Obsessions: Obsessed with proving that she and her ancestors who founded Mindwerks and developed M.O.M. technology were geniuses deserving of worldwide acclaim. To achieve this recognition, Angel believes she must make Mindwerks a power to be feared. She also believes she must destroy Mindwerks' old rival Triax Industries. In addition to extracting vengeance against all the people who tried to ruin Mindwerks or who had mocked and chastised them. In her twisted mind, this has come to include all humans and most humanoids. To achieve these goals she has allied herself with monsters and augments them through the miracles of M.O.M. technology!

- Obsession: Crush Triax.
- Obsession: Subvert, destroy, or conquer the NGR.
- Obsession: Punish all humans for crimes against Mindwerks.
- Obsession: Vengeance against those she perceives as being traitors or enemies. Her revenge is usually painful and prolonged, often letting her foes live, but only after she has inflicted some horrible fate upon them.
- Obsession: To perfect psynetic implants and other M.O.M. technologies and make the world sing of her accomplishments.

Other Insanities: When Angel almost died 250 year ago, she suffered a traumatic rebirth and went from a scrupulous alignment to miscreant. Over the decades, The Angel of Death has become a heartless fiend with delusions of godhood. She sees most humans and D-bees as inferior creatures and the descendants of those who mocked her family and threatened Mindwerks. Consequently to her, they must pay for all the wrongs they and their ancestors have inflicted upon Mindwerks. Most life forms, intelligent or otherwise, are seen as little more than lab animals. Angel is cruel and sadistic in the extreme. What makes her all the more inhuman and menacing is her condescending and motherly demeanor. Even when she is inflicting pain or destruction, she always seems to have a wicked smirk on her face and softly spoken words roll off her tongue. Human suffering provides her with great amusement.

Regarding Mindwerks, Angel is secretive about its location and resources to the point of paranoia. Victims brought to the facility from the surface are always unconscious, blind folded or imprisoned in such a way that they have no idea where Mindwerks is located. As for Angel's involvement with the Brodkil Empire and the world at large, she typically prefers to spin her web of treachery behind the scenes and acts as the unseen Prime Mover of terrible events.

If the Mindwerks complex should ever fall to the enemy, or be destroyed, it will push The Angel of Death over the brink and she will become a completely merciless and murderous monster bent on destroying those responsible.

Psionic Powers: None. Her completely bionic shell prevents the use of psynetic devices. Angel had no natural psionic powers to begin with.

Magic Knowledge: Only lore and legends. Recently she has learned about bio-wizardry, which she finds fascinating.

Combat abilities: Hand to hand: basic (15th level proficiency).

Combat/Attacks Per Melee Round: Five

Bonuses (includes all bonuses): +3 on initiative, +7 to strike, +9 to parry, +10 to dodge, +4 to roll with impact, +4 to pull punch, +13 to S.D.C. damage, critical strike on unmodified 19 or 20, knockout or critical strike from behind, kick attack (1D6 S.D.C.), and judo style body throw/flip (1D6 damage and victim loses initiative and one melee attack). +4 to save vs psionic attack, +5 to save vs horror factor (special), and as a cyborg she is impervious to poison, heat, and many other types of physical afflictions.

Hand to Hand Combat Note: A power punch or leap kick inflicts 1D6 M.D. but counts as two melee attacks. A power stab with the vibro-blade does 3D6 M.D. but also counts as two melee attacks/actions.

Skills of Note (I.Q. bonus included): Medical Doctor, M.D. of cybernetics, pathology, biology, chemistry, basic and advanced math, computer operation, computer programming, radio: basic, electrical engineer, robot electronics, mechanical engineer, pilot hovercraft, swim, lore: demons & monsters, dance, literacy: German, and speaks old Pre-Rifts German, Euro, Dragonese, and Brodkil; all these skills are at 98% proficiency. She also is literate in Euro and Dragonese at 87%, speaks American, Gargoyle and Demongogian at 87%, W.P. knife (15th level), and W.P. energy rifle, all at 10th level proficiency.

Appearance: A slender cyborg with human female proportions and features. Usually only her youthful face appears to be human, but from time to time The Angel of Death will cover her entire body with synthetic flesh. She may also wear a wig. All this is usually done when she wants to look more human and/or innocent and vulnerable. she enjoys games of seduction, subterfuge and misdirection. She looks to be around 30 years old but is really over 330! She stands 6 feet, 2 inches (1.88 m) tall.

Weapons & Equipment of Note: The Angel of Death has all the resources of Mindwerks at her disposal, as well as many others through her connections with the Brodkil Empire. In addition to Mindwerks' own weapons, bionics and bots, she can lay her hands on most Triax weapons, body armor, equipment and many vehicles. Her wardrobe is filled with a vast range of clothing from slinky nightgowns to military fatigues.

When she goes into a combat situation, she is often armed with the TX-22 Precision laser pistol or M-12 plasma pistol and the M-30 Dual energy rifle — but rail guns and other weapons may be used in their place.

Bionics: A full conversion borg with a main body of 280 M.D.C. plus light infantry armor (worn into combat) with an additional 270 M.D.C.; bionic lung with gas filter and oxygen storage cell, molecular analyzer, built-in radio, headjack and ear implant, amplified hearing (bonuses have been added to combat bonus section), sound filtration system, modulating voice synthesizer, multi-optic eyes, gyro-compass, clock calendar, dosimeter/radiation detector and the M.O.M. eternal brain implant!

Bionic Weapons: Utility/scalpel laser finger (1D6 or 3D6 S.D.C.), retractable finger blades (1D4 S.D.C. each), retractable vibro-blade (2D6 M.D.) in the right arm, wrist needle and drug dispenser in the left arm (all drugs are available), a concealed ion rod (4D6 M.D., 2000 ft/610 m range) in the right leg, secret compartment (one, large) in the left leg used to conceal other weapons and items.

Money: The Mindwerks complex is worth billions, including millions of credits' worth of bionics, implants and robots! The Angel of Death has approximately 500 million universal credits available at any given time.

Alliances & Allies: The Death Witch is closely allied to the hierarchy of the Brodkil Empire and loosely associated with the Gargoyle Empire. She is respected and feared by most brodkil and many gargoyles, vampires, simvan and other monsters of Europe. Angel and her daughter really are considered to be demi-gods by many of the D-bees and monsters.

Note: In addition to Mindwerks, The Angel of Death has established two body-chop-shops on the surface in the heart of Brodkil territory. These shops are headed by Mindwerks cyber-docs loyal to Angel and dedicated to the advancement of M.O.M. technology. Like the Death Witch, they too engage in experimentation on helpless captives brought to them by the brodkil. Typically 50% of psynetic implants and all crazies implants are available. The psynetic items are usually locked away in a secret vault that can be destroyed if the shop falls under siege or if the vault is forced open (no psynetic implants will survive). There is also a 15% chance that The Angel of Death will be visiting and a 25% chance that the Angel of Vengeance or Marsalis may be present (or near by).

Angel of Vengeance

Unlike her adopted mother, The Angel of Vengeance (also known as Death's daughter, the Hand of Vengeance and simply as Vengeance) never tries to look human. She discarded her human body ages ago and with it, her humanity. She is completely obsessed by hate and vents her anger by destroying all who offend and annoy her and her mother. The poor child (now over 250 years old!) is demented and believes she is a real god of vengeance. She is completely loyal to The Angel of Death and obeys her without question. Anybody who dares betray or attack her mother must face the wrath of Vengeance! To even infer anything negative about The Angel of Death is to face grim punishment; if one is lucky, he'll only be tortured or beaten within an inch or his life.

The Angel of Vengeance is a courageous and deadly warrior who enjoys the thrill of combat. In recent years, she has become increasingly bold and aggressive. There have been many confrontations with local inhabitants, gypsies, vampires, rogue demons, the Minions of Splugorth and NGR troops. However, few of her opponents, especially humans from the New German Republic, have any idea who or what they are fighting. She is best known among the brodkil, simvan, and gargoyles. The Polish and German defenders believe she is a psychotic cyborg bandit who kills wantonly.

German Name: der Engel der Vergeltung (pronounced en gel der fair gel tung)

True Name: Bridget Herrenisel (the names of her biological parents are unknown and she has been adopted by Angel Herrenisel)

Alignment: Diabolic

Attributes: I.Q.: 14, M.E.: 12, M.A.: 19, P.S.: 30, P.P.: 24, P.E.: not applicable, P.B.: 8, Spd.: 176 (120 mph/192 km). All physical attributes are bionic.

Hit Points: See M.D.C.; full conversion borg, The Angel of Vengeance is more machine than woman.

M.D.C. By Location:

Arms (4) — 110 each

Hands (4) — 35 each

Prehensile Tail (1) — 120

Head — 130 (reinforced, as well as protected by the M.D.C. cords that simulate hair).

Main body — 280 M.D.C. for the main bionic body; Vengeance wears light or heavy infantry armor into combat (light provides an additional 270 M.D.C., heavy 420 M.D.C.).

Note: Depleting the M.D.C. of the main body will effectively destroy her artificial body, but emergency systems will keep the brain and vital organs alive for 36 hours. Recovery of the body will enable cyber-docs to place the character on life support and transplant her into a new bionic body. Both the Angel of Vengeance and the Angel of Death have three spare borg bodies at Mindwerks; prepped and ready to go at a moment's notice. The operation will take four and a half hours if performed by Angel or seven hours by a cyber-doc.

P.P.E.: One point

O.C.C.: Cyborg

Level of Experience: 10th

Disposition: Cunning, defiant, brave, resourceful and merciless. She loves to fight, kill and dominate others. She tends to become obsessed with acts of vengeance.

She loves her adopted mother and will fight to the death to defend her. If The Angel of Death is ever slain (or seriously injured), The Angel of Vengeance will hunt down those responsible and slay them. She tends to be vicious and extreme in her methods and has been known to slaughter entire villages to force an enemy's hand or to extract what she considers just retribution. The Angel of Vengeance sometimes joins brodkil and other demons in combat or missions of destruction.

Insanities: Obsessed with avenging every wrong, slight or attack against her, The Angel of Death, and Mindwerks. The Angel of Vengeance is even more of a megalomaniac than her mother; Vengeance believes she _is_ a demi-god without any shadow of a doubt. She is also extremely sadistic and loves to belittle, abuse, hurt and torment other creatures, especially humans and those who dare to defy her. These acts of vengeance are usually painful, bloody and several times more atrocious than the act she is avenging.

Psionic Powers: None. Her bionic shell prevents the use of psynetic devices and she had no natural psionic powers to begin with.

Magic Knowledge: Only lore and legends.

Combat abilities: Hand to hand Expert (10th level proficiency).

Combat/Attacks Per Melee Round: Six

Bonuses (includes all bonuses): +3 on initiative, +8 to strike, +11 to parry, +10 to dodge, +2 to roll with impact, +2 to pull punch, +15 to S.D.C. damage, critical strike on unmodified 18, 19 or 20, paired weapons, kick attack (1D6 S.D.C.), and judo style body throw/flip (1D6 damage and victim loses initiative and one melee attack). +2 to save vs psionic attack (brain implant), +6 to save vs horror factor (implant), and as a cyborg she is impervious to poison, heat, and many other types of physical afflictions.

Skills of Note: Basic and advanced math 90%, navigation 85%, computer operation 85%, radio: basic 95%, electrical: basic 75%, pilot hovercraft 95%, pilot tank/APC 77%, pilot: jet pack 78%, read sensory equipment 85%, weapon systems 90%, first aid 90%, lore: demons & monsters 70%, literacy: Euro, and speaks Old German, Euro, Gobblely, Brodkil and Demongogian, all at 95%, and Dragonese, Gargoyle and Spanish at 70%. Weapon proficiencies include W.P. sword, W.P. energy pistol, W.P. energy rifle, W.P. heavy energy, and W.P. archery (all 10th level).

Appearance: A female cyborg with four arms, a prehensile tail, a crown of spikes, and a demonic face. The Angel of Vengeance never tries to appear human and likes to evoke fear with her menacing presence. It is impossible to tell her age (over 220 years old) and she stands 10 feet (3 m) tall!

Weapons & Equipment of Note: The Angel of Vengeance has most of the resources of Mindwerks at her disposal, as well as many of those from the Brodkil Empire. In addition to Mindwerks' own weapons, bionics and bots, she can lay her hands on any Triax weapons, equipment and many vehicles. Her wardrobe is limited to a variety of bionic body armor, a royal blue cloak with a crimson lining and a white cape with a gold lining.

When she goes into a combat situation, she usually wears heavy body armor (420 M.D.C.) and may use a jet pack for greater mobility and speed. Typical armament includes a M-12 plasma pistol, M-30 Dual energy rifle, TX-41 giant laser pulse rifle, Kittani plasma sword (human-sized so it functions as a short sword sidearm) and a giant, six foot (1.8 m) long, greater rune sword called Striker. It has an I.Q. of 16, diabolic alignment, inflicts 1D6 × 10 M.D., can cast four elemental spells equal to a 6th level warlock (globe of daylight, fire ball, blue flame, and flame friend) and possesses all sensitive and physical psionic powers plus psi-shield, group mind block and hydrokinesis (see **Rifts Atlantis**, page 128, for more details about rune weapons).

Bionics: A full conversion borg with a main body of 280 M.D.C. plus light bionic infantry armor (270 M.D.C.) or heavy bionic infantry armor (420 M.D.C.); bionic lung with gas filter and oxygen storage cell, molecular analyzer, built-in radio, built-in language translator, loudspeaker, headjack and ear implant, amplified hearing (bonuses have been added to combat bonus section), sound filtration system, multi-optic eyes, gyro-compass, clock calendar, dosimeter/radiation detector and the M.O.M. eternal brain!

Bionic Weapons: Four arms and a tail.

The upper right arm has a particle beam forearm blaster (6D6 + 6 M.D.; 1000 ft/305 m range) and a concealed E-clip arm port. The right index finger has a utility laser (1D6 or 3D6 S.D.C.), and the fingers have retractable blades (1D4 S.D.C. each).

The lower right arm has a chemical spray system built into the wrist and arm (any of the chemicals can be used). A garrote wrist wire is concealed in the wrist and shooting knuckle spikes can be fired at will (explosive types doing 3D6 S.D.C. each).

The upper left arm has a retractable vibro-blade (2D6 M.D.) in the forearm and the fingers also have retractable blades (1D4 S.D.C. each). A climb cord is concealed in the wrist and explosive knuckle spikes can be fired.

The lower left arm also has a chemical spray system, as well as a concealed arm laser (1D6 M.D., 800 ft/244 m range). The first two fingers have concealed cameras.

Both legs have large secret compartments that usually contain a universal credit card or gems worth 50,000 credits, a silver cross, a fusion block, three hand grenades and a spare E-clip or other weapons and items.

The prehensile tail is used as a whip to hit, entangle or strangle. The tail has a reach of 12 feet (3.2 m) and adds +10% to climb.

The three head spikes can be used to impale victims with a head butt or fired at will, inflicting 1D6 M.D. each; range 500 feet (153 m).

Hand to Hand Note: A power punch or leap kick inflicts 1D6 M.D. but counts as two melee attacks. A power stab with the vibro-blade does 3D6 M.D. (counts as two melee attacks).

Money: The Angel of Vengeance has access to the wealth and resources of Mindwerks, including its bionics, implants, bots and weapons. She has approximately 100 million universal credits available to her at any given time (and millions more in hardware).

Alliances & Allies: Even the gargoyles and Minions of Splugorth respect the Avenger, although she is most closely allied to members of the Brodkil Empire. Many lesser beings will flee rather than stand against her, and powerful monsters may bow to her superiority to win her favor. There can be no doubt that Mindwerks is a growing force in the area.

Marsalis

Marsalis is an alien who was captured when he stepped through a Rift. Exactly what he is or where he comes from is unknown. Even before being subjected to M.O.M. implants, the creature was evil and insane. The Angels of Death and Vengeance took an immediate liking to him and the three became friends and allies. Marsalis has worked and fought at the side of the two so-called angels for 60 years. His psynetic implants serve to amplify his already formidable psionic powers.

The red skinned D-bee is as sadistic and cruel as his two mistresses, taking delight in acts of brutality and torture. He has no love for humans, elves and dragons, and absolutely despises vampires, temporal raiders/mages/warriors, shaydorians, naruni (see **Rifts Mercenaries**), zembahk and True Atlanteans (see **Rifts Atlantis** for several of these races).

Marsalis wears a gold helmet that fits over and helps protect his M.O.M. implants and skull (40 M.D.C. for the helmet). The two black lenses of the visor combined with his lower skeletal jaw, exposed yellow teeth and two air slits in place of a nose makes him look all the more skeletal and demonic, adding to the "death" legends and monstrous image of Mindwerks.

Although Marsalis started his life with the Angels as a slave, he has grown to be a unofficial partner. As such he has complete access to all of Mindwerks and is also allowed to conduct his own excursions and schemes on the surface (as long as they don't endanger Mindwerks). Marsalis is completely loyal to both the Angel of Death and of Vengeance and will fight to the death to protect them and Mindwerks. Whatever Marsalis may be, he is the only one of his kind on Earth.

True Name: Mhr-salzs
Alignment: Miscreant
Attributes: I.Q.: 15, M.E.: 23, M.A.: 11, P.S.: 17, P.P.: 14, P.E.: 20, P.B.: 3, Spd.: 22 (15 mph/24 km).
Hit Points: 80, S.D.C. 80; also see M.D.C. and psionics/psynetics.
M.D.C.: Via TK force field, 180 M.D.C. He may also wear environmental body armor into combat (100 M.D.C.).
P.P.E.: 9
Horror Factor: 13
O.C.C.: Psynetic Crazy
Level of Experience: 9th level psynetic crazy (was an alien mind melter).
Disposition: A sinister character who is also sadistic, manipulating, and treacherous. He tends to avoid other people except to cause mischief, suffering and destruction. He is completely loyal and dedicated to the two mistresses of Mindwerks.
Insanities and Side effects: Paranoid Schizophrenic: A voice regularly warns the character not to trust the words and actions of other people, especially humans, True Atlanteans, temporal raiders/mages/warriors, zembahk, shaydorians, naruni, and vampires.

Affective Disorder: Obsessed with cleanliness and washing his hands.

Phobia: Terrified of losing the respect and trust of the Angels of Death and Vengeance. He will never betray them or do anything that would make them angry with him. Marsalis is −5 on initiative and −5 to strike, parry and dodge should he ever be compelled to oppose either one.

Random Insanity: Recluse; prefers to be alone or in the company of the Angel of Death and/or Angel of Vengeance.

Side effects: Energy burst and loss of control (see Side Effects Table, number one) and his mouth and eyebrow twitches uncontrollably when angry or ready for combat or tormenting others.
Psionic Powers:

Original/natural psionic powers: Healing: detect psionics, exorcism, increased healing, psychic diagnosis, and psychic surgery. Physical: ectoplasm, levitation, telekinesis, impervious to fire, and death trance. Super: bio-regenerate (super), bio-manipulation, mind bolt and mind block auto-defense.

Psynetic implant & powers: Advanced sixth sense, amplified telemechanics, psynetic eye (right), TK force field auto-defense (180 M.D.C.) and psychometric booster (increases psi-strength).
Magic Knowledge: None
Combat abilities: Hand to hand: expert (9th level proficiency).
Combat/Attacks Per Melee Round: Four
Bonuses (includes all bonuses): +2 on initiative, +2 to strike, +4 to parry, +5 to dodge, +4 to roll with impact, +4 to pull punch, +2 to S.D.C. damage, critical strike on unmodified 18,19 or 20, kick attack (1D6 S.D.C.), and judo style body throw/flip (1D6 damage and victim loses initiative and one melee attack). +4 to save vs psionic attack, +5 to save vs horror factor (special, natural ability).
Skills of Note: Basic and advanced math, paramedic, radio: basic, read sensory equipment, computer operation, computer programming, computer hacking, lore: demons & monsters, pilot hover vehicle, W.P. energy pistol, W.P. energy rifle, and W.P. Energy heavy. Languages include Euro, Gobblely, Brodkil and Demongogian, all at 95% and old German at 55%; literate in Euro at 65%.
Appearance: A demonic, red-skinned alien with a skeletal head and features. Marsalis is over 100 years old and stands 7 feet (2.1 m) tall; average life span: 250 years.
Weapons & Equipment of Note: Marsalis has all the resources of Mindwerks at his disposal, as well as many of those of the Brodkil Empire. In addition to Mindwerks' own weapons, bionics and bots, he can lay his hands on any Triax weapons, body armor, equipment and many vehicles.

Bionics: An artificial left hand (lost in combat) with a utility/scalpel laser finger (1D6 or 3D6 S.D.C.), a gyro-compass, clock calendar, brain wave identifier, tracker, M.O.M. hyper senses and the M.O.M. eternal brain!

Money: Marsalis has access to the resources of Mindwerks including its bionics, implants, bots and weapons. He has approximately 50 million universal credits available to him at any given time (and millions more in hardware).

Alliances & Allies: Marsalis is well liked by many of the brodkil war chiefs and respected by most brodkil. He has also been favorably received by Emperor Zerstrun, ruler of the Gargoyle Empire, and has had some cautious contact with a gene-splicer who calls himself Sobius.

Typical Human Technician

40% Cyber-docs; all experts in M.O.M technology
25% Operators skilled in robotics
5% Operators skilled in computers and hacking
10% Operators skilled in electronics
10% Psynetic Crazies
10% Traditional Crazies

Most technicians are human (80%) and are descendants of the original Mindwerks survivors. The rest are brodkil and D-bees. Most technicians have minimal combat training: hand to hand: basic and two weapon proficiencies (typically W.P. knife and energy rifle).

75% have two M.O.M. implants (psionic or physical) and a special tracking device, brain wave identifier and an explosive chip implanted in their brain. About 40% have a controller chip as well. See the description for *Other Implants of Note* in the following section for complete details about these special chips.

Note: The Angel of Death also commands approximately 48 brodkil cyborgs, 24 brodkil psynetic borgs, 24 D-bee and 16 human psynetic borgs, 36 psi-bloodhounds, 13 ecto-travelers, and 20 human and 30 D-bee crazies and a handful of others (half are usually away from Mindwerks on special assignments).

Typical Mindwerks Cyber-doc (technician): Rather than list all of the various types of technicians, I have presented only the Mindwerks cyber-doc. Operators and other personnel will be similar. Most have minimal combat skills and training — they are skilled professionals, not warriors.

Typical Alignment: Selfish or Evil

Attributes of Note: I.Q.: 14 or higher, M.E.: 10 or higher, P.P.: 12 or higher, all others can fall within any range.

Hit Points: Human

M.D.C.: Not applicable unless a partial or full conversion borg.

O.C.C. (example): Cyber-Doc

Average Level of Experience: 1D4+4

Disposition: Cold; little regard for life. Obedient and loyal to the three lords of Mindwerks. Many dislike humans of Rifts Earth in general and the people of the NGR and Triax specifically.

Insanities: Many are sadistic and cruel bullies. Many are obsessed with M.O.M. development and experimentation regardless of the cost to intelligent life. Many suffer from delusions of grandeur. 10% worship the Angels of Death and Vengeance as gods.

Psionic Powers: Varies. About 35% have one or two psynetic implants.

Magic Knowledge: Only lore.

Combat abilities: Hand to hand: Basic

Bonuses: Depends on natural attributes, combat training, bionic augmentation and M.O.M. technology. However, only about 10% have undergone partial bionic reconstruction and although 75% have some minor M.O.M. augmentation, most are human beings made of flesh and blood.

Skills of Note (cyber-doc): Basic and advanced math, medical doctor, M.D. of cybernetics, biology, chemistry, computer operation, radio: basic, electrical engineer, mechanical engineer, read sensory equipment, weapon systems, demons & monsters, literacy: Euro and old German, languages: old German, Euro, and Gobblely. Weapon proficiencies include W.P. knife, W.P. energy pistol, W.P. energy rifle.

Appearance: 80% are humans.

Weapons & Equipment of Note: Surgical scalpels, laser scalpel, silver plated knife, silver cross, energy pistol or vibro-blade, and/or an energy rifle, lab coats, surgical equipment, and access to M.O.M. implants, cybernetics, optics, sensory equipment, operating rooms, laboratories, and other Mindwerks facilities.

Bionics: Most of the technicians are human. Only 10% have major bionic augmentation.

M.O.M. Implants: 75% have a special tracking device, brain wave identifier and an explosive chip implanted in their brain. About 40% also have a controller chip. 50% have enhanced endurance and healing or other physical M.O.M. augmentation. 35% have two psynetic M.O.M. enhancements; specific ones will depend on the character and G.M., but most augmentation components are usually items that will help them in their work.

Money: Limited access to the resources of Mindwerks, including good food, recreation facilities and creature comforts. Less than 15%, the elite, are allowed to accumulate a personal fortune (4D6×10,000 credits).

M.O.M. Technology

Who can get M.O.M. (crazies) Implants?

Humans, True Atlanteans, Altara warrior women, ogres, orcs, elves, simvan, most D-bees, and most intelligent, mortal life forms in general, including brodkil and gurgoyles can be physically and/or psionically augmented by M.O.M. technology. **Note:** Like other bionic systems, practitioners of magic avoid them because the artificial devices interfere with the use of magic. Many people avoid M.O.M. augmentation because of the terrible insanity and other side effects that come with them!

M.O.M. implants and cybernetic systems will NOT work on most supernatural beings or creatures of magic. Remember, just because a D-bee may look demonic or monstrous, does not mean the creature is a supernatural demon. The brodkil, although they possess supernatural strength and bio-regeneration, and are considered to be demonic by humans, have insignificant supernatural powers. Consequently, brodkil are acceptable candidates for the M.O.M. procedure. Most gargoyles and all gurgoyles possess comparatively few supernatural abilities (actually, even less than the brodkil) and are considered by most beings to be *sub-demons* — little more than monstrous D-bees. Thus, they too can receive M.O.M. implants. The only exceptions are gargoylites and gargoyle mages who are both creatures of magic, and gargoyle lords because the lord can transform into living stone.

A good rule of thumb is that any creature that can perform any type of metamorphosis, change size, or other feats of shape changing (yes that includes dragons, werebeasts and changelings), can regenerate lost limbs, possesses natural magic powers (like faerie folk), or is clearly a supernatural or magic creature, then that being is ineligible for M.O.M. implants (they don't work and/or the body expels the artificial device). If the creature cannot use bionics, it cannot get M.O.M. or psynetic devices either; both are just another type of cybernetic implant.

Giants can handle the implants better than humans and human-sized characters, suggesting that the problem with the implants may be the micronization process. Working on giants such as gurgoyles, gargoyles, brodkil and ogres is easier than working on the smaller, fragile humans. Brodkil leaders and most inhuman M.O.M. volunteers don't mind paying the price of insanity for more power (see the two side effect tables described elsewhere). Note that ogres, although comparatively giant in size, are almost identical to human physiology (they can even mate with humans, which means they are giant versions of the same species) and can receive the traditional "Crazies" augmentation or the new psionic implants.

Non-humans with exceptional or superhuman strength and/or physical abilities, including all types of invulnerabilities, increased healing, and so on, cannot be physically augmented more than they already are. Thus, the standard "crazy" M.O.M. conversion cannot be used on most giants or physically powerful D-bees — it is effective only on humans, elves and human-like D-bees. However, the brodkil, ogres and other super-strong beings have happily submitted to psynetic enhancements; M.O.M. brain implants that instil or boost psionic powers. The brodkil also love to get conventional bionic augmentation.

Crazies' Mind-Over-Matter (M.O.M.) brain implants are intended to cause a physical improvement to the recipient of the M.O.M. augmentation. Unfortunately, the character suffers mental and emotional side effects.

M.O.M. Side Effect Tables

Side effects Table Number One: Physical Manifestations

Physical manifestations are side effects resulting from the M.O.M. implants in addition to the more infamous insanities and other mental aberrations. All effects and penalties are accumulative. The Game Master may select specific maladies or have the player make random roll determinations (Personally, I like the random approach). If the same side effect comes up again from a random roll, ignore it and roll again.

01-10 Brain damage: Reduce I.Q. by 25%, but the character is impervious to all forms of mind control, +4 to save vs magic illusions and +4 to save vs horror factor.

11-20 Brain damage causes a reduction of the character's I.Q. by half, but instills savant powers! The character can either perform 1D4+1 known skills or one previously unknown skill (player's choice) at 98% efficiency regardless of experience level. Only medical, physical and W.P. skills are excluded. In most cases, the character has limited total recall in regard to the savant skill(s). For example, if the character is a savant in the area of *military intelligence* he will instantly recognize and accurately remember things pertinent to that skill, such as ranks, uniforms, insignias, weapon capabilities, ranges, troop compositions, military procedures/tactics/conduct common to that branch of the military, and so on. If the savant knows mechanics, he can engage in expert repairs or sabotage vehicles and machinery but may have trouble tying his shoes.

Special considerations: In the case of the *language* skill, the savant can understand and speak languages he knew before the implant at 98% and can learn a new language in a matter of days at 90% proficiency. The same applies to the literacy skill. In regard to mathematics, a savant automatically knows advanced mathematics but will not casually use the ability on his own. Instead, he functions like a living calculator who can answer most math questions, computations and equations put to him. Basic math questions can be answered in 1D4 seconds, while advanced math questions may take as long as 1D6×10 seconds (98% proficiency for all). As for playing a musical instrument or singing, the character can remember and play or sing a song perfectly after hearing it only once (limited total recall).

Penalties: All other skills are performed at −20% (−40% if the character's I.Q. is reduced to 1, 2, 3 or 4).

21-25 Constant dull headache causing some difficulty sleeping and concentrating; −5% on all skills.

26-30 Involuntary spasms from nerve damage, usually affecting the hands, arms and face. The spasms may only occur once or twice a day under stress-free conditions, but will increase dramatically when under intense stress. When nervous, frightened or angry the mouth may twitch and may cause some stuttering or make him appear nervous or fearful. A muscle spasm of the hand or arm will ruin an attack (-5 to strike) and the character loses one melee action. If the spasm occurs while working/preforming a skill, the limb will jerk and a hand-held tool or other item may be dropped. The character loses one melee action but can continue with his work. **Note:** Even when under considerable amounts of stress, the spasms in limbs will not come any more frequently than every five or 10 minutes, although the mouth or eyebrow may twitch every 30 seconds or so.

If the character is absolutely terrified, such as fearing imminent death or torture, his entire body may go into convulsions for 1D4 melee rounds. During that period, the character cannot speak or take any action. Nor is he aware of what's transpiring around him (temporarily blacks out).

31-35 Sudden and intense pain as if somebody suddenly stabbed a sharp, hot poker in the character's brain. The pain lasts for 1D4 melee rounds (15 to 60 seconds), during which time the character is limited to two melee actions/attacks per round, all combat bonuses are reduced by half, and all skills are −30%.

36-45 Horrendous pain and psychic scream! A stabbing pain shoots through the character's head. It is so terrible that the character screams in agony, grabs his head and drops to his knees. The pain lasts one melee round, during which the character is impervious to ALL psionic attacks, but cannot concentrate enough to perform any skills, use his psychic powers or even move. The character cannot attack or flee — only scream. This pain can happen at any time during the day or night, but especially under stressful conditions and/or when the psychic is using his/her powers a great deal.

As an additional side effect, every person within 1000 feet (305 m) will feel similar pain, although thankfully, less intense. Everybody, including other psionics, lose one melee round action/attack and are −1 on all combat bonuses; no saving throw. Psychic characters must also roll to save vs psionic attack. A failed roll means the psychic loses another melee action and iniative.

46-55 Psionic outburst. Whenever the character uses a psionic energy attack, there's a 50% chance that the energy will surge out of control, inflicting more damage than intended. A roll of 01-50 means everything is okay; no additional damage. 51-00 means a psychic outburst occurs, doing double the maximum damage from that psionic attack. This includes the powers of bio-manipulation, empathic transmission, mind bolt, telekinesis, hydrokinesis, electrokinesis, pyrokinesis, and psi-sword.

56-65 Uncontrolled psychic flash. When the character is in a stressful situation, including combat, he or she may suddenly be struck by a precognitive type vision. The vision comes without warning and lasts only a few seconds. It almost always reflects events currently in motion around him or involving others he knows or cares about up to 2000 miles away! Glimpses of the future are seldom more than 10 minutes forward. The most typical flash of insight will be a vision of the enemy responsible for or directing the attack, a flash of a friend in imminent danger (a booby trap, a grenade about to be thrown, an enemy about to attack, an ally falling/getting struck down, an important item falling to the enemy, danger to somebody away from the main conflict, kidnapping, fire, magic, a rift opening, etc.).

Such an uncontrolled psychic flash can be helpful, but it is also temporarily debilitating as the psychic is temporarily blinded by the vision, loses one melee attack and cannot defend himself from any attack that may be directed at him at that split second (if he's lucky he won't be involved in melee combat that exact moment, or if he is, the enemy misses or inflicts only minor damage). **G.M. Note:** The player character has absolutely NO control over when the flash might occur or what/who/when it may be about. There are times when the character may receive a flash of insight on a daily or weekly basis, or even several times within an hour depending on the situation, and then not get a psychic flash for weeks or months. This is a completely random happening. Furthermore, it doesn't matter whether or not the character has any other psychic sensitive or psionic powers at all.

66-75 Random paralysis. 1D4 times a day, the neural synapses that link the mind to the body are disrupted and part of the character's body becomes temporarily paralyzed. Roll percentile dice to see which part of the body is affected.

01-25 The left arm and hand becomes limp and useless for 2D4 melee rounds.

26-50 The right arm and hand becomes limp and useless for 3D4 melee rounds.

51-75 One of the legs becomes paralyzed for 2D4 minutes. Reduce speed and the abilities to climb, swim, perform gymnastics, acrobatics or piloting of a vehicle by 50%!

76-00 Vocal cords become paralyzed. The character cannot speak and has difficulty swallowing for 2D6 minutes.

SIEMBIEDA · 93

76-85 An uncontrolled telekinetic outburst. Once or twice a day, usually while the character is sleeping, telekinetic energy leaks from him and affects people and objects within a 20 foot radius of the character. A total of 1000 pounds (450 kg) can be affected. Typically, the uncontrolled TK energy will cause a variety of objects and people to rise 2D6 feet into the air, where they swirl around at a speed of seven (about 5 mph/8 km). Other times only objects weighing one pound or less (0.45 kg) are affected, but they fly around randomly, bouncing off of larger objects and people at a speed of 9 (about 10 mph/16 km)! These items can cause damage to people, property and to themselves. The incident is certainly annoying and causes confusion.

The incident will last 6D6 minutes or until the character causing it wakes up/regains consciousness and control. An uncontrolled telekinetic outburst can also occur when the character is awake but dazed, stunned, feverish, or suffering from delusions (magical or drug induced). **Note:** In most instances, the character doesn't normally have telekinetic powers available to him/her. Whether or not the individual normally has telekinetic powers has no effect on the TK outburst.

86-92 Energy burst and loss of control. Whenever the character becomes excited, happy, frightened, angry or stressed, the brain pumps in too much adrenaline and other stimulants. On the positive side, the character is temporarily +3 on initiative, +6 to damage, gets one additional attack/action per melee round, and speed is increased by 50%.

On the negative side, the character is so hyped and pumped up that he doesn't know his own strength, loses control of his actions, and is likely to hurt himself or others. **Penalties:** −3 to strike, −2 to parry and dodge, −6 to pull punch, −6 to roll with impact, plus he or she is likely to overshoot targets when leaping or lunging, hit harder than intended, accidentally strike somebody else, break things, knock things over, crush delicate items in his hands, trip over his own fast moving feet, talk so fast that he slurs his words (−30% to be understood), and generally acts, reacts and overreacts without thinking.

The adrenaline burst lasts about 1D4+1 minutes (no less than 8 melee rounds), but when the energy burst is over, the character feels tired and slow. For the next 2D4 minutes the character is −1 on initiative, −1 to strike and loses one attack per melee round. After this period the character returns to normal. An energy burst can occur as often as once every 15 minutes and happens at happy, exciting times as well as moments of duress. This character should be thought of as a clumsy, accident prone klutz — a bull in a china shop.

93-00 Hyper-active: This talkative and inquisitive character gets a bonus of +1 on initiative, but has trouble staying focused and concentrating on anything, especially boring things, for more than 20 minutes. After twenty minutes, the character is −10% on skill performance and −30% after 60 minutes. This is not the guy to put on guard duty because he'll fall asleep, read, talk with others, draw pictures in the dirt, or does something else other than concentrate on the job at hand. This character also tends to be chronically late by 2D6 minutes.

Side Effects Table
Number Two: Insanities

01-10 Phobia regarding the Angel of Death and her top henchmen; quakes in terror and pleads for them not hurt him/her. Cannot attack any of these characters unless seriously provoked, and even then the poor soul is −5 on initiative and −5 to strike, parry and dodge.

11-20 Schizophrenic! A voice (sounds a lot like the soft voice of The Angel of Death) suggests things, often tempting things, contrary to one's alignment. Very disturbing! The character must constantly fight with himself to follow his original alignment!! He or she may eventually change alignment, at which point the voice suggests things contrary to the new alignment. A maddening situation.

21-30 Phobic of brodkil with bionics or M.O.M. implants. Nervous around crazies and cyborgs in general.

31-40 Phobic of cybernetic implants (M.O.M. implants in particular). The character will NEVER get another implant of any kind ever again! He will warn others likewise and tell them frightening stories about the horrors, insanity and evil of Mindwerks. Bionic prosthetics, especially bio-systems, are acceptable but even they make the character nervous.

41-50 Paranoid Schizophrenic! A voice regularly warns the character not to trust the words and actions of other people, especially beings and O.C.C.s that the character has a dislike or distrust for to begin with.

51-60 Intimidated by cyborgs and crazies; tends to be frightened of them and avoids them whenever possible. Even the toughest character with this affliction will be polite, humble, apologetic and submissive to these beings, taking an amazing amount of verbal and even physical abuse (slaps, shoves, spit, etc.) from them. If forced or provoked to face them, the character is −3 on initiative and −1 on all other combat bonuses.

61-65 Sadistic; the character likes to inflict pain. This can be physical pain and/or emotional mental pain via intimidation, threats, and lies.

66-70 Multiple personalities (see **Rifts RPG,** page 59).

71-75 Roll on the affective disorder table in the Rifts RPG.

76-83 Roll on the neurosis table found in the Rifts RPG.

84-92 Roll on the Random Insanity Table in the Rifts RPG as a result of trauma.

93-00 Roll on the psychosis table found in the Rifts RPG.

Physical M.O.M. Augmentation

Maximum number of implants: A typical character can get two physical augmenting M.O.M. implants without having to change his Occupational Character Class to the Crazy O.C.C. (occasionally three implants are possible if the Game Master allows it). Typically getting three or more M.O.M. implants means the character must become a **Crazy,** receiving all of that O.C.C.'s powers, bonuses and insanities (see the **Rifts RPG,** page 56).

Combining crazy implants with psynetic types is difficult and dangerous. If a character is a crazy, he can only get <u>one</u> lesser psynetic M.O.M. implant (optional; G.M.'s decision). If the character has three or more psynetic implants he or she can only get <u>one</u> physical, crazy M.O.M. implant (optional; G.M.'s decision). To use any other combination is to cause severe brain damage (as described in Side Effects Table number one) and 1D4 additional insanities (select from or roll on Side Effects Table number two). M.O.M. implants cannot be combined with bionic systems other than the occasional bio-system or prosthetic limb (an artificial limb will not have the same strength, prowess or reaction time because it is not part of the natural body augmented by the M.O.M. implants).

Note: Unlike the psynetic implants which are usually designed to explode if tampered with, crazy M.O.M. implants can be removed, replaced and repaired with little difficulty. However, any insanities or other side effects are permanent whether the implants stay or are removed.

List of Available M.O.M. Implants
(traditional physical augmentation)

Brain Programming
Enhanced Healing
Enhanced Speed
Enhanced Strength
Enhanced Endurance
Eternal Brain
Hyper Sense
Standard Full Crazy Conversion (see O.C.C.s)
Others (special cybernetic items)

> Brain Wave Identifier
> Controller Chip
> Explosive Chip
> Tracking Device

Brain Programming

Scientists have argued for years that the human mind cannot be instantly implanted with knowledge like programming a computer. Humans, they say, must learn and remember. Mindwerks has proved them wrong. The brain program implant can give a character any five skills at 88% efficiency regardless of his or her I.Q., training, or level of experience! The character is not conscious of this knowledge and the skill abilities do not increase with experience, but they can be performed whenever the need arises. The character just knows how to do them. There is no restriction as to what abilities are available, thus one can select several skills from the same skill category or each of the five from a different category. Likewise, these skills do not have to conform with the character's normal O.C.C. or other requirements.

Special Penalties and Insanities (roll percentile dice):

01-40 ALL skills ever "learned" by the character are permanently −30%! Of course this does not include the implanted programmed skills.

41-60 ALL skills "learned" are −10% and the character has trouble concentrating and focusing his attention. Penalties: −1 on initiative, −2 to save vs horror factor, illusions and mind control. The character is easily distracted and tricked.

61-80 ALL skills "learned" by the character are −15%, plus he or she suffers from short-term memory loss, is habitually 4D6 minutes late, and the character has difficulty learning new things (new skills are learned at half the normal rate).

81-00 The character permanently forgets eight of his old skills (player's choice). This is frustrating because the character does remember that he once knew the skills, but no matter how hard he tries, he cannot remember how to do them. This may include things as simple as driving a car or singing. The lost skills cannot be relearned (mental block)!

Note: Crazies can get this programming as an additional implant with one of the above penalties.

Enhanced Healing

The recipient of this M.O.M. implant heals twice as quickly as normal people, is +2 to save vs poison, drugs and disease, and +5 to save vs coma/death.

Special Penalties and Insanities (roll percentile dice):

01-45 Feels superior to other humans and will eventually become cold and indifferent toward "lesser" beings.

46-85 Becomes reckless and takes foolish chances.

86-00 No penalties or insanities.

Enhanced Physical Endurance

The character adds 3D4×10 to his or her S.D.C. and is +2 to save vs magic, poison and disease, and +10% to save vs coma/death. Furthermore, the character can carry two times more than a normal person of equivalent strength and can last 10 times longer before feeling the effects of exhaustion.

Special Penalties and Insanities (roll percentile dice):

01-25 Brain damage: Reduce I.Q. by 20%, but the character is impervious to all forms of mind control, +2 to save vs magic illusions and +2 to save vs horror factor.

26-50 The bulked up character reduces his speed by 10% and is −1 attack per melee round.

51-75 Add another 1D4×10 points to S.D.C. but reduce speed by half.

76-00 Stiffness in joints, reduce speed by 20% and the character is −1 on initiative, −1 to parry and dodge and −2 to roll with impact or fall.

Enhanced Speed

The character adds 3D6 to the Spd attribute (minimum Spd. is 19). Plus the character can leap 12 feet (3.6 m) across and 8 feet (2.4 m) high.

Special Penalties and Insanities (roll percentile dice):

01-50 Increased metabolism! The character eats twice as much as a normal person and still can't gain a pound. To eat a normal amount of food is to lose five pounds (2.3 kg) a day. After a week the character will feel weak; reduce speed by 10%, −1 on initiative and all combat bonuses and tires twice as quickly. There are no penalties if the character has plenty to eat.

51-70 Speed freak! Likes to go fast — the faster the better. Loves motorcycles, hover cycles, jets packs, jet aircraft, and so on. Tends to take foolish risks when piloting a vehicle.

71-80 Roll on Side Effects table number two (insanities).

81-90 Compulsive about being on time. Usually 3D6 minutes early. Hates being late (or even only a minute early) and gets cranky and snide when delayed by others.

91-00 Feels aggressive and superior toward weaker, slower beings; the character tends to be tough, cocky and may eventually become a bully or sadistic.

Enhanced Strength

The character adds 2D4 to the P.S. attribute (minimum P.S. is 19) and adds 4D6 points to his or her S.D.C.

Special Penalties and Insanities (roll percentile dice):

01-40 The bulked up character reduces his speed by 10% and is −1 on initiative.

41-80 Add another four points to the character's P.S. and 10 points to S.D.C. but reduce speed by half and I.Q. by one point; big and strong, but slow.

81-90 Passive and tries to avoid violence; the character may eventually become a paranoid or recluse.

91-00 Feels aggressive and superior toward weaker beings; the character tends to be tough, cocky and may eventually become a bully or sadistic.

Eternal Brain

This is The Angel of Death's secret process for keeping the brain from physical deterioration and enabling it to live without the effects of old age for as long as its physical body survives (flesh and blood or artificial body — The Angels of Death and Vengeance have lived over 200 years as cyborgs).

Some unexpected side effects include a prolonged life, a reduction of the aging process (doubles the average life span of humans; increases most D-bees by a mere 50%), +2 on initiative, +2 to save vs psionic attack, +1D6 to save vs horror factor, and an enhanced immune system (+3 to save vs poison, drugs and disease, +10% to save vs coma and death).

Special Penalties and Insanities (roll percentile dice):

01-40 Feels superior to other humans and will eventually become a megalomaniac or cold and indifferent to "lesser" beings. The character loses his kinship to his fellow man.

41-52 Roll on Side Effects table number one (see psynetics).

53-65 Roll on Side Effects table number two (see psynetics).

66-85 Becomes paranoid or falls prey to the *Invasion of the Body Snatchers* neurosis (see the Rifts RPG).

86-00 No penalties or insanities.

Hyper Sense

Range: Touch or 5 feet (1.5 m) per level of experience.
Duration: Two minutes per level of experience.
I.S.P.: 10
Saving Throw: Not applicable

This implant enhances the five senses and makes the character very alert. The character is a light sleeper and is not easily surprised. Bonuses: +2 on initiative, +1 to parry, +2 to dodge, +2 to roll with impact or fall, +2 to pull punch and +1 to save vs horror factor.

01-25 Has trouble sleeping and tends to be jumpy, over-reacting to sights and sounds.

26-50 Hyper and fidgety: taps fingers, cracks knuckles, hums, whistles, sighs, or may talk all the time and tends to get on other people's nerves.

51-75 Becomes reckless and takes foolish chances.

76-00 No penalties or insanities.

Other Implants of Note

The Angel of Death uses cybernetic devices implanted in the brain as a means to control her minions. Everybody who works at Mindwerks or at one of her surface body-chop-shops or who is taught her secrets of M.O.M. technology, have the first three devices. The only exceptions are Marsalis, Angel of Vengeance and herself; but all three have brain wave identifiers in their heads. **Note:** These devices can be installed and removed without causing insanities, special powers or strange side effects to appear in the recipient. They should be considered to be just another type of cybernetic implant.

1. Brain wave identifier: All brain patterns are as distinctive as a fingerprint. This implant allows various Mindwerks security systems and psynetic crazies to identify a character by his or her brain waves. Some top security locations can only be accessed by a handful of personnel who are admitted only when their brain waves are identified. Those with the identifier implant can be scanned and recognized by security systems in three seconds. The brain wave identifier is a fool proof means of accurately identifying people. No matter how perfect a physical disguise, the infiltrator cannot mask his brain waves.

2. Controller Chip: This device works similarly to a hypnotic suggestion to enforce the Angel of Death's control over trouble-makers, captives, and experimental subjects. The recipient of the chip will respond in a specific way to a particular situation. All situations and responses deal with things that involve either the Angel of Death or Angel of Vengeance, but not both. The controller chip will respond to the character's chemical, nervous and mental reactions when faced with doing one of the following or when forced to face/answer to the Angel of Death or Vengeance. About 40% of Angel's minions and 50% of her most important (for the moment) experimental subjects have been implanted with a controller chip.

Situations (select a maximum of two): Attack/hurt (the Angel of Death or Vengeance), lie to or betray (the Angel of Death/Mindwerks), steal from Mindwerks/Angel of Death, do anything to sabotage Mindwerks, gives less than one's all at work (must give at least 95%), cooperate with or protect known enemies, reveal Mindwerks' location to outsiders, or leave Mindwerks.

Reactions (select one): Paralysis, blindness, uncontrolled sobbing, incapacitating head or stomach pain, or uncontrolled stuttering and trembling.

In each case, the character is reduced to one attack/action per melee, all combat bonuses are reduced to zero, and skills to 10% when facing the situation (defying orders) and/or when facing the Angel of Death (only 20% are programmed to respond to the Angel of Vengeance in this way). In 98% of the cases, the reaction will prevent the character from doing the deed he or she is programmed not to do. Even if the character can force himself to persevere, he will be extremely impaired in carrying out his act of defiance.

3. Explosive Chip: Simply a tiny device implanted in the brain that can be detonated by the Angel of Death, Angel of Vengeance or Marsalis at any time; provided the chip is within 1000 feet of Mindwerks or one of those three characters. The explosive is detonated by a special, hand-held detonator. Only Angel, Vengeance and Marsalis have such a detonator. However, such an extreme tactic is used as a last resort. The lords of Mindwerks prefer to use greed, intimidation, fear and torture to keep troublemakers in line. It is usually enough to threaten detonation to keep workers under control.

If the chip is detonated, the small internal explosion in the brain will cause the following results:

01-50 Instant Death!

51-75 Brain damage: Alive but paralyzed and in a vegetative state.

76-00 Brain damage: Alive, but I.Q. is reduced to 1D4 points, 2D4 × 10% of all memories are lost, all but the most rudimentary skills are also lost and even those that remain are −50%, and the character has a maximum of two attacks/actions per melee. Character may be child-like in his or her perceptions and reactions to the world (roughly equal to a five or six year old).

4. Tracking device: A tiny device implanted in the brain that can be located and tracked anywhere inside the Mindwerks complex or within 1000 feet (305 m) with a hand-held scanner. The tracker is also used to help locate and identify subjects of experimentation. 80% of the Mindwerks personnel and 40% of captives scheduled for M.O.M. experimentation and release are implanted with a tracker.

Psynetics

Psynetics are cybernetic brain implants that instil, boost or augment a character with psionic powers. Typically the recipient of psynetics M.O.M. implants is a minor, major or master psionic — the greater the psychic ability to begin with, the better.

Some people are likely to draw comparisons between psynetic implants and techno-wizard devices. While it's true both can be powered by psionic inner strength points (I.S.P.), psynetics are unique bio-implants that are implanted directly into the brain. The implants enable the recipient to tap into a greater reservoir of psychic energy locked within his mind and body. By contrast, techno-wizard devices are a melding of magic and technology that are created, powered and accessed by mystic or psychic energy. While it is true a clever techno-wizard <u>may</u> be able to create a few devices with similar responses (such as telekinetic extensions), techno-wizard items are not related to psynetic implants in any way.

K. SIEMBIEDA · 94

Who can get Psynetic M.O.M. Implants?

All the same fundamental limitations that apply to Crazies (described previously) apply to psynetic augmentation. Only humans, True Atlanteans, Altara warrior women, ogres, orcs, elves, simvan, most humanoid D-bees and mortal life forms in general, including brodkil and gurgoyles, can receive psynetic M.O.M. brain implants. The Angel of Death has made and/or outfitted entire armies of brodkil, ogres and gurgoyles with psynetic and bionic augmentation.

Psynetic implants and most cybernetic systems will NOT work on powerful supernatural beings, shape-changers and creatures of magic. Practitioners of magic avoid them and most types of bionics because the artificial devices interfere with the use of magic. Many people avoid M.O.M. augmentation because of the debilitating and personality changing insanities and side effects that come with them.

Maximum number of implants: A typical character can get two psynetic implants without having to change his or her Occupational Character Class (occasionally three if they instil minor psi-powers and the Game Master allows it). To get more than three psynetic implants turns the character into a **psynetic crazy** — a creature of great psionic power, many of which are derived from the artificial brain implants.

Combining crazy implants with psynetic types is difficult and dangerous. If a character is a crazy, he can only get one lesser psynetic M.O.M. implant (optional; G.M.'s decision). If the character has three or more psynetic implants he or she can only get one physical, crazy M.O.M. implant (optional; G.M.'s decision). Any other combination will cause severe brain damage (as described in Side effects Table number one) and 1D4 additional insanities (select from or roll on Side effects Table number two). M.O.M. implants cannot be combined with bionic systems other than the occasional bio-system or prosthetic limb. An artificial limb will not have the same strength, prowess or reaction time because it is not part of the natural body augmented by the M.O.M. implants.

General penalties: Characters who are of an O.C.C. other than Crazies or Psynetic Crazies permanently loses one skill for every one psynetic implant. Receiving three or more implants means the character is −5% on all the remaining skills because he or she becomes so dependent on the psionic powers.

Availability: Only from Mindwerks. Nobody else has ever been able to create M.O.M. implants that can give a person psychic powers.

Protecting the secrets of psynetic M.O.M. technology: An anti-tamper explosive device is part of most psynetic implants (Marsalis is one notable exception). Remember, the Angel of Death is paranoid and does not want her secrets of psynetic augmentation to fall into the hands of her enemies. Also remember that captives given her "gift" of power are considered expendable experiments, so she has little regret for causing a character's head to explode! The implant will typically explode only when it is surgically tampered with. Most M.O.M. implants of all kinds can take an incredible amount of bangs, bumps, and jarring without the slightest chance of detonation. It is only when the implant is being disconnected from the brain or the character dies (30 hit points below zero and no chance of recovery) that an electromagnetic/psionic trigger activates the explosive. Any cyber-doc worth a credit will recognize this danger the moment he examines the device. Only an insane doctor will risk getting his hands blown off (or killed) trying to remove it. Furthermore, the denotation of a psynetic implant will cause all the other implants to explode, killing the character with the implants, inflicting 2D6 M.D. to a five foot (1.5 m) radius and unleashing a psychic scream that is three times more severe and damaging than that listed in Side effects table number one.

This extreme measure of protection means nobody has been able to examine and knock-off any psynetic device! Only the Angel of Death and her technicians at Mindwerks can remove, replace, or install psynetic implants.

Available Psynetic M.O.M. Implants

Advanced Sixth Sense
Amplified Telemechanics
Ectoplasmic Disguise
Kinesis Machine
Psionic Defense System (ideal for non-psychics)
Psionic Inducer (for non-psychics)
Psionic Nullifier (negates psionics)

Psychometric Amplifier
Psychometric Booster
Psynetic Eye
Nano-Amplifiers
Telekinetic Extensions
TK Force Field Auto-Defense
Telepathic Senders (for non-psychics and psychics)

Advanced Sixth Sense

Range: Varies; typically touch
Duration: Instant or 15 seconds
I.S.P.: Varies; none, 6 or 12
Saving Throw: Not applicable
Special Penalties and/or Insanities: Roll on Side effect Table number two.

This power is available only to characters with some degree of psychic power to begin with. Advanced sixth sense has elements of sixth sense, clairvoyance and object read all rolled into one, but limited to specific elements of imminent danger.

The character will instantly and automatically sense if something is dangerous to him without activating the psionic power or using I.S.P. points. For example: If his food is poisoned or drugged he will sense danger the second he picks up the fork or touches a morsel. If his drink is poisoned he knows there's danger the moment he raises the glass. If a container, door, or vehicle is booby-trapped he knows it the instant he touches it! This power automatically activates without I.S.P. cost before the character touches an item that will explode or trigger a trap. Under these circumstances, the character does not know exactly what the danger is, but he is aware of its presence and may be able to make an accurate guess as to its nature.

To clearly identify the danger, the individual must expend six I.S.P. points. When this is done, he receives a psychic flash showing exactly what the danger is. If it is poison or drugs the character knows exactly what the dangerous substance is and what it will do to people who drink/eat it (kill, damage, paralyze, induce sleep, hallucinations, etc.). If a booby trap, he will know its exact nature, how it works, what it will do (explode, release a toxic gas, activate concealed lasers, etc.), how to avoid activating it, how to deactivate it (but only a 55% chance of success) or how to activate it but avoid getting hurt (a 65% chance of success).

Furthermore, for the cost of 12 I.S.P., the character can use his advanced sixth sense to sweep a small area to sense traps and danger. The range is limited to a three foot (0.9 m) radius per level of experience and lasts only one melee round (15 seconds). During that time the character cannot move or perform any other skills, but must focus entirely on sensing danger. This power will reveal the exact location (within range) and nature of the danger: traps, concealed weapons, concealed surveillance devices, wards and magic guardians, ambushes, invisible supernatural beings laying in wait and so on.

Note: The psychic insight does NOT reveal who is responsible for the danger, or who constructed any traps, nor his or her motives. Nor can it be used to locate secret doors or passageways. This psychic insight is limited completely to things that represent a danger to the character.

Amplified Telemechanics

Range: Touch or 5 feet (1.5 m) to use normal telemechanics power or touch to use the amplified powers described below.
Duration: Three minutes per level of experience.
I.S.P.: 10 or 30
Saving Throw: Not applicable
Special Penalties and/or Insanities: Roll on Side Effects Tables number two.

Limitations: Can be implanted only in characters who already possess some degree of psionic ability, including crazies.

The character with this implant has all the usual telemechanics powers as described on page 127 of the **Rifts RPG**, but also has the ability to seize complete mental control of most high-tech weapon or computer systems with the following effects:

1. Temporarily off-line (10 I.S.P.): The system isn't shut off, it just will not respond in any way until the psychic releases the machine. This can be used on sensory and communications systems, computers, weapon systems, relay junctions, etc.

2. Usurp control (30 I.S.P.): The psychic can mentally control the machine to override any other commands. Thus, he can make weapon turrets turn a different direction and shoot at whoever he desires (including the vehicle itself), increase or decrease the damage (applicable only to weapons with variable settings), fire wildly, expending all of its payload, not fire at all, and so on. This power can also be used to make vehicles speed up, slow down, stop, turn off, fire weapons, make radio contact, etc. Computers and sensory devices can be mentally controlled to provide false or erroneous data (whatever he wants).

In all cases, the character must be in physical contact with the machine. Although this character can seize control of robots, power armor and exo-skeletons, this power does <u>not</u> work against cybernetic or bionic systems; presumably because they are linked to an organic brain/intelligence and tissue. Likewise, this power will not work against A.R.C.H.I.E. Three, robots controlled by a transferred intelligence/life essence, bots directly controlled by virtual reality link, sophisticated artificial intelligences that simulate the human brain, bio-wizard items, techno-wizard items or items linked to magic in any way. Some alien devices may also be impervious to this power.

Note: The character cannot perform any other skills, attacks or tasks while he or she is overriding and controlling the machine. To do something else instantly breaks mental contact and he/she must then spend another 30 I.S.P. to regain control.

Crazies with this implant tend to be maniacs and love to use high-tech weapons and machines to reap mayhem. Most find chaos, riots, panic, and destruction to be exhilarating.

Ectoplasmic Disguise

Range: Self
Duration: 5 minutes per level of experience.
I.S.P.: 10 to cover face/change features, 35 to cover the entire body.
Saving Throw: Not applicable.
Special Penalties and/or Insanities: Roll once on Side Effects Table number one.
Limitations: Can be implanted only in characters who already possess some degree of psionic ability, including crazies.

This implant enables the character to create solid, flesh-like ectoplasm to cover his body. The character can mentally mold and shape the ectoplasm to change his facial features or the shape of his entire body (restricted by body armor and tight clothing). For this particular use, the character can create an instant disguise (takes about one minute).

The ectoplasm disguise is most effective when the character has some time to plan and can add make-up, a wig, hat, cape, and other articles of clothing to help complete the illusion. Ectoplasm always has an unnatural, waxy look to it and only has two shades of color, pink or grey. Consequently, this disguise never holds up to close scrutiny. However, the character can quickly change his shape to resemble other races, change distinctive features (big nose, completely bald, hunched back, add extra limbs, antenna, a tail, etc.), look older or younger and so on. Basic disguise skill/success ratio is 80% from a distance, in a crowd, or in shadow, but only 40% up close and a mere 12% under close inspection.

Kinesis Machine

Range: Self; range of the powers is increased by 10 feet (3 m).
Duration: Same as psionic power (see Rifts RPG for descriptions).
I.S.P.: Same as the psionic power.
Saving Throw: Same as the psionic power.
Special Penalties and/or Insanities: Roll once on Side Effects Table number two.
Limitations: This implant can be installed on psychics and non-psychic characters, but the non-psionic does NOT get the range bonus and must also roll once on Side Effects table one as well as number two. Non-psychics get their M.E. ×5 as their base I.S.P. reserve and do not get additional I.S.P. as they increase in experience.

This psynetic implant instills any one of the kinetic psi-super powers: electrokinesis, hydrokinesis, pyrokinesis or telekinesis. As many as two of these implants can be installed to provide two different types of powers, but in each case the character must roll for a side effect from table number two.

Nano-Amplifiers

Range: Self
Duration: Permanent as long as the nano-implants are functioning.
I.S.P.: Special: additional 1D6×10 I.S.P. while the nanites are functioning.
Saving Throw: Not applicable.
Special Penalties and/or Insanities: See "complete mental melt-down."
Limitations: Can only be implanted in characters who have minor or major psionics (don't work in master psionics or non-psychics).

Nano robots enter the brain via the inner ear and bury themselves at key psionic centers of the brain. They stimulate the brain, creating new psionic powers in psychics. These tiny bots can only be used on humans and D-bees who already possess minor or major psionic powers. They do not work on master psionics or those without psychic powers.

The nano-bots increase the range, duration and damage of existing psionic powers by 50%. They also provide an additional 1D6×10 I.S.P. and the character receives all the powers from either the healing or physical psionic categories (player's choice)!

As the nanites deteriorate, the character's control over his powers diminishes and they soon become uncontrollable — new nano-bots must be installed to avoid a complete "mental melt-down!" Nanites begin to deteriorate at a rate of 1D4×10% per month after only five months.

At a 40% to 79% deterioration level, the use of psionic powers is unpredictable. Roll on the following table every time a psi-power is used.
01-20 Half as powerful
21-40 50% more powerful
41-50 Two times more powerful.
51-60 Twice the range but half as powerful.
61-70 Half the normal range, but at the usual level of power/damage and duration.
71-80 Half the duration but normal strength and range.
81-90 Doesn't work and half the I.S.P. necessary is expended; try again.
91-00 Wrong power engages at full strength! G.M. picks power.
Complete "mental melt-down" at 80% deterioration or greater! The character suffers with the following penalties and problems.

Penalties:
- Feels like he's loosing control and needs to prove himself. May take foolish chances and is easily provoked. 01-40% become depressed and dependent on drugs and/or alcohol.
- −4 to save vs mind control and possession (but +2 to save vs horror factor).

- Lacks confidence; performance of all skills is −25%.
- −1 on initiative
- Psychic overload. The use of any psychic sensitive powers like telepathy, empathy, etc., cannot be focused toward any one person, item or place. Instead the psychic sees/hears/senses a jumble of a hundred different things — like trying to listen to a hundred different people all talking at once (and loudly too). Sensitive powers are rendered virtually useless.
- Psychic shut-out. Whenever the character uses a mind block he cannot turn it off until the maximum duration has expired, and feels disoriented, as if his other senses were partially blocked as well. The character will be unable to accurately identify tastes and smells (only 50% chance), won't notice things and seems dazed or preoccupied; −4 on initiative and is −1 on all combat rolls.

Roll on the following table every time a psionic power is used by a character suffering from a complete mental melt-down: The character cannot control his powers and may hurt those around him. Furthermore, every time he uses any psionic power, even those he had before the nano-amplifiers, it causes a dangerous, often painful reaction.

01-20 Wrong power engages at double strength and duration.

21-40 Wrong power engages at half strength.

41-60 Right power but at one-quarter the normal duration, range and damage/strength.

61-70 No control! Inflicts triple damage and the character cannot turn the power off once it is activated! He must let it run the maximum normal duration.

71-80 Incredible head pain — as if somebody has stabbed a burning knife behind his eyes. For the next 2D6 minutes the character is temporarily blind (all he can see is a blinding white light; −8 to strike, parry and dodge, no initiative), attacks/actions per melee round are reduced by half, he cannot concentrate to use his psionic powers and skill performance is reduced by 60%!

81-00 Horrendous pain and psychic scream! A stabbing pain shoots through the character's head. It is so terrible that the character screams in agony, grabs his head and drops to his knees. The pain lasts one melee round, during which the character is impervious to ALL psionic attacks, but cannot concentrate enough to perform any skills, use his psychic powers or even move. The character cannot attack or flee — only scream.

As an additional side effect, every person within 1000 feet (305 m) will feel similar pain, although thankfully, less intense. Everybody, including other psionics, lose one melee round action/attack and are −1 on all combat bonuses; no saving throw. Psychic characters must also roll to save vs psionic attack. A failed roll means the psychic loses another melee action and initiative.

The final penalty: When the last of the nano-amplifiers are gone, the character loses his bonus I.S.P. and all the powers the tiny machines gave him. Thankfully, with the nano-bots gone, all of his skills and abilities return to normal, but his remaining psionic powers function at half his real experience level (i.e. a sixth level character has psionic powers equal to a third level character). Getting new nano-amplifiers will restore his natural powers back to normal strength/level and provide the bonus I.S.P. and additional powers.

Psionic Defense System

Range: Self
Duration: Permanent as long as the implant is functioning.
I.S.P.: Special: This device is actually designed for characters who don't have psionic powers. Its installation will reduce a character's base P.P.E. by 33%!
Saving Throw: Not applicable.
Special Penalties and/or Insanities: Roll once on Side effect Tables numbers one and two. Furthermore, the nature of the implant is such that it destroys the psychic's ability to use telepathy, empathy or empathic transmission.
Limitations: Suitable only for NON-psionic characters because using the device in psychic individuals closes the character off from the psychic world.

The recipient of this M.O.M. implant has limited invulnerability to psionic attacks and probes. The character is impervious to see aura, sense evil, sense magic, detect psionics, psychic diagnosis, telepathy, empathy, and hypnosis. He is also +4 to save vs possession, mind control, horror factor, and empathic transmission, and +2 to save vs all other types of psionic attacks.

Note: A psychic character can get this implant and would also be impervious to the psionic probes listed above, but the psychic cannot use any of those powers himself and will find his available I.S.P. constantly at half (P.P.E. is not affected)! Furthermore, the range, duration and damage inflicted by the character's other psi-powers are at half (similar to the psionic nullifier).

Psionic Inducer

Range: Self
Duration: Permanent as long as the implant is functioning.
I.S.P.: Special: Permanently reduces P.P.E. base by 25%
Saving Throw: Not applicable.
Limitations: Two psionic inducers maximum.
Special Penalties and/or Insanities: Roll once on Side Effects Table number one for the first inducer and on number two if a second inducer is installed.
Limitation: This M.O.M. brain implant can only be used on characters who do NOT have natural psionic powers.

One implant can give the character 1D4 random psionic powers from the healing, sensitive or physical category (G.M. can assign each power a number in numerical order, then he or the player can roll the appropriate number of dice. The number that comes up indicates the random power. Roll again if the same power is rolled more than once).

The inducer also gives the character an I.S.P. base of 3D6+10 points. Unlike natural psychic characters, the recipient of the implant does NOT gain additional I.S.P. with subsequent levels of experience. A maximum of two psionic inducers can be implanted for a possible total of 2-8 psionic powers. **Note:** This implant cannot be used with the psionic defense system or on characters who already have any degree of psychic power.

Psionic Nullifier

Range: Self
Duration: Permanent as long as the implant is functioning.
I.S.P.: Special: This device is designed to prevent psychic individuals from using their powers! Its installation will reduce a character's I.S.P. by 75%!!
Saving Throw: Every time the character tries to use one of his psionic powers, he must roll a 14 or higher to save against the implant. A failed roll means he was unable to summon forth the inner strength to use his psi-power; no I.S.P. is expended from a failed attempt.
Special Penalties and/or Insanities: Roll once on Side Effects Tables one and two.
Limitations: Effective only on characters with psionic powers.

This brain implant inhibits the use of psionic powers by psychic individuals; a terrible and traumatic fate, especially for those who possess major and master psionics. Each and every time the character tries to use a psionic power, he or she must concentrate intensely and roll to save vs the nullifier implanted in the brain (14 or higher).

A successful roll to save vs the nullifier (14 or higher; master psionics are +1 to save) means the psychic can summon forth enough I.S.P.

to use one particular power, but at half the duration, range and damage! Furthermore, only 25% of the psychic's full amount of I.S.P. is available to him and the recovery of I.S.P. takes twice as long as normal.

Note: A M.O.M. conversion specialist or Mindwerks technician can remove the implant with only a 1% chance of fatality. A cyber-doc can also try with a 5% chance of fatality or brain damage. In either case, a successful removal will completely restore the character's I.S.P. and psionic powers. However, any insanities and side effects are permanent; the experience is traumatic and damaging.

KEVIN SIEMBIEDA - 93

Psychometric Amplifier

Range: Self
Duration: Permanent as long as the implant is functioning.
I.S.P.: Standard per power.
Saving Throw: Not applicable.
Special Penalties and/or Insanities: Roll once on Side Effects Table number one for the first amplifier and on number two if a second amplifier is installed.
Limitations: The amplifier is applicable only to humans and D-bees who already possess minor or major psionic powers.

The psynetic device can be used to instil three additional psionic powers of choice from the three more common psionic categories or one super-psionic power! Furthermore, the character's I.S.P. base is increased by 2D6 + 10 points. Additional I.S.P. gained through subsequent levels of experience are unchanged but get a bonus + 2 points.

A maximum of two psychometric amplifier can be implanted for a possible total of two to six psionic powers. Remember, M.O.M. implants do not work on demons, supernatural beings or creatures of magic.

Psychometric Booster

Range: Self
Duration: Permanent as long as the implant is functioning.
I.S.P.: Special: Permanently reduces I.S.P. base by 10%!
Saving Throw: Not applicable.
Special Penalties and/or Insanities: Roll once on Side Effects Table number one.
Limitations: This unique and powerful device is applicable only to humans and D-bees who already possess psionic powers.

The implant increases the range, duration and damage of all existing psi-powers as follows: Physical, healing and super-psionic powers are increased by 50%. Psychic sensitive powers see their range and duration doubled! Remember, M.O.M. implants do not work on demons, supernatural beings or creatures of magic.

Psynetic Eye

Range: Varies as described.
Duration: Varies as described.
I.S.P.: Varies
Saving Throw: Not applicable
Special Penalties and/or Insanities: Roll once on Side Effects Tables numbers one and two.
Limitations: Applicable only to characters who possess psionic powers.

A psionic brain implant that is directly linked to a modified cybernetic eye (bio-systems are not suitable). In the alternative, the psynetic eye can be linked to a visor or Heads Up Display of a visor with the same effects but at half the range (Marsalis has this system). The psynetic eye provides the following enhancements:

Mechanical Abilities:

1. Telescopic: 6× magnification, range: 6000 feet (1830 m)

2. Passive night vision: range 2000 feet (610 m)

3. Laser Distancing: Measures and indicates precise distance; range 6000 feet (1830 m).

Psionic Abilities: Powers one and two are automatic and constant, but the implant reduces the character's overall I.S.P. by 5%.

1. See the invisible, including entities, elementals, energy beings, and those turned invisible via magic. Range: 120 feet (36 m).

2. See astral beings. The psynetic eye enables the character to see astral travelers normally invisible even to most psychics! Range: 20 feet (6 m) plus 5 feet (1.5 m) per level of experience.

3. See aura; same as the psionic power. Plus, the auras of most psionic characters flare just before they are about to use a psionic attack. Those with a psynetic eye can see this and take action to attack first, parry, dodge, or flee; +4 on initiative or +2 to dodge under this condition. Note that the use of defensive and passive psionic powers are impossible to see. Range: 20 feet (6 m) plus 5 feet (1.5 m) per level of experience. I.S.P. Cost: 6, Duration: Two melee rounds (30 seconds).

4. Electromagnetic energy blast: 3D6 S.D.C. damage costs 6 I.S.P. or a 1D4 M.D. blast costs 40 I.S.P. The range for both is limited to 20 feet (6 m) plus 5 feet (1.5 m) per level of experience and line of sight. This attack can also be used against astral beings. The number of blasts possible is subject to available I.S.P., Duration: Instant, Bonus: +1 to strike.

Telekinetic Extensions

Range: Varies as described.
Duration: Varies as described.
I.S.P.: Special: Permanently reduces I.S.P. base by 10%, until the limbs and implants are removed!
Saving Throw: Not applicable
Special Penalties and/or Insanities: Roll once on Side Effects Tables numbers one and two.
Limitations: Applicable only to characters who possess major or master psionic powers. The telekinetic power instilled by the implant is limited to the use of extension limbs and cannot be used as an area affect power like normal telekinesis.

Artificial, bionic type hands, arms, tentacles, or weapon arms controlled/animated by telekinesis via a special brain implant. The M.O.M. implant instills telekinetic powers that are linked to special mechanical appendages or extensions. The special neural-psi-connectors in these appendages enable the character to channel his new telekinetic powers into the artificial limbs to manipulate them like an extension of his own body. This means the limbs are powered by psychic energy and do not need an artificial source of energy! Furthermore, the psionic cyber-limbs are keyed to respond only to the character's specific psychic energy signature (like a fingerprint, the brain waves and psychic auras of an individual have a unique signature).

A maximum of six TK limbs/attachments/extensions can be installed. The TK attachments can be designed to replace limbs lost through injury or as additional appendages. Each *pair* of additional TK extensions adds one attack/action per melee round. A typical TK extension/limb has a P.S. of 1D6 + 12 and a P.P. of 1D6 + 10. Legs have a speed of 1D6 + 10. TK arms and/or hands respond and function just like the human appendages. Tentacles and tails are prehensile.

A TK weapon appendage/extension is a telekinetic extension (usually an additional appendage) that has a weapon built into it (usually in place of a hand). All characters can fire a TK-round or kinetic weapon (pistol, rifle, etc.), because he has telekinesis to begin with and the power is already channelled into the artificial limbs. To have a psionic weapon that fires fire/plasma bolts, electricity and so on, he would also need that particular kinesis-power to fire it. Thus, electrokinesis is needed to fire an electric energy weapon extension or pyrokinesis to fire a plasma weapon extension or psionic flamethrower. Note that a character with two or more kinetic powers can have a weapon designed for each appendage, if he so desires.

The weapon extension can only fire one of the following:

TK-Rounds: A rail gun or rifle style weapon that fires TK energy bolts that leave no casings, bullets or muzzle flash. To fire a 3D6 S.D.C. bolt costs 2 I.S.P., to fire a 1D6 M.D. bolt costs 10 I.S.P.; range: 3000 feet (910 m) — the farthest of all the available types of weapons.

Telekinesis can also be used to fire conventional "kinetic" energy drive weapons such as a revolver, pistol, rifle, shotgun, grenade launcher, and even a rail gun. The range of these weapons is the same as usual, but rail guns can't fire farther than 3000 feet (910 m).

Electrokinetic Rounds: An electrical energy bolt is fired, inflicting either a 4D6 S.D.C. bolt costing 3 I.S.P., or a 2D6 M.D. bolt costing 15 I.S.P.; range: 300 feet (91 m).

Pryrokinetic Rounds: A plasma energy bolt is fired, either a 4D6 S.D.C. bolt costing 3 I.S.P. or a 2D6 M.D. bolt costing 15 I.S.P.; range: 300 feet (91 m). A psionic flamethrower appendage can fire a stream of fire 100 feet (30.5 m), doing 6D6 S.D.C. at a cost of 3 I.S.P. or 4D6 M.D. at a cost of 20 I.S.P.

Hydrokinetic Rounds: A blast of water is fired, inflicting 2D6 S.D.C. at a cost of 3 I.S.P. (does 4D6 M.D. to vampires); range: 300 feet (91 m).

TK Force Field Auto-Defense

Range: Self
Duration: Five minutes per level of experience.
I.S.P.: 20
Saving Throw: Not applicable
Special Penalties and/or Insanities: Roll on Side effect Table number two.
Limitations: Applicable only to characters who possess psionic powers.

The psychic instantly erects a force field of telekinetic energy around his body the instant danger is perceived on a conscious or subconscious level. As a result, it is almost impossible to catch the character off-guard without his personal force field going up and protecting him (it is impossible if the character has the power of sixth sense or clairvoyance; instantly pops up as needed). The only negative aspect of this automatic defense system is that it snaps into place and uses up I.S.P. whether the psychic consciously wants to use it or not. Every time it is engaged the 20 I.S.P. are used up.

The force field has 20 M.D.C. per level of experience. If a danger/attack persists, the force field will automatically reengage an instant (about 2 seconds) after the first shield is depleted. This force field cannot be cast around other people nor is it a power available to natural psionics.

Telepathic Sender

Range: Self
Duration: Permanent as long as the implant is functioning.
I.S.P.: Fundamentally the same as the power of telepathy.
Saving Throw: Standard
Special Penalties and/or Insanities: None.
Limitations: This device can be implanted in psychics and non-psionics to instil limited telepathy.

The implant provides the telepathic power as described in the **Rifts RPG**, page 123, but the maximum range is only 20 feet (6 m). However, the character can communicate with other characters who have telepathic senders at a range of 1000 feet (305 m)! Furthermore, master psionics who already possessed telepathy will find their range of communication with other sender devices to be an incredible one mile!

The power to telepathically "send" a message works much like a mental television signal in which the sender can transmit and receive words and images to and from others with this same implant. The telepathic sender cannot reach out and touch those without the brain implant unless the character is within the 20 foot (6 m) general psychic range.

Mindwerks Robots

All Mindwerks Robots and Vehicles have the following features.

1. Nuclear Powered: Which means they have an effectively unlimited fuel capacity and power source. Average life, 20 years.

2. Radar (standard): Can identify and track up to 48 targets simultaneously at a range of 30 miles (48 km).

3. Combat Computer: Calculates, stores, and transmits data onto the heads up display (H.U.D.) of the pilot's helmet. It is tied to the targeting computer.

4. Targeting Computer: Assists in tracking and identification of enemy targets. 30 mile range (48 km).

5. Laser Targeting System: Assists in the selection and focusing of specific targets and adds a bonus of +1 to strike when using long-range weapons. Does not apply to hand to hand combat.

6. Thermo-Imaging and Infrared Optics: Optic systems that can see heat images and the infrared spectrum of light. 2000 (610 m).

7. Telescopic Zoom: 2× to 20× magnification.

8. Video: Most Mindwerks bots have video recording and transmitting capabilities. Range: 6000 feet (1830 m).

9. Radio communication: Long-range, directional communication system with an effective range of about 500 miles (800 km). As well as a directional, short-range radio. Range is 5 miles (8 km). Plus a built-in loudspeaker; 80 decibels.

10. External Audio Pick-up & Loudspeaker: A sound amplification listening system enables the bot pilot to pick up, amplify and hear a whisper 300 feet (91.5 m) away. The loudspeaker allows the pilot or crew to communicate directly with people outside the bot. Range is roughly 4000 feet (1219 m), depending on ambient noise.

11. Internal Language Translator: Most Mindwerks bots have a language translator built-into its communication system. The computer knows the nine major languages, including Euro, American, Dragonese/Elf and Gobblely, plus Brodkil, Gargoyle, Simvan, Kittani, Demongogian, as well as, Pre-Rifts German, Polish and Latin/Greek. The level of accuracy is 98.7% when translating the words of one speaker. That accuracy drops to 78% when three or more people are speaking at the same time. There is a 3 second delay from the spoken word to the translation.

12. Distress Homing Beacon: Most robots are equipped with a scrambled, radio homing signal used for extraction from combat zones.

13. Spotlights/Searchlights: Many of the bots have a searchlight. They may also have headlights or several smaller identification lights. Typical range is 600 feet (182 m).

14. Self-Destruct: All of Mindwerks' robots (and M.O.M. implants for that matter) have a self-destruct mechanism to prevent the robot and Mindwerks technology from being captured by the enemy. The explosive damage is mostly contained inside the robot, destroying most of the internal systems, all computer and film/video data and inflicting 2D6×10 M.D. within a five foot (1.5 m) radius. It is very likely, 1-89% chance, that the nuclear power system will spew forth deadly levels of radiation.

M-1000 Panther

The M-1000 Panther is a defense and security robot controlled by an artificial intelligence. The bot is obedient and is programmed to recognize key members of Mindwerks, allies and enemies. Although it is reasonably efficient, it cannot make subjective decisions or act on hunches. The M-1000, M-1200 and M-1400 are all automated killing machines that function within the parameters of their programming. Although the Angel of Death or Marsalis may change or add programs to specific units, most are given the same basic abilities and tasks.

The M-1000 Panther is designed as a multi-purpose robot programmed for three tasks: security/defense, seek and capture or destroy, and general assistance.

1. Defense: 50% of the M-1000s are programmed to monitor, secure, and defend the factory complex. Most are found underground, but a number are assigned to secure the grounds above and around the secret base. Creatures identified as the enemy are attacked and destroyed. NGR/Triax robots, NGR troops, humans in general, D-bees, vampires, dragons and creatures of magic are usually considered the enemy. Brodkil, gargoyles, simvan, and a handful of others are typically identified as allies.

The bot can be also be programmed to defend a specific area, terminating all intruders. Only a handful of people who are recognized as having clearance are allowed in the restricted area. At top security locations, the panther will be linked to a more sophisticated security system that identifies characters by their brain waves (see identifier implant) — a

security system that can see through the best disguises and shape-changers. Typically, only the three masters of Mindwerks and one or two trusted assistants are allowed into a restricted area.

2. 25% are used for seek and destroy (or capture) mission, unleashing the panther on the unsuspecting surface world to search for, capture and return with test subjects for Mindwerks experiments, retrieve runaways, or extract vengeance against an enemy. They can be dispatched as lone hunters, in pairs, or in small groups of 3 to ten. They can also be members of a larger robot force assigned for whatever reason.

3. The panther is also designed as an all-purpose unit and can be used to assist in mechanical repairs, construction, hauling, transportation, delivery, communication, investigation, and so on.

The panther gets its name from the fact that it is comparatively small, fast and silent — an excellent prowler and stalker.

The oblong bubble in the center of the head is a combination sensor eye and video-recorder/transmitter that can be used by the Angel of Death or her minions like a camera to see everything the bot sees. Optic systems have a range of about 2000 feet (610 m) and transmission range is limited to 200 miles (320 km). Six hours of data can also be recorded and stored for viewing later (typically the last six hours of the bot's experiences are on file). The drone has a handful of built-in weapon systems and can also use hand-held weapons of any sort, including energy weapons and rail guns.

M-1000 Panther
Part of the Mindwerks Defensive Line
German Name: der Panther (pronounced pont air)
Model Type: M-1000
Class: Robot Combat Drone — Unmanned
Crew: None; artificial intelligence
M.D.C. by Location:
    Side Wings (2) — 50 each
    Main Jets (6) — 80 each
    Arms (2) — 90 each
    Mini-Missile Launcher (1, top back) — 150
    Headlights (2; head next to sensor eye) — 5 each

Plasma Rifle (1 or 2) — 70
* Sensor Eye (1; center of head) — 15
* Sensor Clusters (2) — 25 each
* Head — 110
** Main Body — 250

   * Destroying the head or sensor eye of the bot will eliminate all forms of optical recording and transmission as well as impair sensory systems. The robot will respond more slowly: reduce attacks per melee round and combat bonuses by half.

   If the sensor eye or head and two sensor clusters are destroyed, the robot will thrash about and strike at anything it touches (unless shut down by a special code known to the Angel of Death and her top henchmen). In this condition, the robot has only one attack per melee and is −6 to strike, parry and dodge.

   Note: The head and sensor clusters are small and difficult targets to hit. Consequently, they can only be struck when a character makes a *called shot* and even then the attacker is −3 to strike.

   **Depleting the M.D.C. of the main body will destroy the robot completely.

   Note: Destroying three of the hover jets will reduce the bot's speed by half. Destroying four or five will reduce the speed by 75%. Destroying all six immobilizes it — can crawl, using its arms, at a speed of six.

Speed: The powerful hover jet propulsion system enables the panther to hover stationary up to 1000 feet (305 m) high or fly at a maximum speed of 400 mph (640 km)! Cruising speed is considered to be 50 to 150 mph (80 to 240 km).

   It can also travel on top of the water like a hydrofoil at a maximum speed of 80 mph (128.7 km) and travel underwater at a maximum speed of 30 mph (48 km); maximum depth 600 feet (183 m).

Statistical Data
Height: 7 feet (2.1 m) from the top of its head to the bottom jets.
Width: Wings down: 5 feet (1.5 m)
             Wings extended: 7 feet (2.1 m)
Length: 4 feet, 6 inches (1.4 m)
Weight: 1.5 tons
Physical Strength: Equal to a P.S. 40
Cargo: None
Power System: Nuclear, average energy life is 20 years.
Black Market Cost: Not available; exclusive to Mindwerks.
Note: The current stock-pile at Mindwerks is roughly 300 units, but with sufficient materials and incentive, the Mindwerks factory could produce 60 a month.

Weapon Systems

1. Head Lasers: A pair of short-range lasers is mounted in the mouth/chin section of the head. They can move side to side about 30 degrees or fire straight forward.
Primary Purpose: Assault
Secondary Purpose: Defense
Mega-Damage: 2D6 M.D. per individual blast or 4D6 M.D. per simultaneous double blast (counts as one melee attack/action).
Rate of Fire: Six per melee round.
Maximum Effective Range: 1200 feet (366 m)
Payload: Effectively unlimited.
2. Top Mounted Mini-Missile Launcher: The lager canister or hump on the back of robot is a mini-missile launcher.
Primary Purpose: Anti-Aircraft
Secondary Purpose: Defense
Missile Type: Any mini-missile can be used; fragmentation (5D6 M.D.), armor piercing (1D4 × 10 M.D.), plasma (1D6 × 10), smoke or stun/riot control.
Mega-Damage: Varies with missile type.
Range: Usually about a mile.

Rate of Fire: One at a time or in volleys of 2, 4, or 6.
Payload: 48
3. Energy Rifles or Light Rail Guns and other hand-held weapons can be substituted in an emergency or used as a back-up weapon.
Hand to Hand Combat: Rather than use a weapon, the bot can engage in mega-damage hand to hand combat.
   Normal Punch — 1D6 + 1 M.D.
   Power Punch — 2D6 + 2 M.D.
   Body Block/Ram — 1D4 M.D. at low speed, add 1D6 for every 100 mph (160 km).
Combat Bonuses: Six attacks per melee round; +1 on initiative, +5 to strike and parry, +7 to dodge, +2 to roll with impact, and +4 to pull punch. Of course as a robot, the M-1000 is impervious to mind control, horror factor, and normal heat and cold.
Skills of Note: Prowl 80%, climb 60%, detect ambush 60%, detect concealment 60%, and land navigation, navigation, basic and advanced math, basic mechanics, basic electronics, radio: basic, intelligence, identify plants/fruits, T.V./video, and photography, all at 88%; plus W.P. blunt, W.P. sword, W.P. energy pistol, W.P. energy rifle and W.P. energy heavy (all equal to a 5th level soldier). In addition, the bot has a built-in language translator (all major and local languages).
Sensor System Note: The panther has full optical systems, including laser targeting, telescopic, passive night vision (light amplification), thermo-imaging, infrared, ultraviolet, polarization and all the standard features.

M-1200 Lion Assault Robot

   The M-1200 lion is a heavy defense and security robot bristling with weapons. The bot has an artificial intelligence, is obedient and is programmed to recognize key members of Mindwerks, allies and enemies. Although it is reasonably efficient, it cannot make subjective decisions or act on hunches. Like the M-1000 and M-1400, the M-1200 is an automated killing machine used for security, defense, assault and seek and destroy missions.

M-1200 Lion
Part of the Mindwerks Defensive Line
German Name: der Lowe (pronounced low veh)
Model Type: M-1200
Class: Robot Combat Drone — Unmanned
Crew: None; artificial intelligence
M.D.C. by Location:
   Main Jets (3; large) — 140 each
   Large Arms (2) — 120 each
   Small Arms (2) — 60 each
   Weapon Arms (2) — 80 each
   Rail Gun (1; side) — 80
   Mini-Missile Launchers (2, top back) — 70 each
   Exhaust Tubes (2) — 50 each
   Headlights (2; small, above the large eyes) — 2 each
   Plasma Rifle (1 or 2) — 70
   * Sensor Eye (1; center of head) — 15
   * Sensor Clusters (2; eyes) — 35 each
   * Head — 120
   ** Main Body — 350

   * Destroying the head or sensor eyes of the bot will eliminate all forms of optical recording and transmission as well as impair sensory systems. The robot will respond more slowly: reduce attacks per melee round and combat bonuses by half.

   If the sensor eye or head and two sensor clusters (eyes) are destroyed, the robot is blind and will thrash about and strike at anything it touches (unless shut down by a special code known to the Angel

of Death and her top henchmen). In this condition, the robot has only four attacks per melee and is −10 to strike, parry and dodge and has no combat bonuses.

Note: The head and sensor clusters are small and difficult targets to hit. Consequently, they can only be struck when a character makes a *called shot* and even then, the attacker is −3 to strike.

**Depleting the M.D.C. of the main body will destroy the robot completely.

Note: Destroying one of the hover jets will reduce the bot's speed by one third. Destroying two will reduce the speed by 66%. destroying all three immobilizes it — can crawl, using its arms, at a speed of six.

Speed: The powerful hover jet propulsion system enables the M-1200 to hover stationary up to 800 feet (244 m) high or fly at a maximum speed of 220 mph (352 km)! Cruising speed is considered to be 50 mph (80 km).

It can also travel on top of water, like a hydrofoil, at a maximum speed of 45 mph (72 km) or travel underwater at a maximum speed of 30 mph (48 km); maximum depth 800 feet (244 m).

Statistical Data

Height: 11 feet (3.4 m)

Width: 7 feet (2.1 m)

Length: 6 feet (1.8 m)

Weight: 2 tons

Physical Strength: The two large arms have a P.S. 40, the small ones have a P.S. 30.

Cargo: None

Power System: Nuclear, average energy life is 20 years.

Black Market Cost: Not available; exclusive to Mindwerks.

Note: Current stockpile at Mindwerks is roughly 200 units, but with sufficient materials and incentive, the Mindwerks factory could produce 30 a month.

Weapon Systems

1. **Laser Weapon Arm (1):** The lower center arm is a long-range laser. The arm is a tentacle-like appendage that can point in all directions and can parry and strike an opponent as well as shoot him.

Primary Purpose: Assault

Secondary Purpose: Defense

Mega-Damage: 3D6 M.D. per blast

Rate of Fire: Nine! Equal to the number of combined hand to hand attacks of the bot.

Maximum Effective Range: 4000 feet (1200 m)

Payload: Effectively unlimited.

2. **M-44 Dual Ion Cannon Arm (1):** The largest weapon arm has a dual ion weapon. The largest barrel is a long-range ion cannon. The small barrel fires a short-range ion beam. The arm can rotate 360 degrees and can point up and down and side to side 180 degrees.

Primary Purpose: Assault

Secondary Purpose: Defense

Mega-Damage: The short-range ion beam inflicts 5D6 M.D. per single blast. Long-range ion beam does 1D4 × 10 M.D. (much of the energy of the blast is expended to go the long distance).

Rate of Fire: Equal to the bot's hand to hand attacks (9).

Effective Range: Short-range gun: 1000 feet (305 m); long-range cannon: 3000 feet (914 m).

Payload: Effectively unlimited.

3. **Large Arms (2):** These two large arms and hands have a P.S. 40 and are heavily armored. These human-like appendages can use any type of hand-held weapon, including rail guns. Furthermore, each arm has a concealed compartment that can hold five hand grenades in each or two fusion blocks, two vibro-knives, or other odds and ends. The first fingers of each hand has a mini-laser for cutting and welding.

Damage: Laser finger: 1D6 × 10 to 2D6 × 10 S.D.C. or 1D6 M.D.

Rate of Fire: Equal to the bot's hand to hand attacks (9).

Effective Range: 100 feet (30.5 m)

Payload: Effectively unlimited.

4. **Small Extendable Arms (2):** The small arms are connected to a hydraulic system that gives the arms a maximum reach of 15 feet (4.6 m). Many a troublemaker about to leap over a high fence or from a rooftop has been snared by these arms. The extendable hands/arms also enables the predatory bot to reach into narrow places like storm drains, ventilator shafts, tunnels, holes, into crates and other narrow cavities. Both arms are connected to a housing that can rotate 360 degrees. P.S. 30; can use most weapons, including light rail guns.

5. **ML-Rail Gun (1):** Built-into a side turret is a gatling gun style rail gun. The gun can shoot up and down and side to side in a 90 degree arc of fire. It can fire one bullet, a 15 round short burst, or a maximum damage burst of 30 rounds. Few rail guns are as versatile. If two rail guns are used, one in each hand, only one can be connected to an ammo drum.

Primary Purpose: Anti-armor

Secondary Purpose: Defense

Mega-Damage: A full damage burst fires 30 rounds and inflicts 1D4 × 10 M.D. A short burst of 15 rounds does 4D6 M.D. and a single round does 1D4 M.D.

Rate of Fire: Equal to the bot's hand to hand attacks (9 bursts).

Maximum Effective Range: 6000 feet (1828 m)

Payload: 3000 round drum and is capable of firing 100 full damage bursts (30 rounds) or 200 short bursts (15 rounds)! Reloading a drum will take about three minutes for those not trained, but a mere one minute by somebody trained in the use of power armor. A strength of 28 or higher is required to handle the drum.

6. Top Mounted Mini-Missile Launchers: The long canisters on the lion's back are mini-missile launchers.

Primary Purpose: Anti-Aircraft and Anti-Missile

Secondary Purpose: Anti-Armor

Missile Type: Any mini-missile can be used; fragmentation (5D6 M.D.), armor piercing (1D4 × 10 M.D.), plasma (1D6 × 10 M.D.), smoke or stun/riot control.

Mega-Damage: Varies with missile type.

Range: Usually about a mile.

Rate of Fire: One at a time or in volleys of 2 or 4.

Payload: 20 total

7. Energy Rifles or Hand-held Rail Guns and other hand-held weapons can be used by any of the hands/arms. Standard issue is one or two M-40 ion rifle tubes (see weapon description at the end of this section) and a second hand-held weapon.

Hand to Hand Combat: Rather than use a weapon, the bot can engage in mega-damage hand to hand combat.

　　Normal Punch — 1D6 + 1 M.D.

　　Power Punch — 2D6 + 2 M.D.

　　Body Block/Ram — 1D4 M.D. at low speed, add 1D6 for every 100 mph (160 km).

Combat Bonuses: 9 attacks per melee round! +1 on initiative, +6 to strike, +10 to parry, +6 to dodge, +2 to roll with impact, and +4 to pull punch. Of course as a robot, the M-1200 is impervious to mind control, horror factor, and normal heat and cold.

Skills of Note: Prowl 40%, climb 75%, swim 75%, detect ambush 60%, detect concealment 60%, and land navigation, navigation, basic and advanced math, radio: basic, radio: scrambler, computer operation, intelligence, track (humanoids), track animals, all at 88%; plus W.P. blunt, W.P. knife, W.P. sword, W.P. automatic pistol, W.P. sub-machinegun, W.P. automatic rifle, W.P. energy pistol, W.P. energy rifle and W.P. energy heavy (all equal to an 8th level soldier). In addition, the bot has a built-in language translator (all major and local languages).

Sensor System Note: Full optical systems, including laser targeting, telescopic, passive night vision (light amplification), thermo-imaging, infrared, ultraviolet, polarization, motion detectors, and all the standard features.

M-1400 Tiger

The M-1400 tiger is designed as a hunter/killer assault bot with a wide variety of deadly weapon systems. The bot is suitable for activity in all environments, from forests to city streets. Consequently, it is a roughly man-sized (7 feet, 6 inches tall/2.29 m) biped unit that can easily be mistaken as a borg.

The M-1400 is utilized by Mindwerks as an instrument of vengeance, sending it against known enemies, deserters and adventurers who get too close to Mindwerks or its secrets. Each of the body-chop-shops secretly operated by Mindwerks has a half dozen tiger bots who serve as both protectors and enforcers for the organization.

M-1400 Tiger
Part of the Mindwerks Defensive Line
German Name: der Tiger (pronounced tig air)
Model Type: M-1400
Class: Robot Combat Drone — Unmanned
Crew: None; artificial intelligence
M.D.C. by Location:
　　*Claw Hands (2) — 30 each
　　*Arms (2) — 90 each
　　*Elbow Blades (2) — 15 each
　　Legs (2) — 120 each
　　Mini-Missile Launcher (4, top back) — 70 each
　　*Infrared Searchlights (2; eyes) — 3 each
　　* Sensor Head — 100
　　** Main Body — 250

　* Destroying the sensor head will blind the bot; −10 to strike, parry and dodge and eliminate all combat bonuses. The robot will thrash about and strike at anything it touches (unless shut down by a special code known to the Angel of Death and her top henchmen).

　Note: Everything marked by a single asterisk indicates a small and difficult targets to hit. Consequently, they can only be struck when a character makes a *called shot* and even then, the attacker is −3 to strike.

　**Depleting the M.D.C. of the main body will destroy the robot completely.

Speed: 150 mph (241 km) running. The powerful legs also enable the monstrous robot to leap 30 feet (9 m) high or lengthwise; double when it has a running start at speeds in excess of 40 mph (64 km) and triple when running at speeds of 100 mph (160 km) or greater. The bot can also travel underwater by walking on the river bed: maximum speed is 30 mph (48 km) maximum depth is 500 feet (153 m) or swim through water at a speed of 40 mph (64 km).

Statistical Data

Height: 7 feet, 6 inches (2.29 m) from head to toe.

Width: 4 feet (1.2 m)

Length: 4 feet (1.2 m)

Weight: One ton fully loaded

Physical Strength: Equal to a P.S. 40

Cargo: None

Power System: Nuclear, average energy life is 20 years.

Black Market Cost: Not available; exclusive to Mindwerks.

Note: The current stockpile at Mindwerks is roughly 200 units, but with sufficient materials and incentive, the Mindwerks factory could produce 40 a month.

Weapon Systems

1. **Head Lasers:** A pair of short-range lasers is mounted in the mouth/chin section of the head. They can move side to side and up and down with about 30 degrees or fire straight forward. In the center above the two lasers is an ion blaster with the same range of movement.

Primary Purpose: Assault

Secondary Purpose: Defense

Mega-Damage: 2D6 M.D. per individual blast or 4D6 M.D. per simultaneous double blast (counts as one melee attack/action). The ion blaster does 3D6 M.D. per blast or can be combined with the lasers to inflict 1D4×10+2 M.D.

Rate of Fire: Equal to the number of combined hand to hand attacks of the bot.

Maximum Effective Range: Lasers 1600 feet (488 m); ion blaster 1200 (366 m)

Payload: Effectively unlimited.

2. **Top Mounted Mini-Missile Launchers:** The lager canisters on the back of robot are mini-missile launchers.

Primary Purpose: Anti-Aircraft

Secondary Purpose: Defense

Missile Type: Any mini-missile can be used; fragmentation (5D6 M.D.), armor piercing (1D4×10 M.D.), plasma (1D6×10), smoke or stun.

Mega-Damage: Varies with missile type.

Range: Usually about a mile.

Rate of Fire: One at a time or in volleys of 2 or 4.

Payload: Total of 20, five mini-missiles in each tube.

3. **Energy Rifles or Light Rail Guns** and other hand-held weapons can be substituted in an emergency or used as a back-up weapon. The blade fingers make the use of a hand-held weapon awkward so the robot does not get the usual W.P. bonus for an aimed shot.

4. **Extendable Hydraulic Claw Hands/Arms:** The hands are connected to a hydraulic system similar to those once used by remote control robots and medical bots. The clawed hands can extend the robot's reach by three feet (0.9 m; for a total reach of 8 feet/2.4 m). Many a troublemaker about to leap over a high fence or from a rooftop has been grabbed by his leg or shirt collar or impaled on the bot's finger blades. The extendable hands/arms also enables the predatory bot to reach into narrow places like storm drains, ventilator shafts, tunnels, cavities, holes, into crates and other narrow cavities.

The three fingers and thumb are all long, mega-damage blades. They are excellent in hand to hand combat but not as good for holding and carrying items. The M-1400 tiger can hold and fire rifle-like weapons and operate basic equipment but such operations are a bit more difficult for the bot, so it does not get the usual bonuses to strike from the W.P. skill. Likewise, it can operate most hover vehicles, open doors, etc., but not quite as quickly or easily as a human or robot with fully articulated fingers. In many instances, the tiger will smash or hack through S.D.C. or light M.D.C. doors and walls.

Hand to Hand Combat: Rather than use a weapon, the bot can engage in mega-damage hand to hand combat.

Normal Punch/Slap — 1D6 M.D.

Claw Strike/Slash/Stab — 3D6 M.D.

Power Claw Strike — 6D6 M.D., (counts as two melee attacks)

Elbow Blade Strike — 2D6 M.D.

Kick — 1D6 M.D.

Leap Kick — 3D6 M.D. (counts as two melee attacks)

Body Block/Ram — 1D4 M.D. at low speed, add 1D6 for every 100 mph (160 km).

Combat Bonuses: Seven attacks per melee round; +2 on initiative, +6 to strike, +8 parry, +5 to dodge, +2 to roll with impact, and +2 to pull punch. Of course as a robot, the M-1400 is impervious to mind control, horror factor, and normal heat and cold.

Skills of Note: Prowl 60%, climb 60%, swim 90%, detect ambush 60%, detect concealment 60%, and land navigation, navigation, basic and advanced math, radio: basic, radio: scrambler, pick locks (with finger blades), intelligence, track (humanoids), track animals identify plants/fruits, pilot hover vehicle, pilot motorcycle, and pilot jet pack, all at 88%; plus W.P. knife, W.P. sword, W.P. automatic rifle, W.P. energy pistol, W.P. energy rifle and W.P. energy heavy (all equal to a 5th level soldier). In addition the bot has a built-in language translator (all major and local languages).

Sensor System Note: Full optical systems, including laser targeting, telescopic, passive night vision (light amplification), thermo-imaging, infrared, ultraviolet, polarization and all the standard features.

M-1600 Bear

The bear is the only, truly giant robot in the Mindwerks arsenal. It is a robot vehicle operated by a single pilot. The M-1600 Bear is extremely easy to operate and is much faster and more agile than its bulk would suggest (always an advantage on the field of battle). The war machine wields an array of weapons, making it suitable for close combat in confined conditions, like those of Mindwerks' underground complex and urban settings, as well as the wide open wilderness. Many of the close combat/urban features are meant to disperse crowds/attackers, making the enemy easier to handle by the other, smaller drones and/or brodkil forces. This walking tank is intended to combat a wide range of foes with an equally wide range of results, from suppressing and dispersing tactics to infantry support and front-line assault. For example, tear gas and smoke missiles can be substituted for explosive missiles. It can also be used to capture intruders, criminals, and subjects for experimentation, as well as fight rogue gargoyles, giants and giant combat Triax robots. In a pinch, the giant bot can also be used in building and hauling.

German Name: der Baer (pronounced bear)

Model Type: M-1600

Class: One-man Strategic Infantry Assault Robot

Crew: One (pilot), plus one human-sized passenger can be squeezed in, but it's a tight, uncomfortable fit.

M.D.C. by Location:

Shoulders (2) — 150 each

Rear Cooling Tubes (4, small) — 80 each

Hands (2) — 100 each

Lower Arms — (2) — 180 each

Legs (2) — 240 each

Feet (2) — 160 each

* Smoked Dispensers (2; lower leg) — 50 each

* Laser Knuckle Blasters (3; right hand) — 40 each

* Grenade Launchers (2) — 100 each

Mini-Missile Launchers (4; back) — 130 each

Multi-Weapon Arm (1; left forearm) — 180

* Retractable Vibro-Sword (1; right forearm) — 80

* Tri-Barrel Head Gun (1) — 50

* Searchlight (1, center of the head) — 5
* Armored Sensor Head — 180
   ** Main Body — 580

   * Items marked with a single asterisk are small and difficult targets to hit and requires the attacker to make a called strike, and even then the character is −3 to strike.

   Destroying the head of the robot will eliminate all forms of optical enhancement and sensory systems. The pilot is forced to rely on his own human vision and senses. Furthermore, all bot combat bonuses to strike, parry, and dodge are lost!

   **Depleting the M.D.C. of the main body will shut the armor down completely, making it useless.

Speed

Running: 60 mph (96 km) maximum. The bot can also travel underwater by walking on the riverbed: maximum speed is 20 mph (32 km), maximum depth is 1000 feet (305 m).

Leaping: The robot can leap up to 25 feet (7.6 m) high or 50 feet lengthwise (15 m) from a running start.

Flying: None

Statistical Data

Height: 25 feet (7.6 m) from head to toe.
Width: 13 feet (4.0 m)
Length: 10 feet (3 m), including the missile launch tubes.
Weight: 21 tons
Physical Strength: Equal to a P.S. 50
Cargo: None

Power System: Nuclear, average energy life is 20 years.
Black Market Cost: None! Exclusive to Mindwerks.
Note: Current stockpile at Mindwerks is roughly 56 units, but with sufficient materials and incentive, the Mindwerks factory could produce 20 a month. 24 have been traded away to the Brodkil Empire (piloted by human-sized D-bees) and two are concealed at each of the secret, Mindwerks sponsored and controlled body-chop-shops.

Weapon Systems

1. Canister Grenade Launch Tubes (2): The two short and somewhat wider tubes in the back of the robot are canister launch tubes. They fire smoke and/or stun/flash grenades (but fragmentation grenades can be substituted).

Primary Purpose: Close range anti-personnel and riot control.

Grenade Type: Canister style grenades — usually no mega-damage.

Stun/flash grenades are designed to disorient and confuse terrorists or criminals who are holding hostages in confined places. The grenade makes a loud exploding boom and emits a bright flash followed by a shower of white-hot sparklettes and some white smoke. The flash, burning sparks and smoke should blind and startle any character without environmental armor and shielded visor. Victims of the stun/flash grenade are −8 to strike, parry and dodge, −1 on initiative and lose one melee attack/action for the next 1D4 melee rounds (15 to 60 seconds). Even those in armor should be momentarily distracted for 1D4 seconds and lose initiative.

Tear gas grenades release a gas that will instantly affect all characters without gas masks or environmental body armor. The eyes burn, sting and water profusely, causing great discomfort and makes seeing clearly impossible. The gas also makes breathing difficult and irritates exposed skin. The effects last for 3D4 minutes. The 25 foot (7.6 m) cloud dissipates in about five minutes unless blown away by wind in 1D4 minutes. Victims of tear gas are −10 to strike, parry and dodge, −3 on initiative and lose one melee attack/action for each of the next 1D6+1 melee rounds. Those in environmental armor are completely unaffected. Note: Tear gas is usually only half as effective against brodkil, gargoyles, and some of the more powerful and alien D-bees.

Smoke grenades release a thick cloud of smoke that covers a 20 foot (6 m) radius. The smoke obscures vision in and through the cloud from those on the outside of it. Infrared cannot penetrate a smoke cloud or be used within one. Those inside the cloud will be blinded and have trouble breathing. Those who are not protected by environmental suits or gas masks and goggles will be −5 to strike, parry and dodge and −1 on initiative. Attackers firing into/through the cloud are shooting wild. Note that passive nightscopes will work in a smoke cloud.

Fragmentation grenades can be substituted for infantry combat missions. These grenades inflict 2D6 M.D. with a 20 foot (6 m) blast radius).

Mega-Damage: Varies with grenade type.

Range: 25 feet (7.6 m) minimum to 150 feet (46 m) maximum.

Rate of Fire: One at a time or a volley of two or four.

Payload: A total of 64; 32 in each canister. Typically, one canister holds stun and/or tear gas grenades and the other, smoke and/or fragmentation grenades, or 16 of each of the four types. Any combination of grenades can be fired.

2. Top Mounted Mini-Missile Launchers: The taller two canister tubes on the back of the robot are mini-missile launchers.

Primary Purpose: Anti-Aircraft

Secondary Purpose: Defense

Missile Type: Any mini-missile can be used; fragmentation (5D6 M.D.), armor piercing (1D4×10 M.D.), plasma (1D6×10), smoke or stun/riot control.

Mega-Damage: Varies with missile type.

Range: Usually about a mile.

Rate of Fire: One at a time or in volleys of 2 or 4

Payload: A total of 32; 16 in each launch tube.

3. Tri-Barrel Head Blaster (2): The triple-barreled lasers are mounted in a small turret located to the left side of the chin on the robot's head. The turret can rotate 360 degree and the three barrels can spread open like fingers to about 45 degrees. This enables the weapon to fire a wide spray to try to hit three different targets or fire a random spray at a mass of enemy troops or the three barrels can be drawn close together to fire at one specific target.

Primary Purpose: Assault

Secondary Purpose: Defense

Mega-Damage: 2D6 M.D. per individual blast, 4D6 M.D. per simultaneous double blast or 6D6 M.D. per triple blast (simultaneous blasts count as one melee attack/action).

Rate of Fire: Equal to the number of combined hand to hand attacks of the pilot (typically 6-8).

Maximum Effective Range: 2000 feet (610 m)

Payload: Effectively unlimited.

4. Multi-Weapon Arm (1): The left arm is a triple-barreled weapon cannon. The small, recessed barrel on the middle is a laser, the top barrel fires an ion beam and the lower one fires a particle beam.

Primary Purpose: Anti-Gargoyles/Giants

Secondary Purpose: Anti-Personnel

Mega-Damage: Laser: 3D6 M.D., Ion beam: 1D4×10 M.D., Particle beam 1D6×10 M.D.; a dual ion beam and particle beam blast inflicts 2D4×10+20 M.D. Only two of the three weapons can be fired at the same time.

Maximum Effective Range: All have a range of 3000 feet (914 m)

Cannon Rate of Fire: Equal to number of combined hand to hand attacks (usually 6-8).

Cannon Payload: Effectively unlimited.

5. Laser Knuckle Blasters (3): The three housings on the knuckles of the right hand fire wide-beam laser blasts.

Primary Purpose: Assault

Secondary Purpose: Defense

Mega-Damage: 3D6 M.D. per individual blast, 6D6 M.D. per simultaneous double blast or 1D6×10 M.D. per triple blast (simultaneous blasts count as one melee attack/action).

Rate of Fire: Equal to the number of combined hand to hand attacks of the pilot (typically 6-8).

Maximum Effective Range: 3000 feet (914 m)

Payload: Effectively unlimited.

6. Forearm Vibro-Sword (1): Located in the right forearm is a concealed, extendable and retractable vibro-sword. The weapon is five feet long (1.5 m).

Primary Purpose: Defense

Mega-Damage: 3D6 M.D.

7. Smoke-Dispenser (2): In the rear of each lower leg is a housing that can release a cloud of smoke. The smoke is typically used to create cover and to confuse the enemy.

Mega-Damage: None. Same effect as the smoke grenade described under number 1.

Rate of Fire: Once per melee round.

Range: A smoke cloud appears around the robot.

Payload: 12 total smoke releases.

8. A Giant-Sized Energy Rifle and Rail Gun or other hand-held weapon can be also be carried and used (right hand only).

Hand to Hand Combat: Rather than use a weapon, the pilot can engage in mega-damage hand to hand combat.

Bonuses & Damage from the M-1600 Bear Combat Training

Restrained Punch — 1D6 M.D.

Full Strength Punch — 2D6 M.D.

Power Punch — 4D6 M.D. (counts as two attacks)

Crush, Pry or Tear: 2D4 M.D.

Kick/Knee — 2D6 M.D.

Leap Kick — 5D6 M.D. (counts as two attacks)

Body Flip/Throw — 1D6 M.D.

Body Block/Ram — 2D6 M.D.

+1 on initiative	+2 to dodge
+3 to strike	+2 to roll with impact
+3 to parry	+2 to pull punch

+1 melee action/attack at levels 1, 3, 6, and 10. Note: The additional attacks and combat bonuses are in addition to those of the pilot!

Sensors of note: Full multi-optics, long and short-range radio broadcasting and scanning capabilities as well as a distress homing beacon.

Mindwerks Weapons

M-12 Plasma Pistol

A powerful, short-range energy pistol that fires plasma bolts. Like most of Mindwerks' weapons, the pistol is designed for use by large humanoids 8 to 15 feet (2.4 to 4.6 m) tall. This means humans find the weapon awkward to hold and fire (-2 to strike). It comes standard with a telescopic sight and laser targeting ($+1$ to strike).

Weight: 15 lbs (6.8 kg)

Mega-Damage: 4D6 M.D. per blast

Rate of Fire: Equal to the number of combined hand to hand attacks (usually 3-7).

Effective Range: 500 feet (152 m)

Payload: 12 shot E-clip. The weapon also has a self charging energy supply that can fire one plasma bolt per hour without an E-clip.

Note: The Mindwerks E-clip is different than the Triax or CS style clips which means clips produced by manufacturers other than Mindwerks must be specially modified to fit this weapon. Such modifications cost about 3500 credits. This weapon is depicted with the Angel of Vengeance.

M-30 Dual Energy Rifle

The M-30 dual energy rifle is a versatile and powerful weapon designed specifically to be used by large creatures with superhuman strength. The rifle comes in two sizes: medium and large. The medium-size is heavy and big, making it awkward to use by most humans (-2 to strike), but is ideal for use by cyborgs, ogres, brodkil and other beings that stand about seven to 10 feet tall (2.1 to 3 m) and who have a P.S. of 20 or higher. It is roughly equivalent to a large cyborg rail gun.

The large-sized weapon is designed for giants roughly 14 to 20 feet (4.2 to 6 m) tall although slightly smaller or larger beings can use it, provided they have a P.S. of 24 or greater.

The upper barrel of the gun fires a particle beam. The lower barrel, a longer range laser. A laser targeting beam can be fired from the upper shield and provides a bonus of $+1$ to strike.

Weight: Medium: 40 lbs (18 kg); Large: 90 lbs (40.8 kg).

Mega-Damage (regardless of size): The particle beam inflicts $1D4 \times 10 + 6$ M.D.; the laser beam does 4D6 M.D. per blast.

Rate of Fire: Equal to the number of combined hand to hand attacks (usually 3-7).

Effective Range: Medium-sized rifle: 1600 feet (488 m) for the particle beam, or 2000 feet (610 m) for the laser.

Large rifle: 2000 feet (610 m) for the particle beam or 3000 feet (914 m) for the laser.

Payload: Medium-sized rifle: 40 shot E-clip. Large rifle; 60 shot E-clip. The weapon also has a self charging energy supply that can fire four laser beams or one particle beam per hour without an E-clip.

Note: The Mindwerks E-clip is different than the Triax or CS style clips which means clips produced by manufacturers other than Mindwerks must be modified to fit this weapon.

M-25 Firebrand Giant Rifle

This rifle is a giant-sized knock-off of the Coalition State's C-14 Fire Breather, assault laser and grenade launcher. Exactly how the CS weapon found its way to Mindwerks is not known. Like its human-sized counterpart, the weapon has an over-and-under firing capability and is known for its durability and reliability in action. The top barrel is a laser, the bottom is the grenade launch tube, fired like a pump action shotgun. The weapon comes standard with a passive nightvision scope.

Weight: 45 lbs (20 kg)

Mega-Damage: 4D6 M.D. per single laser blast. The grenades inflict 4D6 M.D. to a blast area of 14 feet (4.3 m).

Rate of Fire: Equal to the number of hand to hand attacks.

Effective Range: Laser is 2000 feet (610 m); grenade is 1000 ft (305 m).

Payload: Laser: 20 shot E-clip.

M-18 Ion Pulse Pistol

Another powerful, short-range energy pistol from Mindwerks. It too is designed for use by large humanoids 8 to 15 feet (2.4 to 4.6 m) tall. This means humans find the weapon awkward to hold and fire (-2 to strike).

Weight: 10 lbs (4.5 kg)

Mega-Damage: 2D6 M.D. per single blast or 6D6 per multiple pulse (three simultaneous shots).

Rate of Fire: Equal to number of combined hand to hand attacks (usually 3-7).

Effective Range: 500 feet (152 m)

Payload: 18 shot E-clip. The weapon also has a self charging energy supply that can fire one ion pulse per hour without an E-clip.

Note: The Mindwerks E-clip is different than the Triax or CS style clips which means clips produced by manufacturers other than Mindwerks must be specially modified to fit this weapon. Such modifications cost about 3500 credits. This weapon is depicted with Marsalis.

M-40 Ion Rifle Tube

This energy rifle is commonly used by the Mindwerks robot defenders. It can also be used by large humanoids 8 to 15 feet (2.4 to 4.6 m) tall, but humans find the weapon awkward to hold and fire (-2 to strike).

Weight: 30 lbs (13.6 kg)

Mega-Damage: 5D6 M.D. per single blast or 1D6 × 10 per simultaneous double blast (like a shotgun).

Rate of Fire: Equal to the number of combined hand to hand attacks (usually 3-7).

Effective Range: 1600 feet (488 m)

Payload: 20 shot E-clip. The weapon also has a self charging energy supply that can fire two ion blasts per hour without an E-clip.

Note: The weapon can be connected to the bot via a hose-like conduit, tapping into the bot's power supply, giving it an effectively unlimited payload. An E-clip may also be used as an energy reserve in case the hose is severed. This weapon is depicted in the illustration of the M-1200 Lion robot.

M-120 Plasma Rifle

A powerful, short-range rifle that fires plasma bolts. Like most of Mindwerks' weapons, the rifle is designed for use by large humanoids and robots 8 to 15 feet (2.4 to 4.6 m) tall. This means humans find the weapon awkward to hold and fire (-2 to strike). It comes standard with a telescopic sight and laser targeting (+1 to strike).

Weight: 35 lbs (15.7 kg)

Mega-Damage: 5D6 M.D. per blast

Rate of Fire: Equal to number of combined hand to hand attacks (usually 3-7).

Effective Range: 1200 feet (365 m)

Payload: 12 shot E-clip. The weapon also has a self charging energy supply that can fire one plasma bolt per hour without an E-clip.

Note: The Mindwerks E-clip is different than the Triax or CS style clips which means that clips produced by manufacturers other than Mindwerks must be specially modified to fit this weapon. Such modifications cost about 3500 credits. This weapon is depicted with the M-1000 panther robot.

Optional M.O.M. O.C.C.s

Full Standard Crazy
Full Conversion Borg
Null Psyborg
Psi-Bloodhound
Psynetic Crazy
Ecto-Traveler

An Important Note: The Angel of Death turns unwilling people into cyborgs, crazies and other things for the following reasons:

1. As a favor or trade with the brodkil and gargoyles;
2. For her own sadistic pleasure;
3. As a means of torture and/or punishment;
4. To expand her knowledge of M.O.M. technology via continuous experimentation.
5. She believes she is a "god" and that it is a god's duty to "create" and instigate change. Many of her "creations" are the product of this twisted view of life and her delusions of divinity.

Frequently, her "creations" are released into the world (away from the Mindwerks complex). Once the Angel of Death or Vengeance is done with a creation, they are discarded like yesterday's garbage. In some instances she studies them, like Earth scientists of old who placed identification tags on wild animals, turned them loose and observed the animal in its natural habitat. She always enjoys encountering or watching her "creations" in action, even if they try to oppose her or her forces.

The Angel of Death and the Mindwerks techs always make a tremendous effort to prevent captives from knowing the location of Mindwerks (less than 1% ever have any idea about its location). Only the most loyal, submissive and controlled "creations" are allowed to live at the secret complex.

Full Standard Crazy Conversion

This elaborate process turns the recipient into a superman! See the Crazies O.C.C. in the **Rifts RPG**, page 56. This process can be used on humans and most human-like D-bees. See the new O.C.C.s and psynetic implants for artificially induced *psionic powers*.

The physically augmented crazy cannot receive any psynetic implants. To try to combine the two (the Angel of Death has tried to do so many times) will cause the character's mind or nervous system to overload, turning him or her into a vegetable or mindless, murderous animal with no sense of self-identity, skills or intelligence — it just lashes out and kills everything it encounters. Such wildmen usually die violently within 2D6 weeks. The process is irreversible. Crazies can get the brain programming implant subject to the additional penalties presented in its description.

Mindwerks Full Conversion Borg O.C.C.

A Mindwerks cyborg is almost always (90%) a full conversion borg! The basic creation is similar to the **Borg O.C.C.** presented in the **Rifts RPG**, (page 47). However, along the way, the Angel of Death adds a few of her own unique touches in the way of brain implants. Angel's test subjects seldom have knowledge of cybernetics, have no desire to become a cyborg and have little or no combat training.

Attribute Requirements: None; although an average or higher I.Q. and M.E. is recommended.

O.C.C. Skills:
Languages: Two of choice (+20%)
Piloting: Two of choice (+10%)
W.P.: Two of choice

O.C.C. Related Skills: 10 of choice from available skill categories. Select two additional skills at levels 4, 8, and 12.
Communications: Any (+5%)
Domestic: Any (+10%)
Electrical: None
Espionage: None
Mechanical: None
Medical: First Aid or paramedic only (+5%)
Military: None
Physical: Any
Pilot: Any (+10%)
Pilot Related: Any (+5%)

Rogue: Any (+2%)
Science: Any
Technical: Any (+10%)
W.P.: Any
Wilderness: Any (+5%)

Secondary Skills: The character can select three at level one and two at levels five and ten.

Standard Mindwerks Full Conversion Cyborg:

Bionic arms and hands: P.S. 22+2D4, P.P. 18+1D6, plus one arm weapon or feature and 1D4 hand weapons or features of choice.

Bionic legs: Speed: 77+2D4×10; plus one concealed weapon rod or secret compartment for each leg (player's choice).

Bionic body: Reinforced full body conversion with 180+2D4×10 M.D.C., plus 270 M.D.C. from light infantry body armor. The armor may have spikes, studs and frightening designs to it. Likewise, the cyborg's head is likely to be the standard "cyclops" design (intended to mock Triax and the NGR), skeletal or demonic looking.

Other Standard Features: Bionic lung, gas filter, oxygen storage cell, built-in language translator, ultra-ear, sound filtration system, and multi-optic eye. Plus the player can select three other cybernetic or bionic features of choice. All additional features can be selected from cybernetic and bionic systems presented in any of the **Rifts** books (see the **Rifts RPG** and **Triax & The NGR**).

Future Bionics Improvements: Other bionic items can be installed as a reward for a job well done or purchased; availability of bionics will vary.

M.O.M. implants:

1. Brain Programming: Select five skills from any categories. Each is at 88% proficiency regardless of the character's intelligence, experience or normal O.C.C. limitations. Some standard Mindwerks skill programs are as follows (pick one):

Combat: Hand to hand: martial arts, boxing or wrestling, W.P. blunt or sword, W.P. energy pistol or sniper, and W.P. energy rifle (all are equal to 7th level experience).

Data: Basic math, advanced math, navigation, computer operation, and read sensory equipment.

Espionage: Intelligence, tracking, wilderness survival, land navigation, and streetwise.

Explosives: Demolitions, demolitions disposal (may include safecracking; see **Rifts Mercenaries**), basic electronics, and basic mechanics.

Electrical: Electrical engineer, robot electronics, computer operation, computer repair, and radio: basic.

General: Land navigation, computer operation, radio: basic, pilot hover vehicle and literacy: Euro.

Language: Speaks four languages of choice and is literate in one.

Mechanical: Mechanical engineer, automotive mechanics, weapons engineer, locksmith, and basic electronics.

Pilot: Five vehicles of choice.

Supernatural: Demon & monster lore, faerie lore, magic lore, astronomy, and streetwise.

Surveillance: Surveillance systems, T.V./video, radio: basic, radio: scrambler, and photography.

Note: Roll on the table under Brain Programming to determine the penalty from this implant.

2. Other secondary implants: All cyborgs who serve Mindwerks have the controller chip (preventing the character from raising a hand against the Angel of Death or the Mindwerks facility), the tracking device, identifier implant and explosive brain chip.

70% of the people captured, transformed and released have the identifier and tracking device; 50% have the explosive chip and/or controller

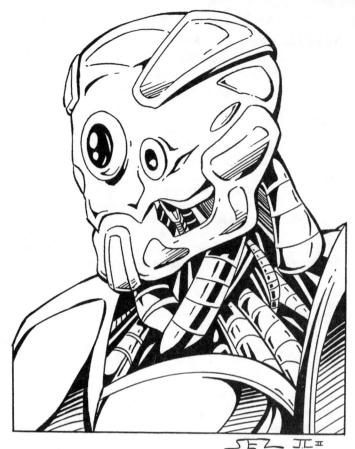

SEZ JC II

implant. See the full descriptions in the M.O.M. implant section. In response to her growing paranoia and megalomania, she has secretly installed tracking and explosive chips in about 60% of the brodkil and gargoyles augmented by Mindwerks. 45% have the controller chip, preventing them from raising a hand against her or the Mindwerks facility.

Standard Issue Equipment: Captives or volunteers turned into Mindwerks borgs and released start with the bare essentials including a utility belt, cape, cloak or robe, knife, Mindwerks or Triax energy weapon of choice (no rail guns) and an energy pistol, vibro-blade or Kittani plasma weapon as a sidearm. Other weapons and equipment must be acquired with time.

Characters who are minions of Mindwerks or the Brodkil Empire can select any two Mindwerks, Triax, or Kittani weapons they desire, including rail guns, get 1D4 hand grenades, and a vibro-blade or other type of sword, battle axe or staff. They also get access to basic resources of their employer/master.

Money: Captives or volunteers turned into Mindwerks borgs and released start with none.

Those who remain under the employment of the Angel of Death or the Brodkil Empire are usually provided food, basic essentials, mechanical repairs, a means of transportation, a modest monthly salary of 1000 credits and a small percentage of booty (may be allowed to keep items scavenged or taken from opponents unless it is extremely valuable).

Note: Psynetic implants won't work in a full conversion borg. Most brodkil prefer limited or partial bionic augmentation and seldom become full conversion borgs.

The Angel of Death turns unwilling people into borgs, crazies and other things out of sadistic pleasure or because she believes it is her duty as a god to "create," change and improve life. When she's done with the characters, they are released back into the world. She and the Mindwerks techs always make a tremendous effort to prevent captives from learning the location of the Mindwerks complex (less than 1% ever have any inkling of its location). Only the most loyal, submissive and controlled "creations" are allowed to live at the secret complex.

Null Psyborg O.C.C.

The null psyborg is a partial reconstruction cyborg enhanced by the Angel of Death's M.O.M. technology. The main emphasis of the null psyborg's powers is an incredible resistance to psionic attacks and mind control. This is made possible through the installation of a more powerful variation on the *psionic defense system* implant and other brain implants linked to the overall null psyborg creation process. This "null system" makes the augmented warrior impervious to many forms of psionic detection and resistant to psionic attack. The null psyborg is the ideal spy or assassin when up against psionic characters.

Special O.C.C. Bonuses & Powers

The entire Mind-Over-Matter conversion process involving this type of enhancement goes beyond the capabilities of the implants described previously, providing additional bonuses and powers.

1. Physical bonuses: +1D4×10 S.D.C., P.P.E. 10+1D4×10, +1 on initiative, +1 to save vs disease and poison, and one extra attack per melee round (not including any TK extensions).

2. Enhanced psionic defense system & psionic bonuses: The null psyborg's aura, alignment and presence cannot be seen or sensed! This brain implant is similar to the more common defense system, but is even more powerful. The character is impervious to see aura, sense evil, sense magic, detect psionics, psychic diagnosis, telepathy, empathy, and hypnosis. He is also +6 to save vs possession, mind control, mind meld, horror factor, and empathic transmission, +4 to save vs all other types of psionic attacks and +4 to save vs magic illusions. All saves against psionics are as if the character was a master psionic to begin with.

3. Psionic disruption: Whenever the null psyborg touches a living being, psychic, human or supernatural being, and uses this power, the character is drained of 1D4×10 I.S.P. or 3D6 P.P.E. points. Or the disruptive touch can be made to affect a psionic ability while it is in use by touching the psychic using the power. The null psyborg's touch reduces the power by half (half range, area affect, damage/effects, and duration). By touching the victim of the psionic attack, the victim gets a new saving throw with a bonus of +4 to save. A successful save has instant results.

To use the disruption power, the null psyborg needs only to touch his target and concentrate on disrupting psionic energy. Each use/touch counts as one melee round action/attack. Note that this ability does not use up the psyborg's P.P.E. nor require I.S.P.; it can be used at will in place of a normal melee action/attack, like a punch or kick.

4. Psionic energy null field: Similar to a nega-psychic (see **Beyond the Supernatural**), the character can draw on his P.P.E. to create an anti-psionic and anti-magic energy field. The field lasts one minute per each P.P.E. point expended and can last as long as the character desires to resist psionics and magic. When the field is up, he is impervious to magic curses, illnesses, and illusions, as well as psionic bio-manipulation, empathic transmission, mind bond, and mind wipe. Furthermore, all friends and allies within a 10 foot radius of the character are +1 to save vs magic, illusions, and mind control.

The character can also use the null field to dispel or drain I.S.P. or P.P.E. contained in magic crystals, talismans, and similar items that store mystic or psychic energy, including techno-wizard devices. This power cannot be used to drain energy from rune weapons, magic weapons, other magic items, magic potions, scrolls, ley lines, symbiotes or living beings. For every one point of P.P.E. temporarily expended by the null psyborg, 10 I.S.P. or 5 P.P.E. points are dispelled/negated. Range: Touch or within a 10 foot (3 m) proximity.

Note: The null psyborg cannot use any form of telepathy or empathy (completely blocked) and any psionic powers the character may have had before are lost.

The Null Psyborg

Attribute Requirements: None; although an average or higher I.Q. and M.E. is recommended.

O.C.C. Skills:
Radio Basic (+10%)
Land Navigation (+10%)
Languages: Three of choice (+20%)
Piloting: Three of choice (+10%)
W.P. Four of choice
Hand to hand:: Expert

Hand to hand: expert can be changed to martial arts (or assassin if evil) for the cost of one other skill.

O.C.C. Related Skills: Select eight other skills, plus two additional skills at levels 3, 7, and 11. All new skills start at level one proficiency.
Communications: Any (+5%)
Domestic: Any (+10%)
Electrical: Basic only
Espionage: Any (+5%)
Mechanical: Basic only
Medical: First Aid only (+5%)
Military: Any
Physical: Any except acrobatics and wrestling
Pilot: Any (+10%)
Pilot Related: Any (+5%)
Rogue: Any
Science: Any
Technical: Any (+10%)
W.P.: Any
Wilderness: Any

Secondary Skills: The character can select three at level one and two at levels five and ten.

Standard Bionic Conversion:

Bionic hand and arm (one or both limbs): P.S. 18+1D6, P.P. 18+1D6, plus three weapons/features for each bionic limb.

Bionic legs: Speed: 44+1D4×10; plus one concealed weapon rod or secret compartment for each leg (player's choice).

Bionic body: Reinforced spine and joints with 100+1D4×10 M.D.C., plus light bionic espionage armor (135 M.D.C.) or other type of body armor.

Other Standard Features: Toxic filter, oxygen storage cell, built-in language translator, multi-optic eye, radiation detector, clock calendar and gyro-compass.

Future Cybernetic Improvements: Other bionic items can be installed as a reward for a job well done or purchased; availability of bionics will vary.

M.O.M. implants:

Nano-amplifiers can be used by the null psyborg but the ranges of all powers are reduced by half because of interference from the bionics (see the full description in the M.O.M. implant section).

Optional Brain Programming: Select five skills from any categories. Each is at 88% proficiency regardless of the character's intelligence, experience or normal O.C.C. limitations. See the Mindwerks' full conversion borg for a complete list of standard programs ready for quick installation. In the case of the null psyborg, the combat, espionage, piloting and surveillance programs are the most commonly used. **Note:** Roll on the table under Brain Programming to determine the penalty from this implant.

Other secondary implants: 80% of the null psyborgs who serve Mindwerks have the controller chip, identifier implant and explosive brain chip.

70% of the people captured, transformed and released have the identifier and tracking device; 50% have the explosive chip and/or controller implant. See the full descriptions in the M.O.M. implant section. In response to her growing paranoia and megalomania, she has secretly

installed tracking and explosive chips in about 60% of the brodkil and gargoyles augmented by Mindwerks. 45% have the controller chip, preventing them from raising a hand against her or the Mindwerks facility.

Standard Issue Equipment: Captives or volunteers turned into Mindwerks borgs and released start with the bare essentials, including a utility belt, cape, cloak or robe, knife, Mindwerks or Triax energy weapon of choice (no rail guns) and an energy pistol, vibroblade or Kittani plasma weapon as a sidearm. Other weapons and equipment must be acquired with time.

Characters who are minions of Mindwerks or the Brodkil Empire have a suit of light bionic espionage body armor (135 M.D.C.) and/or personalized mega-damage body armor (any kind, including Triax, Kittani, or Mindwerks/gargoyle/brodkil armor), a set of dress clothing, black and/or camouflage fatigues, a gas mask and air filter, tinted goggles, and an NG-S2 basic survival pack. The character also owns a vehicle such as a hover cycle, motorcycle or land rover, one energy handgun and rifle, three additional weapons of choice, 1D6 grenades, robot medical kit, IRMSS, infrared distancing binoculars, language translator, passive night-sight scope for rifle, 2D4 sets of handcuffs or manacles, 50 feet of strong cord/rope, utility belt, backpack, knapsack, and 1D4 sacks.

Special Equipment: Pick one (must have appropriate skill; may be stolen from Mindwerks or brodkil)

1. Transportation and Cash: Jet pack or shark bullet bike and 3D6 × 1000 extra credits.

38

2. Power Armor Suit: T-C20 Terrain Hopper, Predator, Triax T-31 Super Trooper, Northern Gun or Kittani types.

3. Magic Armor: One techno-wizard or other magic armor and magic weapon (keep the items reasonable) or magic weapon.

4. Special Vehicle: A souped-up (has weapon system and goes 20% faster than normal) motorcycle, hover cycle, hover vehicle, land rover, jeep or small truck with double the usual M.D.C., an energy weapon mounted on it, radar and long-range radio. Or a robot horse may be selected.

Money: Captives or volunteers turned into Mindwerks borgs and released start with none.

Those who remain under the employment of the Angel of Death or the Brodkil Empire are usually provided food, basic essentials, mechanical repairs, a means of transportation, a modest monthly salary of 1000 credits and a small percentage of booty (may be allowed to keep items scavenged or taken from opponents unless it is extremely valuable).

Note: Most brodkil prefer limited or partial bionic augmentation and many select becoming a null psyborg.

The Angel of Death turns unwilling people into borgs, crazies and other things out of sadistic pleasure or because she believes it is her duty as a god to "create," change and improve life. When she's done with the characters, they are released back into the world. She and the Mindwerks techs always make a tremendous effort to prevent captives from learning the location of the Mindwerks complex (less than 1% ever have any inkling of its location). Only the most loyal, submissive and controlled "creations" are allowed to live at the secret complex.

Ecto-Traveler O.C.C.

The ecto-traveler is created by implanting a cluster of brain implants that is physically debilitating but psychically liberating. The recipient of the implants becomes completely paralyzed and must be sustained by life support systems. The character can speak and open and close his eyes, but all other motor functions are lost! Without a medical life support system, the lungs and/or heart will eventually (within 2D6 weeks without support) cease to function.

Uncooperative or despondent characters may require drugs or psionic stimulation/communication to be motivated, especially at first. For some unwilling victims, the threat of being unplugged from life support (and the promise of eventual restoration) is enough to garner the person's cooperation. However, after awhile, many subjected to the ecto-traveler conversion grow to love their new-found power. Many also become delusional and dangerously maniacal. **Note:** Only the Angel of Death and a handful of her cyber-docs know how to create an ecto-traveler. She has 13 at her disposal and an estimated dozen or so exist outside of Mindwerks (five are known to exist in Poland and two in Germany).

Ecto-Traveler Powers

The powers instilled by this terrible M.O.M. implant process are unique and incredible.

1. Astral Projection: The same as the psionic power described in the **Rifts RPG**, page 119, except to this character, the astral plane seems less confusing and frightening (+20% to find his way back to his physical body). In many ways, the ecto-traveler uses the astral plane as a super-highway in which he or she can travel a thousand miles a second with a mere thought. This is done to travel from one point in the physical plane to another in a matter of seconds.

2. Creating a Physical Body to Inhabit: Normally the astral traveler cannot interact with the material plane. Instead, he is like a ghost who watches events unfold before him. This is not the case with the ecto-traveler! The implants give the character the unprecedented (for humans and most creatures) ability to manifest a physical body out of thin air.

The astral form of the person can use this body to reenter and function in the material plane! This is done by creating an ectoplasm like material drawn from living things in the area, including humanoids, plants and animals (with no ill effect or loss of I.S.P. to those creatures).

The ecto-body looks frightening and ugly, like a pink or grey, protoplasmic blob in a humanoid shape (or a giant, lumpy Pillsbury Dough Boy). The basic shape of the body is always the same as the traveler's paralyzed body; i.e. a human will create a roughly human body with a head, two legs, two arms, hands and feet.

The astral traveler can leave the astral plane and rejoin the physical world by entering the ectoplasmic body! At that point, the character's control is so complete that he can create tentacles, extra arms, horn-like protrusions, wings (but can't fly) or other appendages; limited to eight total, in addition to a pair of legs.

3. The ectoplasm body:

Size: 5 to 10 feet (1.5 to 3 m) tall or long; usually humanoid.

M.D.C.: 15 points plus 5 per each level of experience; also see limited regeneration under special abilities.

Attributes of Note: P.S. 9, P.P. 10, P.B. 4, Spd 12, and horror factor: 12. All mental abilities are the same as the paralyzed character (roll as is appropriate for that particular race; humans is 3D6).

The Physical Plane: While the astral body inhabits the physical ectoplasm body, the character is rooted in the physical plane and is limited only to powers listed in this section. He cannot enter the astral plane again without discorporating his current body (takes 10 minutes) or when the body is destroyed. Discorporation means the traveler reenters the astral plane where he can stay for a while or he can return to his real body. A new ectoplasm body cannot be created for 12 hours if discorporated (turns into vapors and vanishes) and 24 hours if the body is destroyed. The character can stay in the ecto-body indefinitely.

4. Bonuses: +2 on initiative, +1 to strike and parry, +5 to dodge. In many cases the body seems to flow and bend in impossible ways to avoid getting hit — a dodge uses up one melee action/attack. +6 to save vs horror factor, +3 to save vs psionic attack. The ecto-body has a horror factor: 12

5. Special Abilities:

Understands & Speaks All Spoken Languages: Base skill level is 70%; never increases with experience.

Additional limbs: The ectoplasm body can grow as many as eight additional limbs. Each additional limb adds one attack per melee round; 8 limbs means eight attacks per melee round! Limbs can be grown at a rate of two per melee round (15 seconds) and kept or absorbed back into the body (grown back as needed). This also means the creature can regenerate limbs that are atomized by energy blasts.

Regeneration: Lost M.D.C. is regenerated at a rate of 2D6 per hour without expending any I.S.P., or 10 I.S.P. can be directed to self-regeneration, restoring five M.D.C. points instantly. Each act of five M.D.C. regeneration counts as one melee action/attack.

Limited Imperviousness: Remember, the ectoplasm body is not really made of living flesh and doesn't breath, doesn't have blood, or vital organs. It is a physical manifestation of the mind! Thus, blowing off an arm or punching a hole through the body may do damage but does not inflict pain or permanently impair the big glob! Furthermore, it is not affected by the bite of a vampire, possession, disease, drugs, gases, pollution, radiation, fatigue, thirst or hunger (it's not really alive).

Resistance to Damage: Falls, explosions and other types of impacts (punches, kicks, bullets, etc.) inflict half damage. Fire, extreme cold, energy attacks and most types of psionics do full damage. Magic and magic weapons do double damage!

Body Molding: As ectoplasm, the body has a putty or goop-like consistency enabling the character to ooze between bars, squeeze through openings as small as a baseball, squeeze out of handcuffs and manacles, and even slip under doors that are hung one inch or higher above the floor. The oozing process take 1D4 melee rounds to accomplish and another melee round (15 seconds) to regain the body's humanoid appearance. The ecto-body cannot assume the shape of other creatures or specific people.

Enhanced Physical Beauty: At sixth level and higher, the ecto-traveler can mentally sculpt his or her body to look less monstrous and more human. Physical beauty can be increased one point per level of experience (starting at level 6), but also reduces the horror factor by one per each additional P.B. point. Thus, an ecto-body given four P.B. points has a P.B of 8 and a horror factor of 8.

6. Psionic Powers: While in the ecto-body, the character has ALL psychic sensitive powers, plus, electrokinesis, hydrokinesis, mind bolt, psi-shield and psi-sword. Base I.S.P. is 3D6×10+40 plus 1D6 per level of experience. Any psionic powers the character may have had before are only available to him when in his real physical body or in the astral plane.

7. Penalties and Limitations:

Limited senses: The ecto-body does have a sense of touch and the ecto-traveler can see and hear from the astral plane, but the ectoplasmic body does not have a sense of smell or taste. Even its sense of touch is not as acute as a normal human's (roughly 60%).

Cannot Wear Body Armor: Body armor and power armor are too heavy, confining, and uncomfortable, but the character can wear loose fitting clothes, such as a poncho, robe, cape, or cloak.

I.S.P. Limitations: When all I.S.P. are expended, the character cannot use psionic abilities until some of the I.S.P. are recovered through relaxation or meditation. However, no I.S.P. also makes it difficult to maintain the ecto-body; reduce speed by half and the total number of melee round attacks to four regardless of the number of appendages.

Destroying the ecto-body tears the ecto-traveler out of the physical plane and back into the astral plane. The experience is traumatic and the character is dazed, floating aimlessly in the astral plane for 1D6 hours. When he finally regains his senses, he must return to his physical body and cannot astral travel or create a new ectoplasm body for 24 hours.

No life, no ecto-body: The ectoplasm body cannot be created in places that are truly devoid of life, like outer space. Nor can it be maintained for more than 24 hours in such a "dead" environment.

Destroying the Physical Body: To slay the ecto-traveler's real body is to kill him! If the character's body is destroyed, he can continue to inhabit the ectoplasm body for 4D6 days, after which the body discorporates and the character dies. If the ecto-body is destroyed shortly after the physical body, the character is gone forever. Once the real body is destroyed the ecto-traveler cannot create a new ecto-body. Of course the physical body and its life support system is usually hidden and well protected.

8. Insanities & Alignments: Roll once on Side Effects Table number two (insanities) at levels one, three, six, eight, eleven and fourteen. In addition, most ecto-travelers (01-85%) learn to love their bizarre life and don't want to be restored to their human condition. These characters also become obsessed with adventure, exploration, intrigue and travel. Those who don't are people who wish to be restored to human form (even as a cyborg) or be allowed to die.

Those of a selfish or evil nature frequently become deluded with (and addicted to) a sense of power and knowledge that transcends mortal boundaries. Some believe they have become demi-gods or supernatural beings meant to dominate lesser creatures. These villains believe that they are above the laws, morals and concerns of humans and other mere mortals. They tend to grow arrogant, distant, dispassionate, manipulative and cruel. Some become monsters!

Of course, the alignment and integrity of the character will determine how he or she adjusts to the new existence and power of the ecto-traveler.

Many will never become cruel or evil and may become heroic champions who protect and defend the innocent and good-hearted from the forces of evil.

O.C.C. Data

O.C.C. & Secondary Skills: Most ecto-travelers started life in a different profession (when in doubt role up a vagabond). The character gets to keep that skill knowledge but the hands of the ectoplasm body are not quite as articulated and precise as the human body and medical, electrical, mechanical and science skills are −10%. Furthermore, the skill proficiencies are frozen at the level when the character was transformed into an ecto-traveler and NEVER increase. The character relies primarily on his psionic and ecto-body powers.

The ecto-traveler gets only four new skills: Streetwise (+14%), demon and monster lore (+20%), magic lore (+10%; see Triax & NGR, page 155) and land navigation (+30%). All new skills start at first level proficiency, as does the O.C.C. level of experience.

Magic powers/spellcasting cannot be performed by an ecto-traveler! Just one of the limitations of this O.C.C.; however, a mage turned ecto-traveler will retain his knowledge of ley lines, how magic works, and similar magic O.C.C. skills.

Standard Equipment: None per se. Most rely so heavily on their new powers that they don't use much in the way of equipment. Few have more than a utility belt or two with one or two vibro-blades, an energy pistol, an energy rifle and a walkie-talkie. Remember, the ecto-traveler doesn't eat, drink or need clothing.

Money: Whether an ecto-traveler earns and saves money and collects valuables depends on the individual. Although the creature doesn't need food and many of the amenities desired by humans, the traveler may need money to maintain the life support system and protection for his real body, as well as miscellaneous equipment and money for bribes or to help others.

Cybernetics: Absolutely no type of cybernetics can be used in the ecto-body. The paralyzed real body does not respond to exo-skeletons or most cybernetics.

Note: The ecto-traveler brain implants can be removed without killing the character. However, all special powers are lost, insanities remain, and muscles of the real body will be terribly atrophied and require 3D4+6 months of daily therapy and exercise to get back to normal.

Psynetic Crazy O.C.C.

The psynetic crazy, also known as the psi-crazy, is a product of M.O.M. technology that combines both physical and mental powers. Only Mindwerks has perfected this particular blending of M.O.M. technology. The character is not as physically powerful as most crazies, but has psionic powers added to his arsenal of abilities that more than compensates. The psi-crazy tends to be even more wild, insane and unpredictable than the conventional crazy! The character is usually hyper and on edge, like a tiger ready to pounce, and needs only four or five hours of sleep a night. He or she likes to fight and play hard.

Crazies Physical Augmentation

1. Hyper sense: +2 on initiative, +1 to parry, +2 to dodge, +2 to roll with impact or fall, +2 to pull punch and +1 to save vs horror factor. Has trouble sleeping and tends to be jumpy, over-reacting to sights and sounds. The character is also hyper and fidgety: taps fingers, cracks knuckles, hums, whistles, sighs, or may talk all the time and tends to get on other people's nerves. See the full description in the M.O.M. implant section.

2. Enhanced healing: As described previously.

3. Two physical M.O.M. implants of choice: Select from those described in this book. See the Mindwerks borg for some basic brain programming formats (or select five skills of choice — don't forget to roll on the side effects table under that implant).

4. Other standard implants: Controller chip preventing the character to raise a hand against the Angel of Death or the Mindwerks facility, plus the tracking device and a 01-50% chance of having a explosive chip implanted as well (should stay away from Mindwerks). See the full descriptions in the M.O.M. implant section.

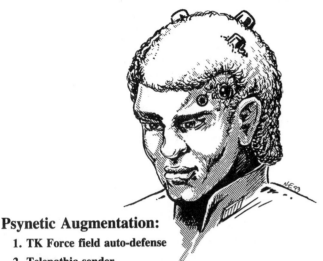

Psynetic Augmentation:

1. TK Force field auto-defense

2. Telepathic sender

3. **Psynetic eye** or psychometric amplifier or booster.

4. **Special: Psionic brain wave identifier:** Not only does the psionic identifier enable Mindwerks security systems to scan and make a positive identification of the character, but the psynetic crazy can sense characters who also have the identifier implant. This alerts him to the fact that the person(s) he faces is a creation of Mindwerks. Furthermore, the Angel of Death or Mindwerks cyber-docs can program the psionic identifier to recognize any ONE specific brain wave signature (Mindwerks records and files the brain patterns of most of its creations and operatives). Thus, the psi-crazy can identify a specific character no matter how much he may have changed or disguised himself. Range 120 feet (36.5 m).

5. **Three psynetic implants of choice (including Telekinetic Extensions).** Roll on the appropriate side effects tables for each, as well as for numbers 1-3.

Special O.C.C. Bonuses & Powers

The entire Mind-Over-Matter conversion process involving this type of enhancement goes beyond the capabilities of the implants described previously, providing additional bonuses and powers.

Bonuses Applicable to all psi-crazies: +1D4×10 S.D.C., +1 on initiative, +2 to save vs psionic attacks, +4 to save vs mind control (drugs or psionic), +6 to save vs possession, and +4 to save vs horror factor. All bonuses are cumulative. All psynetic crazies regain I.S.P. at the same rate as a mind melter: 2 points per hour while active or 12 points per hour sleeping or meditating.

Type one psynetic crazy: The non-psionic: Add 1D6 to the character's P.S. and Spd attributes, +2 to save vs disease and poison, +1 on initiative and one extra attack per melee round. 1D4 random psionic powers from any of the three lesser categories manifest themselves. These are in addition to those instilled by specific psynetic implants. I.S.P. Base: 10+2D4×10 plus 4 I.S.P. per level of experience.

Type two psynetic crazy: Minor or major psionic: +1 to save vs psionic attacks, mind control, possession and horror factor. In addition to any psionic powers the character had naturally and those gained from specific psynetic augmentation, he can select three psionic powers from any of the three lesser categories or one super psionic power. I.S.P. Base: 20+2D4×10 plus 6 I.S.P. per level of experience.

Type three psynetic crazy: Master psionic: +2 to save vs psionic attacks, mind control and possession, +2 to save vs horror factor, plus one extra attack per melee round.

The character can detect psionics and sense evil at three times the usual range. The Master psionic selects 10 psionic abilities in any of the three lesser categories and four super psionic powers, in addition to those provided by specific psynetic implants. Unlike the natural master psionic (mind melter or mind bleeder) the psi-crazy does not gain any new psionic abilities as he increases in experience. I.S.P. Base: 50+3D4×10 plus 10 I.S.P. per level of experience.

The Psi-crazy O.C.C.

Attribute Requirements: None, just a willingness to subject oneself to M.O.M. conversion. Characters with some measure of psychic power are ideal.

O.C.C. Skills:
Languages: Two of choice (+20%)
Radio: Basic (+10%)
Piloting: Two of choice (+10%)
Acrobatics or Gymnastics (+10%; pick one)
Climbing (+10%)
Swimming (+10%)
W.P. Ancient: Two of choice
W.P. Modern or Energy: Two of choice
Hand to Hand: Martial Arts (or assassin, if evil)

O.C.C. Related Skills: Select 8 other skills. Plus, select two additional skills at level three, and one at levels 7, and 11.
Communications: Any (+5%)
Domestic: Any
Electrical: None
Espionage: Any
Mechanical: Basic mechanics and automotive only
Medical: First Aid or paramedic only (+10%)
Military: Any (+5%)
Physical: Any
Pilot: Any (+5%)
Pilot Related: Any
Rogue: Any (+5%)
Science: Math only
Technical: Any (+10% on languages and literacy)
W.P.: Any
Wilderness: Any

Secondary Skills: The character can select three at level one and two at levels five and ten.

Standard Issue Equipment: Captives or volunteers turned into Mindwerks borgs and released start with the bare essentials including 50 feet of strong cord/rope, utility belt, backpack, knapsack, cloak or robe, knife, Mindwerks or Triax energy weapon of choice (no rail guns) and an energy pistol, vibro-blade or Kittani plasma weapon as a sidearm. Other weapons and equipment must be acquired with time.

Characters who are minions of Mindwerks or the Brodkil Empire can select two Mindwerks, Triax, or Kittani weapons (excluding rail guns), a suit of personalized mega-damage body armor (any kind, including Triax/NGR, Gargoyle or other armor), a set of clothing, a gas mask and air filter, tinted goggles, and an NG-S2 basic survival pack. The character may also have access to a vehicle such as a hover cycle, motorcycle or land rover. They may also have access to the basic resources of their employer/master.

Money: Captives or volunteers turned into Mindwerks borgs and released start with none.

Those who serve the Angel of Death or the Brodkil or Gargoyle Empires are usually provided food, basic essentials, mechanical repairs, a means of transportation, a modest monthly salary of 1000 credits and a small percentage of booty (may be allowed to keep items scavenged or taken from opponents unless it is extremely valuable).

Note: Like all of her creations, the Angel of Death frequently releases the psi-crazies into the world to do as he or she pleases. The Angel of Death and the Mindwerks techs always make a tremendous effort to prevent captives from knowing the location of Mindwerks (less than 1% ever have any idea about its location). Only the most loyal, submissive and controlled "creations" are allowed to live at the secret complex.

Psi-Bloodhound R.C.C.

This is a horrible mind and psionic altering M.O.M. process used to transform psi-stalkers and mutant dog boys enslaved by the Brodkil Empire, into savage bloodhound-like trackers and killers. The process enhances the D-bee's or mutant's already formidable tracking and psionic senses but also turns the poor creatures into aggressive, slobbering predators that function more on instinct than intellect.

The psi-stalker bloodhound (also known as the psi-hound) is reduced to a near animal state and is incapable of learning or remembering any but the most basic skills. Many are so aggressive and extremely animal-like that they must be kept caged or on a chain leash or they will run off, looking for prey (starting with supernatural monsters and those they don't like). They are also easily provoked by the words and actions of others and will quickly respond with insults, threats, challenges to combat, shoving, slapping, biting and are always ready to fight — restraint is not one of the psi-hound's virtues.

The character makes an excellent tracker and assassin, driven by an instinct to hunt and kill, with an especially keen bloodlust and tracking ability toward supernatural monsters, master psionics and practitioners of magic.

Special Powers of the Psi-Bloodhound

1. Amplified psionic powers. The natural abilities of the psi-stalker to sense psychic and magic energy, sense supernatural beings, and psionic empathy with animals and other psionic "sense" powers have double the usual range and duration. The same is true of the mutant dog's psychic sensing abilities plus they can track by smell alone at −20%.

2. Animalistic nature and endurance: Savage; loves to hunt, prowl and kill. Very aggressive in combat and when defending friends or property. Supernatural endurance, plus add 1D6×10 S.D.C. and the character fights on even when mortally wounded until hit points are −80 below zero!

3. Recognizes psionic signatures/brain waves of specific psionic individuals just as a dog can recognize a specific scent. The psi-bloodhound will remember the psionic signature of any psychic or

supernatural being who ever attacked it! When that psychic scent is encountered in the future (by using psionics on or near the character; within 90 ft/27.4 m), the psi-hound will recognize the psychic as an enemy, giving the hound a bonus of +1 on initiative and +1 to strike when facing this foe. **Base skill:** 30%+5% per level of experience to accurately identify a psi-scent (+10% against supernatural beings).

4. Berserker Bloodlust: When the psi-bloodhound is angry, frustrated, engaged in serious combat, or injured, he is likely to fly into a berserker fury (01-86% chance). During this rage, the creature is completely merciless and ruthless. In most cases the hound will not stop fighting until he has slain his opponent, he is slain, or he is pulled off his opponent and forcibly restrained. During the rage, the creature will strike out at anybody who gets between him and his prey; including slave masters, friends, family and innocent bystanders.

During the rage, the psi-bloodhound is +3 to save vs magic, psionics, and horror factor, plus he inflicts double damage with every hand to hand strike/bite/attack and can leap 20 feet (6 m) across or lengthwise!

5. Other bonuses: Double I.S.P. and P.P.E., +2 to save vs disease and poison.

6. All the other R.C.C. abilities and bonuses are unchanged; Reduce I.Q. to 2D4; relies mainly on instinct.

The Psi-Bloodhound

Attribute Requirements: See the Psi-stalker and Dog Pack R.C.C.s
Alignment: Any; but the animal nature of the character usually eliminates principled good or aberrant evil.
Skill Modifications: The character is reborn as a psi-bloodhound. Regardless of the character's past R.C.C. skills, training and experience, he or she selects new skills and starts at first level experience. Highly technical skills are no longer available, even though they may have been available to the original R.C.C.
R.C.C. Skills/Instincts:
  Track (+20%)
  Track: Animals (+10%)
  Land Navigation (+20%)
  Swim (+10%)
  Climb (+10%)
  Languages: Speaks two of choice (+10%)
  W.P.: Three of choice.
  Hand to Hand Expert (or assassin if evil)
O.C.C. related skills: Select 7 other skills, plus one additional at levels four, eight and 12.
  Communications: Radio: basic only
  Domestic: Any
  Electrical: None
  Espionage: Sniper and detect ambush only.
  Mechanical: None
  Medical: First aid only (+10%).
  Military: None
  Physical: Any
  Pilot: Horsemanship (+30%), boats (except ship), pilot motorcycle or hover cycle only (all at +10%).
  Pilot Related: None
  Rogue: Any
  Science: None
  Technical: Language, art, and lore only; cannot learn to read.
  W.P.: Any
  Wilderness: Any (+10%)
Secondary Skills: None
Standard Equipment: A suit of light personalized mega-damage body armor (any kind including Triax, Coalition or Kittani), one energy handgun and rifle, three additional weapons of choice, fatigues, tinted goggles or sunglasses, a NG-S2 Basic Survival Pack (see **Rifts Mercenaries**), robot medical kit, IRMSS, infrared distancing binoculars, language translator, passive night sight scope for rifle,

2D4 sets of handcuffs or manacles, 50 feet of strong cord/rope, utility belt, backpack. Psi-bloodhounds are also fond of vibro-blades, Kittani energy blades, blade weapons in general, and magic weapons.

Cybernetics: All have the explosive chip and tracking device, about 65% have the controller chip. The psi-bloodhound can eventually acquire other basic cybernetic implants, but most don't want any. The characters are too ignorant and aggressive to properly use most psynetic implants (they prefer to engage in hand to hand combat).

Money: Psi-hounds can't count and the character has little need or desire for money but may be attracted to gems and gold and understands enough to keep 2D6×100 in credit (or equivalent) for basic needs. The few that collect a treasure trove other than weapons and equipment will have no real concept of just how valuable something is and may rely on somebody else who can tell him. The treasure gathering hound gets enjoyment from thinking he has things of value whether they really are or not.

D-Bees of Germany & Poland

The following section describes some of the non-humans found in and around Northern France, Belgium, Switzerland, Germany, Austria, Poland, Czechoslovakia, Yugoslavia, Hungary, and Romania. Many can also be found throughout Europe and Russia, but in smaller numbers.

In addition to those described here, many of the creatures and optional R.C.C.s found in **Rifts World Book Two: Atlantis, Rifts World Book Three: England** and **Rifts Conversion Book (One)** are also found in Europe.

Rifts England: Mantaz Sectles can be found inhabiting and protecting *most* Millennium Trees around the world. Dabugghs are found in northwestern Europe, including France, Germany and Poland. The giant clamp-mouthed dragonfly is a plague in France and found throughout western Europe. Flash Beetles, Petal Things, and the occasional giant dragonfly inhabit the Black Forest and other parts of Europe, India and Africa. Stone Ball Bugs are found in the garbage dumps of most cities and villages and are one of the few alien scavengers welcomed by humans. Knights and druids are found primarily in England, Scotland, Ireland and France, but small communities and adventurers can be found anywhere in Europe and parts of Asia. Likewise, the users of temporal magic (uncommon) and herbalists (very numerous) can be found throughout Europe, Africa and Asia. Most gypsy bands and every European village will have one or more herbalists among them.

Rifts Atlantis: The Metzla can be found anywhere in the world, but are most common in Atlantis, France, Belgium, Scandinavia and in the Baltic and Mediterranean seas. The Minions of Splugorth, True Atlanteans (all) and Sunaj assassins are generally uncommon but can be found anywhere in the world (in small or great numbers depending on the circumstance). The occasional hawrk-duhk, hawrk-ka, hawrk-ohl, adarok flying mountains, erta, shaydorians (both), yll-tree climbers, and zembahk can be encountered throughout Europe and Asia as lone adventurers, in pairs or small groups.

A growing community of zembahk live in the Black Forest and other woodlands of Germany, Poland and Romania. Many gypsy bands and even some human and D-bee wilderness villages have accepted the zembahk as generous, helpful beings worthy of their friendship. Other people only see the intelligent mystic worms as a valuable commodity that evil alchemists, bio-wizards, gargoyles and Minions of Splugorth are willing to pay a great amount for. The zembahk are generally a gentle, compassionate race who try to help those in need. Unlike humans, the zembahk seldom regard the physical features of other intelligent creatures as important; they try to respect all life forms. The

mystic worms feel most at home among the splendor of the wilderness and among the needy and comparatively friendly wilderness folk. However, they also inhabit some of the cities of the NGR and Poland. Most German authorities see the zembahk as hideous monsters not to be trusted — see Rifts Atlantis, page 82, for details about the zembahk.

Rifts Conversion Book: Gargoyles, goblins, faerie folk, boogie-men, gryphons, perytons, dragondactyls, and drakin, are common to Europe; mainly in forested areas. The occasional wolfen (currently most numerous in Italy and Greece), giant, ogre, troll, dragon wolf, waternix, werebeast, worm of Taut (most common in warm regions), and dragon can also be encountered. Demons, deevils, and supernatural menaces of all kinds are in abundance in Europe, especially in the domains of the gargoyles and brodkil.

Optional R.C.C.s

Azverkan R.C.C.
Lycanmorph R.C.C.
Seeker R.C.C.
Ugakwa Explorer R.C.C.
Simvan Monster Rider R.C.C.
Srrynn Cannibal R.C.C.

Monsters (NPCs)

C'ro Demon Mage NPC
Eurotorpid
Mega-Foot Mastica
Stone Claw
White Slayer Demon

SEL J.I.II

The Azverkan R.C.C.

Knights of the True Vision

The azverkan are a race of D-bees reminiscent of both the psi-stalker and cyber-knight. They are a warrior race who seem to be inexorably linked to the supernatural. If you ask an azverkan warrior, he or she will tell you that their race is both blessed and cursed with the "true vision," the natural ability to sense and see supernatural evil. Their elongated, rectangular eyes are ebony except for a tiny, yellow pupil. These unusual eyes enable them to see a cloudy grey to black aura emanating from vampires and all types of undead, zombies, animated dead, necromancers, ghouls, rune weapons, and individuals possessed by entities, dybbuks, alien intelligences and supernatural forces. They can also see those turned invisible by supernatural or mystical means.

Their unique life essence makes them completely impervious to supernatural possession and resistant to magic. Thus, like the psi-stalker and Atlantean undead slayers, the azverkan have become the eternal enemy of the undead, the Splugorth and all forms of supernatural evil (including those who enslave or use and manipulate others). The majority (about 75%) belong to a pseudo-religious order known as the **Knights of the True Vision**, crusaders dedicated to the eradication of evil supernatural monsters and the protection of the weak and innocent from such diabolical forces. Like most knights, these characters are concerned with righting wrongs of all kind, but they are obsessed with the demonic and supernatural. Consequently, a Knight of the True Vision may abandon "a lesser evil" in mid-conflict to engage a supernatural menace, especially vampires, demons, alien intelligences and necromancers.

The azverkan have been attracted to the conflicts between humans and D-bees with the Gargoyle and Brodkil Empires. Of course, the NGR and most humans don't trust any D-bees and have rejected the azverkan's aid. Thus, the Knights of the True Vision wage a private battle against the dark forces and have become respected heroes to hundreds of D-bee communities (not unlike the cyber-knights of the Americas). The typical azverkan knight travels alone, in pairs, or in a small band (typically 1D4 + 1 knights). One or more may team up with other champions and heroes to fight the good fight or lead an army against the forces of evil.

Note: Only an azverkan can become a Knight of the True Vision. This does not mean they feel superior to other beings, it's just that one must possess "the true vision," a racial trait common only to the azverkan people. They have the utmost respect for Atlantean undead slayers, tattooed men, psi-stalkers, dog boys, masters of temporal magic, knights and heroes of all kinds, but they just can't become a Knight of the True Vision.

Alignment: Any, but generally good or selfish.

Attributes: I.Q.: 3D6, M.E.: 4D6, M.A.: 3D6, P.S.: 3D6 + 8, P.P.: 3D6 + 6, P.E.: 3D6 + 8, P.B.: 2D4, Spd.: 4D6 + 6.

Hit Points: Mega-damage creatures.

M.D.C. (natural body armor): 2D4 × 10 plus body armor; many become partial or full conversion cyborgs.

P.P.E.: 2D4 × 10, but possess no natural magic powers.

Horror Factor: 10

Weight: 200 to 300 pounds (90 to 135 kg)

Size: 6 to 7 feet tall (1.8 to 2.1 m).

Average Level of Experience for NPCs: 1D4 + 3

Natural Abilities: 1. Keen 20/20 normal vision, nightvision 500 feet (152 m), and see the invisible.

2. See the supernatural auras of the undead and evil supernatural beings (sees a cloudy grey to black aura emanating from vampires, zombies and all types of undead, necromancers, rune/bio-wizard weapons, and individuals possessed by supernatural forces).

3. Sense supernatural evil: The character can sense the presence of supernatural evil when they are close by. These powers are similar to the abilities of the psi-stalker. Unfortunately, the azverkan's sense is not as precise as the psi-stalker's, so all the character knows is that there is one or two, a few (3 to 9) or many (10 or more) evil supernatural beings close by, near/medium range or far (at the outer edge of his sensing abilities). Range: 50 feet (15.2 m) + 25 feet (7.6 m) per level of experience. The sensation is also strong enough to tell whether the supernatural being(s) is your average vampire/ demon, high level, or incredibly powerful like a god or alien intelligence.

4. Keen sense of smell. Identify everyday smells at 70% + 2% per level of experience. Identify a specific person's scent 40% + 2% per level, and track by scent 24% + 2% per level of experience.

Natural Bonuses: Impervious to supernatural and psionic possession, impervious to the bite and gaze of vampires (azverkan cannot be turned into vampires), +2 on initiative when fighting the supernatural, +8 to save vs horror factor, +8 to save vs symbiotic union and control, +6 to save vs magic illusions, +4 to save vs all forms of mind control, +4 to save vs necromancy, +2 to save vs magic of any kind. All bonuses are in addition to attributes and skills.

Combat: Azverkan knights get hand to hand: expert (or as per O.C.C.). Attacks Per Melee Round: As per hand to hand. Knights of the True Vision get one additional attack/action per melee and are +2 on initiative and +3 to pull a punch.

Damage:

    Bite — 2D6 S.D.C.

    Body Flip — 2D6 S.D.C.

    Head Butt or a Restrained Punch — 1D6 S.D.C.

    Full Strength Punch — 3D6 S.D.C. plus P.S. bonus

    Power Punch or Leap Kick — 6D6 S.D.C. plus P.S. bonus (counts
    as two melee attacks).

Psionics: Standard; same as humans.

Magic: None.

Appearance: A muscular, hairless alien with pale blue, light green or
blue-grey skin that feels coarse to the touch, like sandpaper. The
head is divided by large, lumpy sections. The eyes are black with
a yellow pupil and pointed, yellow teeth protrude from the lower
lip. The nose dangles down to the chin like a tiny elephant's trunk.

Slave Market Value: 100,000 to 200,000 credits.

Habitat: Any place.

Enemies: Vampires, demons and evil supernatural beings.

Allies: Champions of good.

R.C.C. Skills as a Knight of the True Vision:

    Lore: Magic (+10%, see Rifts Triax)

    Lore: Demons & Monsters (+10%)

    Streetwise (+12%)

    Concealment (+12%)

    Land Navigation (+20%)

    Wilderness Survival (+20%)

    Basic Math (+20%)

    Literacy: Native Azverkan (+20%)

    Radio: Basic (+20%)

    Pilot: Two of choice (+10%)

    W.P. Sword

    W.P.: Any two of choice

    Hand to Hand: Expert

R.C.C. Related Skills: Select eight other skills plus one at levels two,
four, six, eight, ten and twelve.

    Communications: Any (+10%)

    Domestic: Any (+5%)

    Electrical: None

    Espionage: Any

    Mechanical: None

    Medical: First aid (+10%)

    Military: Any

    Physical: Any

    Pilot: Any (+5%)

    Pilot Related: Any (+10%)

    Rogue: Any (+2%)

    Science: Math, astronomy, anthropology only (+10%)

    Technical: Any (+10%)

    Weapon Proficiencies: Any

    Wilderness: Any (+5%)

Secondary Skills: The character also gets to select two secondary skills
at levels one, three, seven and eleven.

Standard Equipment: Sword and three weapons of choice, a silver
plated survival knife, wooden cross, six wooden stakes and a mallet,
mega-damage body armor of choice, short-range walkie-talkie, air
filter, flashlight, backpack, utility belt, compass, language translator, canteen and food rations. The azverkan are attracted to powerful energy weapons, plasma and vibro-blades, power armor and
limited cybernetic augmentation.

Cybernetics & Bionics: None to start, but over the years may acquire
several basic implants and an artificial limb or two.

Money: 1D6×1000 credits and 1D6×1000 credits worth of gold and
artifacts to start.

Note: The Azverkan Adventurer: The rare azverkan who doesn't
become a Knight of the True Vision can select any O.C.C. as an area
of knowledge and expertise, except for cyber-knight, CS soldiers, NGR
soldiers, juicer, tattooed man, and all magic O.C.C.s. Their resistance
to magic prevents them from becoming practitioners of magic. Most
lean toward cyborg, headhunter, bounty hunter (see **Rifts Mercenaries**),
power armor/robot pilot, wilderness scout, and most types of combat
occupations, although about 30% are adventurers and scholars. Few
trust magic, bio-wizardry or M.O.M. augmentation.

Lycanmorph R.C.C.

The lycanmorph is another strange creature from a different dimension
that has found its way to Central Europe and India. What most people
consider its "natural" form is a human-sized, mega-damage humanoid
with bony plates on its chest, shoulders and head. The head is about
as inhuman as one can get. The shape is like that of a crescent, with
a hard plate cranium, huge black eyes, and scaly plates covering the
face. The creature has no apparent nose and the mouth is a stubby,
prehensile trunk protected by a covering of hard lobster-like plates.
From the opening of the mouth, at the end of the trunk, are three to
four inch long fibers that are incredibly sensitive to odors, tastes and
movement in the air. Although its frightening visage might suggest that
the lycanmorph is a blood sucking fiend, the creature is a herbivore
who feeds mainly on fresh and decaying fruits, vegetables, roots, nuts,
and greens, including the leaves from most trees.

They usually live in forests where food is plentiful and the trees offer
a thousand hiding places. They are rare compared to the number of
gargoyles, brodkil, ogres and other d-bees on Earth, and usually avoid
densely populated places. They frequently congregate in small tribes
or communities and often live with other beings. In fact, the D-bee
may adopt a particular tribe, village, farm or person as its own (whether
the person or people want it or not). The Lycanmorph is an inquisitive
and communal creature, so it is naturally attracted to other beings. They
like to play with and help their adopted friends and will engage in battle
to protect them.

Player's Note: These are typically curious, friendly creatures with
the trusting disposition (and educational equivalent) of an eight year
old child. They are not predators and lack the aggressive nature of such
beings, including war-like humans. They usually fight in self defense,
to protect a friend, or attack when frightened or provoked (which usually
takes some doing). However, they are fast and have multiple attacks/ac-
tions per melee and can be a deadly opponent.

When playing this character, the creature should be played as naive,
foolishly trusting and overly curious rather than stupid. They are easily
tricked, misguided and manipulated by cunning and evil characters and
will let their curiosity and friendly disposition lead them into trouble
time and time again. They can sense evil and try to avoid such beings.
They instinctively knowing evil creatures represent danger. When an
encounter is unavoidable, the lycanmorph often falls easy prey to their
tricks and games. The lycanmorph is typically like a happy puppy,
quick to forgive and/or forget all but the most traumatic and painful
offenses. A character hated by a lycanmorph must be responsible for
some terrible (unforgivable) crime; murder and torture of a friend(s) is
one way to create such animosity.

Despite the lycanmorph's naivete, gullibility and lack of aggression,
the character is no saint. They can be extremely mischievous, selfish
and willfully disobedient. They are also given to pouting, whining, and
pranks when they can't get their way.

Alignment: Any, but generally good or selfish.

Attributes: I.Q.: 1D6+2, M.E.: 2D6+1, M.A.: 3D6+2, P.S.:
3D6+10 (supernatural), P.P.: 3D6+6, P.E.: 4D6+4, P.B.: 2D4, Spd.:
6D6+30 (running, climbing and swinging through trees).

Hit Points: Mega-damage creatures.

M.D.C.: See individual metamorphosis and healing metamorphosis.

P.P.E.: 1D6×10, but possess no magic powers unless one includes
the metamorphosis ability.

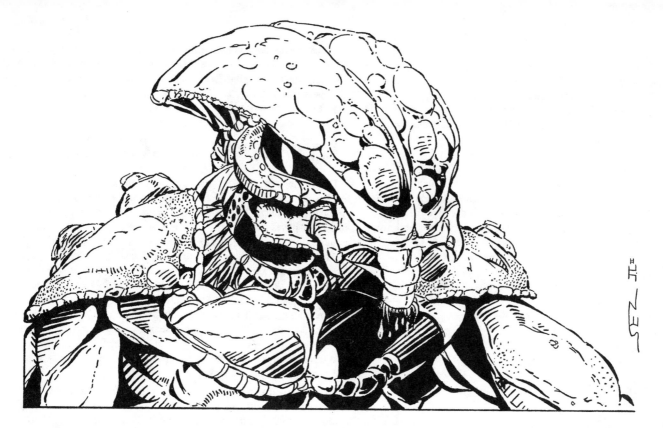

Horror Factor: Humanoid: 9, flyer: 11, or battler: 14.

Weight: See specific metamorphosis.

Size: See specific metamorphosis.

Average Level of Experience for NPCs: 1D6

Natural Abilities: Varies depending on the form the lycanmorph takes. Psionic powers and mental attributes never change in any form. The character also possesses the following skills and instincts in all forms: Climb 95/90%, acrobatics 85%, prowl 70% (half in giant forms), swim 70%, and escape artist 50% (half in giant forms). The lycanmorph also has keen, hawk-like vision, able to see a grapefruit or an enemy a mile (1.6 km) away, and has good nightvision 200 feet (61 m).

Metamorphosis: Another constant is its metamorphosis ability. To change form, the lycanmorph must weave a cocoon. This takes 1D4 minutes. The transformation from one form to another takes 1D4 hours (always a random time period). The creature can change into any of its three shapes without limit other than the time constraints. Once transformed, it can maintain that form indefinitely — days, months or years. The cocoon is a mega-damage structure with 250 M.D.C., but completely dissolves into thin air after the lycanmorph emerges (suggesting that it may be generated in part by ectoplasm). If the cocoon is attacked and destroyed the lycanmorph suffers 4D6×10 M.D. (half if the metamorphosis is nearly complete). If it survives, the creature will try to escape and make a new cocoon to recover and continue its transformation.

Healing metamorphosis: The cocoon can also be used to heal itself. Like the metamorphosis process, a cocoon is spun around the lycanmorph, but the only change is rapid healing — 2D6×10 per hour until all mega-damage is restored to full. During this healing transformation, the creature can emerge at any time without any ill effects (has whatever M.D.C. that has been restored up to that point). The healing metamorphosis can also be used to regenerate missing limbs but takes an additional 2D4 hours per each appendage being regrown.

The three forms of the lycanmorph:

1. In its human-sized, bipedal form, the creature is ambidextrous, double jointed and amazingly acrobatic, fast and silent like a panther. The character stands five to six feet (1.5 to 1.8 m) tall and weighs 160 to 200 pounds (72 to 90 kg). Can leap 20 feet (6 m) up or 15 feet (4.5 m) lengthwise from a standing still position (add 10 ft/3 m with a running start). In humanoid form, ideal for climbing trees and forest living, the character can identify food, plants, herbs, and poisons with a whisk of its sensitive mouth hairs at 85% accuracy.

Attacks/actions per melee: Four; +2 on initiative, +3 to strike, +4 to parry, +5 to dodge, +3 to roll with impact or fall.

Combat damage: 3D6 S.D.C. restrained punch or body flip, 1D6 M.D. full strength punch or kick, 2D6 from a power punch or leap kick. Head butt does 1D4 M.D.

Mega-Damage Capacity in humanoid from: 190 M.D.C.

2. Transformed into a "flyer," the lycanmorph looks like a giant alien beetle; 10 to 15 feet tall (3 to 4.6 m from the rump to the top of the head) and weighs 8 tons. Flying speed is 70+2D6×10 mph, swimming on top of water is 30+1D4×10 mph, swimming underwater is 1D4×10 mph. The four eyes can see the invisible, see into the infrared spectrum, and has nightvision with a range of 600 feet (183 m), plus can see 360 degrees, making it impossible to sneak up on one unawares.

Attacks/actions per melee: Five; +4 on initiative, +4 to strike, +5 to parry, +8 to dodge, +2 to roll with impact or fall.

Combat Damage: 1D6 M.D. restrained punch, 3D6 M.D. full strength punch, stab, or snip, 1D4×10 M.D. from a power punch, stab or scissor snip. Body butt does 1D4 M.D., while a full speed ram does 1D6×10 but counts as two melee attacks.

The Mega-Damage Capacity of the flyer:

Legs (4) — 50 each
Pincer Arms (2) — 200 each
Wings (2 pair) — 100 each
Wing Casings (2) — 220 each
Eyes (4) — 15 each (attackers are −3 to strike)
Main Body — 600

3. Transformed into a "battler," the lycanmorph looks like a giant insectoid robot; 12 to 18 feet tall (3.6 to 5.5 m) and weighs 12 tons. Flying speed is 30+1D6×10 mph, swimming on top of water is 5+1D4×10 mph, swimming underwater is 10 mph (16 km). P.S. is effectively doubled, but speed (running) is reduced by half. This incarnation of the creature is a warrior/defender of considerable power.

The forearms are covered in dense bony plates with three terrible mega-damage claws. Human-like hands are safely concealed on the undersides of the claw-plates, leaving them free to use an additional weapon (sword, energy weapon, etc.; lycanmorphs are especially fond of rune weapons and kittani energy weapons). A restrained punch/slap does 1D6 M.D., a full strength punch/stab does 3D6 M.D., and a power punch does 6D6 M.D.

The triangular protrusion on the top of the forearm fires a powerful electrokinetic blast, inflicting 4D6 M.D. (+1D6 at levels 3, 6, 9, and 12). Range of the blast is 60 feet (18 m) plus 5 feet (1.5 m) per level of experience.

The elbows have a sharp spike that inflicts 2D6 M.D. from an elbow jab.

The head has two large horns used for head butting (1D4 M.D.) and parrying (+6 with head and horns).

Clawed Feet: The lower legs have prehensile, clawed feet that can grab, hold, and tear. A kick inflicts 3D6 M.D., a tearing claw attack does 4D6 M.D. and a tearing claw leap kick does 1D4×10+8 M.D.! The feet can also be used to parry (+5) or to grab, hold or pin a character. The powerful legs can propel the lycanmorph 50 feet (15 m) high or lengthwise from a standing still position (double from a running start)!

Wings: The wings enable the character to fly or hover. Doing either while engaged in combat gives the giant the advantage of speed, maneuverability and height. The powerful legs and prehensile feet provides the equivalent of four slashing arms.

Toxic Spray: The hard plate wing casings not only protect the wings, but each has nine circular openings that can spray an opponent with a toxic chemical similar to a potent tear gas. This spray has the following effect on dragons and supernatural monsters, including vampires: The eyes burn, sting and water profusely, causing great discomfort and makes seeing clearly impossible. The spray also irritates exposed skin. The effects last for 2D4 minutes. Victims are −10 to strike, parry and dodge, −3 on initiative and lose one melee attack/action until the effects wane. Robots, and those in environmental armor, are completely unaffected. The effect of the toxic spray when used against humans and non-mega-damage creatures unprotected by environmental body armor is much more severe. The character suffers 6D6 hit point/S.D.C. damage and must roll to save vs lethal poison (14 or higher). A failed roll means he goes into shock for 1D4 minutes and collapses (cannot attack). When the character comes out of shock, he suffers all the previously described penalties but for three times longer.

Attacks/actions per melee: Seven; +2 on initiative, +6 to strike, +8 to parry, +3 to dodge, +2 to pull punch, and +2 to roll with impact or fall.

Combat Damage: See individual weapons and attacks above.

The Mega-Damage Capacity as a Battler:

Legs (2) — 250 each
Upper Arms (2) — 130 each
Forearms (2) — 160 each
Wings (2 pair) — 100 each
Wing Casings (2) — 180 each
Head Horns (2) — 40 each (attackers are −3 to strike)
Eyes (2) — 15 each (attackers are −5 to strike)
Main Body — 310

Transformed into a "flyer"

Other Bonuses: +4 to save vs horror factor, +5 to save vs symbiotic union and control, +2 to save vs psionic attack, +2 to save vs magic, +3 to save vs poison, drugs and disease. All bonuses are in addition to attributes and skills.

Combat: The lycanmorph's fighting abilities are purely a matter of instinct and body configuration.

Damage: See the individual abilities and descriptions previously described.

Psionics: All lycanmorphs have 3D4×10 I.S.P. plus six per level of experience and the powers of empathy, telepathy, sense evil, sense magic, mind block, and electrokinesis.

Magic: None.

Appearance: See the three metamorphoses described under natural abilities.

Slave Market Value: 300,000 to 700,000 credits; they are coveted by the Splugorth because they are so exotic and exciting in gladiatorial contests, particularly as the "battler."

Habitat: Forests and jungles, the denser the better. They also like Millennium trees.

Enemies: None per se; most aren't very aggressive and tend to avoid trouble.

Allies: Anybody who shows them kindness.

R.C.C. Skills (limited):
    Land Navigation (+20%)
    Wilderness Survival (+20%)
    Identify Plants & Fruits (+30%)
    Track Animals (+10%)
    Basic Math (+10%)
    W.P. Sword
    W.P.: Any two of choice

R.C.C. Related Skills: None.

Secondary Skills: The character can select six skills from the categories of domestic, espionage, physical, rogue (excluding computer hacking and streetwise), weapon proficiencies and wilderness skills. Select an additional two skills at levels four, eight and twelve.

Standard Equipment: The character is a creature of nature and has little need or desire for possessions other than a good sword, one or two other weapons and a nice trinket or two (they like jewelry).

Cybernetics & Bionics: None; their body rejects all forms of implants.

Money: None to start and has little need or desire for money. They may collect some jewelry and magic items that can be worth a lot, but this is not very common either.

Transformed into a "battler"

Seeker R.C.C.

The seekers are a race of giants from another dimension. They are commonly trained and commanded, or owned, by more intelligent and/or powerful dimensional travelers, mercenaries or bounty hunters. The seeker is huge, towering over 20 feet (6 m) when standing erect. They are frequently mistaken as a cyclops because the giant has one huge eye that dominates its head. Two large horns protrude from the sides of the head and help to protect the eye. A comparatively tiny and inconspicuous mouth with blunt teeth is located below the eye. The hands are oversized and powerful. The feet are prehensile hands like those of an Earth ape.

The seeker has a low intelligence, but is an instinctive hunter and works well with other creatures and in groups. The giants are omnivorous, meaning they eat raw meat, fish, fruit, vegetables and other edibles. Their keen senses and vision make them ideal hunters and have led to their capture, enslavement and sale by Naruni Enterprises (see **Rifts Mercenaries**) and other dimensional traders and slavers. The Splugorth have a few of these creatures but not many — this was one market commodity captured and dominated by the Naruni.

Many True Atlanteans, undead slayers and some other dimension spanning champions have made it a point to free enslaved seekers whenever they can. Many undead slayers travel the Megaverse with one or more seekers as their companions. Seekers have a high regard for intelligent life forms, especially humanoids and dragons. This means those of an unprincipled or good alignment avoid wanton murder and destruction. The fearsome giants can show astonishing gentleness and compassion.

Alignment: Any, but generally scrupulous, unprincipled, anarchist or aberrant.

Attributes: I.Q.: 1D4 + 3, M.E.: 4D6 + 2, M.A.: 3D6, P.S.: 4D6 + 20 (supernatural), P.P.: 3D6, P.E.: 3D6 + 6, P.B.: 2D6, Spd.: 4D6 + 10.

Hit Points: Supernatural mega-damage creature.

M.D.C. by Location:
  Hands (4) — 80 each
  Arms (2) — 100 each
  Legs (2) — 100 each
  Horns (2) — 100 each
  Eye (1) — 1D6 × 10
  Main Body — 3D6 × 10 + 60

P.P.E.: 2D4 × 10.

Horror Factor: 14

Weight: 2 to 4 tons

Size: 20 to 25 feet (6 to 7.6 m) tall when standing completely erect, but is usually bent over and walks on his knuckles, like a gorilla, for an average height of 15 feet tall (4.6 m).

Average Level of Experience for NPCs: 1D4 + 1

Natural Abilities: Keen color vision, nightvision 1000 feet (305 m), see in the infrared and ultraviolet light spectrum, see the invisible (including elemental beings and astral travelers), has keen hawk-like vision, able to see a rabbit two miles (3.2 km) away, and track by sight 85%. The creature is ambidextrous and has fully articulated hands in place of feet. The giant can leap 20 feet (6 m) high or 40 feet (12 m) lengthwise from a standing still position or double when running at full speed. Bio-regenerates 4D6 M.D. once per melee round, and is impervious to cold (no damage). The giant eye can be regenerated but takes 2D6 days if completely destroyed (blind until the eye is completely reformed). Hands, horns and limbs can be regenerated within 3D6 days.

Natural Bonuses: +2 on initiative, +2 to pull punch, +2 to roll with impact or fall, +6 to save vs horror factor, +4 to save vs symbiotic union and control, +4 to save vs magic illusions, +4 to save vs poison and disease. All bonuses are in addition to attributes and skills.

Combat: Seekers usually know hand to hand: basic, but get one additional melee attack/action per round.

Damage:

    Bite — 2D6 S.D.C.

    Body Flip — 2D6 M.D.

    Gore or Ram with Horns — 4D6 M.D.

    Head Butt — 1D6 M.D.

    Restrained Punch — 5D6 S.D.C.

    Punches — 1D6 M.D. + P.S. from supernatural P.S.; see **Rifts Conversion Book (one)**, page 22, for supernatural P.S. damage table. A seeker's punch or kick will typically inflict around 4D6 M.D.

Psionics: M.E. ×10. Considered a major psionic. Psionic powers include presence sense, detect psionics, see aura, see the invisible, sense evil, sense magic, psychic diagnosis, telepathy and mind block.

Magic: The seeker can cast a total of five spells a day. All seekers have the following spell abilities: invisibility (self), escape, teleport: greater (self only) and reduce self (in this case to 6 feet/1.8 m tall).

Appearance: A muscular, hairless giant with one huge eye (typically around four feet in diameter), grey skin with patterns of dark grey or black on the back, arms and legs. Two great tusks protrude from the sides of the head.

Slave Market Value: 100,000 to 200,000 credits.

Habitat: Anyplace; indigenous to an alien world.

Enemies & Allies: None per se; as transdimensional slaves and mercenaries they can face any number of foes or have a variety of allies.

R.C.C. Skills:

    Tracking (+20%)

    Track Animals (+20%)

    Detect Ambush (+20%)

    Detect Concealment (+10%)

    Palming (+10%)

    Concealment (+10%)

    Land Navigation (+30%)

    Wilderness Survival (+20%)

    Basic Math (+10%)

    Language: Gobblely (+20%) and one of choice

    Swim (+20%)

    Climb (+20%)

    W.P. Blunt

    W.P.: Any two of choice

    Hand to Hand: Basic; can be changed to expert (or assassin if evil) for the cost of one "other" skill selection.

R.C.C. Related Skills: Select six other skills plus one at levels two, four, six, eight, ten and twelve.

    Communications: Any

    Domestic: Any (+10%)

    Electrical: None

    Espionage: None

    Mechanical: None

    Medical: First aid or holistic medicine (+10%)

    Military: Any

    Physical: Any except acrobatics and gymnastics

    Pilot: None

    Pilot Related: None

    Rogue: Any (+2%), except computer hacking

    Science: Math only (+5%)

    Technical: Any (+5%)

    Weapon Proficiencies: Any

    Wilderness: Any (+10%)

Secondary Skills: The character also gets to select two secondary skills at levels one, three, seven and eleven.

Standard Equipment: Sword or blunt weapon and one or two weapons of choice — the seeker can use giant energy weapons or magic items. The character may also have a giant utility belt and/or back pack, 25 gallon (95 liter) water jug, language translator (tied to horn) and other odds and ends.

Cybernetics & Bionics: None; supernatural being.

Money: 1D6×1000 credits and 1D6×1000 credits worth of gold and artifacts to start.

Ugakwa Explorer R.C.C.

The ugakwa (pronounced you gah kuwah) are a race of dimensional adventurers and mercenaries who have only begun to explore the megaverse. Rifts Earth, with its many dimensional Rifts and anomalies, is one of the worlds discovered by the aliens. Currently, fewer than a thousand ugakwa can be found throughout the world. Unlike some aliens, they have no desire to conquer the Earth or any planet. Instead, they come to explore the wonders, mystery, magic and technology the planet has to offer. Depending on the individual's goals, personality and alignment, the character may be gentle and friendly, gruff and abrasive, self-serving or downright evil. Most are adventurers and mercenaries.

The ugakwa comes from a planet with a thick, gaseous atmosphere and a comparatively light gravity, which enables the aliens to float and *swim* through their atmosphere like fish in the sea or birds in the air. Consequently, their upper bodies are heavily muscled and incredibly strong, while their legs are comparatively thin and weak. As one might expect, on Earth and on Earth-like planets, the ugakwa cannot breathe the air. Being exposed to Earth's oxygen will cause the humanoid to suffocate within 2D4 minutes. To survive on Earth, they must wear a special air tank and helmet that can extract and mix the right gases from the air to create renewable, breathable air. In addition, most explorers wear an exo-skeleton over their legs to help them walk and to keep themselves from tiring quickly. They also wear a force field generator, a jet pack and have a variety of weapons and equipment. **Note:** The Ugakwa are as technologically advanced as Triax, except instead of developing robots and robot vehicles, they developed force field generators, lightweight exo-skeletons, miniaturized/nano-systems, and personal propulsion systems, as well as energy weapons and communications.

Alignment: Any

Attributes: I.Q.: 3D6, M.E.: 3D6, M.A.: 3D6, P.S.: 5D6+12 (equal to supernatural), P.P.: 3D6+6, P.E.: 3D6+6, P.B.: 2D4, Spd.: 1D6 without mechanical enhancements like an exo-skeleton or jet pack.

Hit Points: P.E. attribute number +1D6 per level of experience.

S.D.C.: 3D6×10

M.D.C.: The ugakwa use mega-damage body armor and force fields.

P.P.E.: 2D4×10, but possess no natural magic powers.

Horror Factor: 10

Weight: 300 pounds (135 kg)

Size: 6 to 7 feet tall (1.8 to 2.1 m).

Average Level of Experience for NPCs: 1D4+2

Natural Abilities: 1. Keen 20/20 color vision, natural polarized vision and can see the ultraviolet spectrum of light.

Natural Bonuses: +2 on initiative, +2 to pull punch, +2 to roll with impact or fall, +6 to S.D.C. damage, +2 to save vs horror factor, +1 to save vs psionic attack, +2 to save vs poison and disease. All bonuses are in addition to attributes and skills.

Combat: The Ugakwa get hand to hand: expert (or as per O.C.C.). Attacks Per Melee Round: As per hand to hand.

Damage:

Bite — 2D6 S.D.C.

Body Flip — 2D6 S.D.C.

Head Butt or a Restrained Punch — 1D6 S.D.C.

Full Strength Punch — 3D6 S.D.C. plus P.S. bonus

Power Punch or Leap Kick — 6D6 S.D.C. plus P.S. bonus (counts as two melee attacks).

Psionics: Standard; same as humans.

Magic: None.

Appearance: A muscular, hairless alien with a poerful upper body and spindly legs. Usually clad in a helmet and exo-skeleton.

Slave Market Value: 100,000 to 200,000 credits.

Habitat: Any place.

Enemies: Vampires, demons and evil supernatural beings.

Allies: Champions of good.

R.C.C. Skills of the Ugakwa Explorer:

Radio: Basic (+20%)

Land Navigation (+10%)

Navigation (+20%)

Read Sensory Equipment (+10%)

Computer Operation (+20%)

Basic Math (+20%)

Literacy: Native Ugakwa at 98%

Pilot: Jet Pack (+20%)

Pilot: Two of choice

W.P. Spear/Targeting

W.P. Energy Rifle

W.P.: Any two of choice

Hand to Hand: Expert

R.C.C. Related Skills: Select eight other skills plus one at levels two, four, six, eight, ten and twelve.

Communications: Any (+10%)

Domestic: Any (+10%)

Electrical: Any

Espionage: None

Mechanical: Any (+5%)

Medical: None

Military: Any

Physical: Any, except acrobatics or gymnastics

Pilot: Any (+10%)

Pilot Related: Any (+10%)

Rogue: Any (+2%)

Science: Any (+10%)

Technical: Any (+15%)

Weapon Proficiencies: Any

Wilderness: Any

Secondary Skills: The character also gets to select two secondary skills at levels two, five, nine and twelve.

Standard Equipment:

1. Force Field Generator: This system is even smaller, lighter and more powerful than the Naruni system available in the Americas. The main generator is designed as a portable backpack connected to the life support unit; weight: 15 lbs (6.8 kg). The backpack has 50 M.D.C. and the force field it generates has 200 M.D.C.! 20 M.D.C. can be regenerated per hour. The protective energy field covers the entire body and also prevents infection from alien microbes/disease.

2. Life support system: The ugakwa's atmosphere creation and circulatory system is built-into the helmet along with an air tank that has emergency reserves of six hours. The system also has a cooling unit to keep the temperature around the body (within the force field) comfortable and to reduce exhaustion (fatigues at half the normal rate).

A bionic lung with a gas filter and air storage cell serve as a back-up system and offers additional protection.

* Nano-medical bots, housed in a rechargeable internal container inside the body, provides the same kind of instant medical service as several *IRMSS Internal Robot Medical Surgeon Systems and RMK "Knitters."*

* The Helmet has 60 M.D.C. points and is a difficult target to hit; −4 even on a called shot. It also has a built-in language translator, loudspeaker, long-range radio, radiation detector, and tinted dome that adjusts automatically in response to the ambient light source.

3. Exo-skeleton: A special pair of pants with numerous nano-sensors and stimuli are linked to a lightweight, exterior exo-skeleton that supports the alien explorer's legs. The system enables the character to walk and move faster; add 12 points to the character's speed attribute. If the exo-skeleton is destroyed the character loses the 12 spd points and fatigues more easily (equal to a typical human). The exo-skeleton has 80 M.D.C. points and is a difficult target to hit; −4 even on a called shot.

The feet of the exo-skeleton and a handpad on the right hand are electro-adhesive pads (see **Rifts RPG,** page 247, for details). It also has an independent power supply with a 15 year life.

4. Jet Pack: Attached to the backpack. Lightweight (14 lbs/6.4 kg), effectively unlimited range, can hover stationary, has a maximum altitude of 10,000 feet (3050 m) and a maximum speed of 300 mph (482 km).

5. System Power Supply: Nuclear, with a 25 year life.

6. Concentrated Food Pills: One pill has the nutritional value of a complete meal; has enough food for six months. The ugakwa can also eat the same food as a human but must insert it through a special side opening in the helmet.

7. Other types of equipment such as tools, optics, tents, utility belts, vehicles, etc., can also be acquired.

Standard Weapon Systems:

1. Knuckle Laser (1): Short-range defense and repair system.
Weight: 6 ounces (0.17 kg)
Mega-Damage: One blast 1D6 M.D., two simultaneous blasts 2D6 M.D. or 3D6 M.D.
Range: 25 feet (7.6 m)
Payload: 12 — 1D6 M.D. blasts as an independent item, but is effectively unlimited when tied to the overall power and force field system, which is standard.
Note: Typically worn on the left hand.

2. Forearm Laser Gauntlet (1): This is a laser weapon attached to a ceramic plate, forearm gauntlet. The weapon can swivel to point up and down or to the left and right without moving the arm. The weapon comes with laser targeting and self adjusting targeting system, +3 to strike!
Weight: 1.5 pounds (0.68 kg)
Mega-Damage: 2D6 M.D.
Range: 1600 feet (488 m)
Payload: 20 blasts as an independent item, but is effectively unlimited when tied to the overall power and force field system, which is standard.
Note: One is typically worn on the right hand. The blaster has 20 M.D.C. and the gauntlet, 30. The gauntlet also has four small compartments large enough to hold such things as additional IRMSS and RMK medical bots, a dozen pills, four credit cards, and similar.

3. Plasma Spear (1): This weapon is reminiscent of the Kittani plasma items and can be used as a mega-damage spear or as an energy firing weapon.
Weight: 4 pounds (1.8 kg)
Mega-Damage: 4D6 M.D. per plasma blast or 2D6 as a stabbing weapon.
Range: 3000 feet (914 m) blast range or about 200 feet (61 m) thrown.

Payload: 20 blasts as an independent item, but is effectively unlimited when tied to the overall power and force field system, which is standard.
Note: The spear has 70 M.D.C.

4. High-Power Backpack Lasers (2): The two appendages sticking up from the backpack/jet pack are lasers. They can point straight up (forward when flying in a prone position) or bend over the shoulders to point in the direction the character faces when standing.
Weight: Adds 14 pounds (6.4 kg) to the backpack.
Mega-Damage: 3D6 M.D. per single blast or 6D6 per simultaneous double blast.
Range: 4000 feet (1200 m)
Payload: 60 blasts each before needing recharging. Recharges at a rate of 10 per hour.
Note: Each of the laser appendages has 90 M.D.C.

5. Grenades: 2D4 hand grenades. Basically the same types as those available from Triax/NGR.

6. Plasma Net: A net with bola-like weights at the ends, making it ideal for throwing. It is large enough to encircle a human-sized target and the space-age fibers are as strong as steel cable (60 M.D.C.)
Mega-Damage: When connected to the plasma spear, a charge of plasma energy courses through the net, inflicting 3D6 M.D. as often as twice per melee round (15 seconds); each charge counts as one melee attack and uses up one of the spear's charges. It can also be used as a parrying weapon and the weights at the ends can inflict 2D4 S.D.C. damage when the net is used to hit an opponent.
Range: Thrown 100 feet (30.5 m); swinging to parry or hit, the net extends the reach by about four feet (1.2 m).
Payload: Plasma charges are linked to the energy spear.
Note: The net has 65 M.D.C.; characters entangled in the net will need to use up 1D4 + 1 melee actions/attacks to get loose. A plasma jolt will cause the trapped creature to lose two melee actions.

7. Other weapons such as laser pistols, rifles, etc., can also be used. Ugakwa weapons will be equivalent to Triax or Coalition items. They like powerful energy weapons, plasma and vibro-blades, and limited cybernetic augmentation.

Cybernetics & Bionics: Only those listed previously. Others can be acquired later, but the operation is dangerous on Earth because of the atmospheric conditions (need a special chamber with the Ugakwa's atmosphere, and the cyber-doc in a spacesuit. Both the gene-splicers and Mindwerks could perform such an operation.)

Money: Has 2D6 × 1000 Earth credits to start.

Srrynn Cannibal R.C.C.

The srrynn (seer ryan) cannibal is a predatory D-bee worthy of being considered a demon (although technically it is not). They are a race of hunters and scavengers who have gladly joined the ranks of transdimensional raiders, bandits, mercenaries, and bounty hunters. Many are independent operators or members of freelance mercenary bands. Others work for dimension-spanning alien intelligences, corporations, arms dealers, armies, and minions.

The srrynn have a high metabolism that helps to give them lightning reflexes and speed. Approximately 10,000 srrynn are members of the Gargoyle Empire and another estimated two to four thousand roam Germany, Poland and western Europe as bandits and mercenaries. Most srrynn will feed on the internal organs of a fallen opponent. The blood-thirsty warriors eat other humanoids, including members of their own race. As is common among many warrior races, the srrynn respect strength and power above all else. They are natural and instinctive hunters and love to fight.

Player Character Note: A srrynn player character is likely to be an outcast for some reason — one reason may be an unusual good alignment. Even good characters will be hyperactive, aggressive and violent.

Alignment: Any, but generally selfish or evil.

Attributes: I.Q.: 3D6, M.E.: 3D6, M.A.: 3D6, P.S.: 3D6+10, P.P.: 3D6+10, P.E.: 3D6+8, P.B.: 1D6, Spd.: 4D4×10.

Hit Points: Mega-damage creatures.

M.D.C. (natural): 1D6×10+30 plus body armor and bionics; many become partial cyborgs.

P.P.E.: 1D4×10, but possess no natural magic powers.

Horror Factor: 10

Weight: 200 to 300 pounds (90 to 135 kg)

Size: 6 to 8 feet tall (1.8 to 2.4 m).

Average Level of Experience for NPCs: 1D4+3

Natural Abilities: Ambidextrous, lightning reflexes (see P.P. and combat bonuses), three arms, keen 20/20 color vision and sense of smell, nightvision 90 feet (27 m) and resistant to poison, drugs and disease. It also has an 8 foot (2.4 m) long prehensile tail used to strike like a whip, stab, entangle, strangle and climb.

Natural Bonuses: +5 on initiative, +2 to strike, +2 to parry, +4 to pull punch, +2 to roll with impact or fall, +5 to save vs horror factor, +4 to save vs poison, drugs, and disease, +1 to save vs magic. All bonuses are in addition to attributes and skills.

Combat: The typical srrynn gets hand to hand: expert or assassin plus two additional attacks/actions per melee!

Damage: Same as humans plus P.S. attribute bonus.

Bite does 1D6 S.D.C., head butt does 1D6 S.D.C., kick or leap kick 2D6, and prehensile tail has a sharp blade at the end (1D6 S.D.C. stab, 1D6 whip, 4D6 S.D.C. per melee round to strangle).

Psionics: None.

Magic: None.

Appearance: A three armed, muscular alien with pale yellow skin and reddish brown accent markings. The head is large, the eyes sunken, and the pointed ivory teeth protrude from the upper lip. A pair of tusks and pincers protrude from the jaw, adding to the creature's demonic appearance.

Slave Market Value: 80,000 to 150,000 credits.

Habitat: Any place.

Enemies: None per se — or many; very aggressive.

Allies: Other warriors and monsters.

R.C.C. Skills:
- Track: Humanoids (+15%)
- Track: Animals (+20%)
- Skin & Prepare Animal Hides (+15%)
- Land Navigation (+15%)
- Wilderness Survival (+20%)
- Basic Math (+20%)
- Literacy: Native Srrynn (+20%)
- Language: Native Srrynn at 98% and Dragonese (+20%)
- Radio: Basic (+20%)
- Pilot: Two of choice (+15%)
- W.P. Sword
- W.P. Energy Pistol
- W.P. Energy Rifle
- W.P.: Any two of choice
- Hand to Hand: Expert (or assassin if evil)

R.C.C. Related Skills: Select eight other skills plus one at levels two, four, eight, and twelve.
- Communications: Any (+10%)
- Domestic: Any
- Electrical: None
- Espionage: Any
- Mechanical: None
- Medical: First aid (+10%)
- Military: Any
- Physical: Any
- Pilot: Any (+10%)
- Pilot Related: Any (+10%)
- Rogue: Any (+2%)
- Science: Math, astronomy, anthropology only (+10%)
- Technical: Any (+10%)
- Weapon Proficiencies: Any
- Wilderness: Any (+5%)

Secondary Skills: The character also gets to select two secondary skills at levels one, five and eleven.

Standard Equipment: Spear and three weapons of choice, a silver plated knife, six wooden stakes and a mallet, short-range walkie-talkie, flashlight, backpack, utility belt, compass, language translator, canteen and food rations. The character is attracted to powerful energy weapons, magic weapons, vibro-blades, and bionic augmentation.

Cybernetics & Bionics: One limb will be bionic with 1D4 weapon features, plus 1D4 other cybernetic/bionic items (optics and amplified hearing are always high on the list). Others can be acquired with time.

Money: 2D4 × 1000 credits and 1D6 × 1000 credits' worth of gold and artifacts to start.

The Simvan
The Monster Riders of Europe

The inhabitants of the American and Canadian west know the simvan monster riders well. A race of intelligent humanoid cannibals who can control wild animals and monsters from the Rifts. In the Americas the simvan arrived through the infamous Calgary rift. In Europe they have arrived through one of the portals in the evil millennium tree located in the Black Forest. These nomads travel in tribes that number as few as 1D4 × 100 to 4D6 × 100 members. Thousands have joined the Gargoyle and Brodkil Empires, particularly the latter. The simvan are far more numerous in Europe than any other continent, with the greatest concentration (the NGR estimates 3 to 5 million) inhabiting the countries once known as Germany, Austria, Poland, and Czechoslovakia.

The simvan culture is not unlike most nomadic societies. The men are the builders, hunters and protectors, while the women are the homemakers, bearing and raising children, preparing food, making clothes, etc. The women are also the tribal healers and possess natural psionic healing abilities.

A tribe will settle in one area for weeks or months at a time. Sometimes they may inhabit the same specific area as long as a year, but eventually they move on, especially when the hunting grows poor (usually seasonal) or the environment becomes threatening (weather, monsters, humans, etc.). Some tribes follow a seasonal pattern that doesn't change for generations, then one day they are gone — off to explore a new frontier.

The males and females are aggressive, quick tempered and violent, although acts of violence within the same tribe and between family members rarely draw blood. Among their own, the simvan are amazingly gentle, patient, kind, considerate, cooperative and always cheerful and laughing. They create a strong community held together with bonds of friendship, family and loyalty to each other and the tribe as a whole.

It must be understood that the simvan see only themselves as the true people, one with the land; all others are generally seen as fools or food. The simvan are meat eaters with a definite preference for human and humanoid flesh. They are aggressive, belligerent, demeaning, arrogant and deadly dangerous toward other humanoids and rival tribes. On their homeworld, during times of famine and hardship, rival tribes will go to war. The losers becoming slaves and the fallen are eaten. It is also tradition to eat a worthy foe to show one's respect to a valiant enemy. They believe the hand of fate may deem to impart some of the fallen's strength, courage or wisdom to those who feast on his bones. This legend of strength probably stems from the strength and life that food provides to the starving.

Simvan men are capable hunters and merciless warriors. Their skills as trackers and hunters outshine the wilderness scout and as warriors they are nearly equal to any headhunter or knight. The men, like all simvan, have a wild devil-may-care attitude toward life. They love to take risks and accept challenges that will test their strength, courage and skills. As cannibals, the ultimate triumph and honor is to vanquish and eat a valiant and worthy opponent. The warriors see combat as a means of proving their own bravery, power, and skills, as well as making life exciting and worth living. Courage, combat skill, and honor to one's people are the most important values among the simvan.

The Simvan are not stupid and will not attack enemies with vastly superior numbers or superior firepower, unless defending the tribe or family. However, they do love to fight and encourage settling disputes or proving one's honor through combat with the opposing or accusing person or through trial by combat (often with a monster/animal). For example: A tribesman who has been disgraced in combat (cowardice or accused of treachery) must either fight his accuser, often to the death, or face some other physical challenge or contest. If many accuse him, the offender is banished from the tribe but can redeem himself by going into the wilderness with no armor and only ancient types of weapons

to fight and slay a terrible beast (bear, lion, monster, etc.). If he returns with its head, he may be allowed back into the tribe. Likewise, outsiders who wish to speak to the shaman or tribe leader may be forced to prove themselves by hand to hand combat (not to the death).

Although the simvan are cannibals and man-eaters, they do not attack and eat anybody they happen upon. They frequently trade animal furs and offer scouting, tracking, and hunting services to other humanoids in trade for mega-damage weapons, E-clips, body armor and supplies. Likewise, they are often acquaintances (and even friends) with human and D-bee gypsies, mountain men and wilderness scouts in the area. The simvan's favorite humanoid associates are gypsies, brodkil, azverkan, seekers, psi-stalkers and intelligent mutant animals. The psi-stalkers and intelligent mutant animals are often allowed official membership into a tribe as long as they obey tribal law and customs. The Simvan's favorite humanoids to eat are humans and those most like humans. Simvan respect and fear faerie folk and elementals.

These wildmen are known as "Monster Riders" because they have the psionic power to tame even ferocious predators and use them as mounts, companions and beasts of burden. The monsters selected are frequently creatures believed to be untamable and are frequently carnivorous. In Europe such monsters include the eurotorpid, stone-claw, mega-foot mastica, gryphon, peryton, dragondactyl, melech, and others. Tribe members will often have wolves, dogs, bears, wild boars and mountain lions as pets.

Player's Note: Simvan player characters may be tribal outcasts and may be marked as an enemy if he supports humankind or fights against either the Gargoyle or Brodkil empire. The Brodkil Empire has the vast majority of simvan pledged to it, but there are tribes, clans and individuals allied to the gargoyles or who operate as independent, non-allied forces.

European Simvan Monster Riders
Alignment: Any, although most NPC villains are likely to be anarchist, aberrant or other evil alignment.
Horror Factor: 12
Size: 5 feet 7 inches (1.7 m) to six feet (1.8 m) tall.
Weight: 150 to 200 pounds (67 to 90 kg)
Attributes: I.Q.: 3D6 M.E.: 4D6, M.A.: 2D6, P.S.: 4D6, P.P.: 4D6, P.E. 5D6, P.B.: 2D6, Spd. 4D6
P.P.E.: 4D4
Hit Points: 1D4×10, **S.D.C.:** 2D6×10
M.D.C.: By body armor or magic.
Natural Abilities: Keen vision, nightvision 120 feet (36.5 m), and psionic powers.
Psionic Powers, Males: I.S.P.: 2D4×10+M.E. points. Empathy, telepathy, sixth sense, mind block, and mind bond (super), as well as a psychic affinity with animals similar to those of the psi-stalker (see **Rifts**, page 106, #8), only it applies to all types of animals, including monsters with an animal intelligence. This power automatically gives the simvan male the horsemanship skill at +30% and horsemanship: exotic animals at +20%
Psionic Powers, Females: I.S.P.: 4D4×10+M.E. Detect psionics, deaden pain, exorcism, healing touch, increase healing, psychic diagnosis, and psychic surgery.
Combat: Two attacks per melee plus those of the hand to hand training. Most Males are 3rd to 9th level fighters (roll 2D4+1); assassin hand to hand.
Skills of Males: All wilderness skills (+20% bonus on all), wilderness survival (+30%), track humanoids +20%, horsemanship +30%, monstermanship +20%, dance and sing both at +10%. Physical skills: Hand to hand expert or assassin, body building, general athletics, running, climbing, and select three others (boxing and acrobatics not available). Weapon Proficiencies: Archery and targeting, knife, energy rifle, and select four additional. Most simvan speak Simvanese (98%), Brodkil, Gobblely and Euro all at +20%.

Player characters (or more elaborate NPCs), male or female: Select a total of six skills from the following: Radio: basic, escape artist, pick pockets, palming, concealment, pilot motorcycle, pilot automobile, pilot hover craft, pilot sail- or motor-boat, monster lore, faerie lore, any languages and art. No bonuses applicable.
Skills of Females: All domestic (+30% on all) and wilderness skills (+10%), wilderness survival (+15%), horsemanship (+20%), horsemanship: exotic animals (+15%), holistic medicine (+20%), herbology (+20%; see **Rifts England**) and speak Simvanese (98%), Brodkil, Gobblely, Euro and one of choice (+20%). Physical skills: Hand to hand basic, running, climbing, and select two others. Weapon Proficiencies: Blunt, knife, and select two others. A female is typically the clan or tribe shaman.
Weapons & Equipment: Knife and two energy weapons of choice, and/or bow and arrows (can include high-tech or magic arrows). Favorite weapons include the vibro-blades, Kittani plasma blades, mega-damage arrows, and Triax energy weapons. They like magic items, especially mega-damage swords, knives, axes, bows, staffs and spears, but don't seek them above any other good weapon. Most Simvan wear light mega-damage body armor, but any kind can be worn.
Bionics & Cybernetics: Tend to avoid them for many reasons, but will consider a more powerful prosthetic limb if the natural one is lost. Most simvan also avoid M.O.M. implants, but some have elected to get some, usually for increased psionic powers.
Money: The typical simvan will have only 1D6×100 credits and 1D4×1000 credits' worth of furs and precious metals.

C'ro Demon Mage (NPC)

The c'ro (pronounced crow) demon mage is a supernatural monster from another dimension whose powers and scarcity place them in the category of greater demon. As the name suggests, this creature possesses magic and spell casting abilities. The demon mage may associate with other demons and supernatural kin, but tend to conduct their business as independent operators with their own agenda. They are selfish, brutal creatures who seldom let anything stand in the way of what they want. Most are attracted to wealth and power. It is not surprising to find these fiends trying to position themselves into places of power as lords, kings, emperors and even gods.

There are at least three c'ro demon mages known to have expressed an interest in Europe. In each case, the demon sees the current conflict as a free-for-all that offers some excellent opportunities for those who can take advantage of them. The demon mage is a master of deceit and manipulation, but their actions and words can only lead to trouble and dismay.
Note: The demon mage is intended as a non-player character (NPC) villain and is not available as a player character.
Alignment: Selfish or evil; most are miscreant and diabolic.
Attributes: I.Q.: 2D6+8, M.E.: 3D6+8, M.A.: 3D6+6, P.S.: 3D6+6, P.P.: 3D6+6, P.E.: 3D6+6, P.B.: 2D4, Spd.: 4D6
Hit Points: Mega-damage creatures.
M.D.C.: 1D4×100+100 (never uses body armor).
P.P.E.: 1D4×100+250
Horror Factor: 15
Weight: 200 to 300 pounds (90 to 135 kg)
Size: 6 to 7 feet tall (1.8 to 2.1 m).
Average Level of Experience for NPC Villains: 1D4+4
Natural Abilities: Nightvision 90 feet (27.4 m), keen color vision, see the invisible, dimensional teleport 75%, bio-regeneration 4D6 per melee round (severed limbs regenerate completely within 48 hours), impervious to normal fire and cold, mega-damage and magic fire and cold inflicts half damage, impervious to disease, and magically knows all languages.

Natural Bonuses: Impervious to supernatural and psionic possession, impervious to the bite and gaze of vampires, impervious to symbiotic union and control, +3 on initiative, +3 to strike, +6 to parry, +3 to pull punch, +2 to roll with impact or fall, +6 to save vs horror factor, +3 to magic, +2 to save vs psionics and +6 to save vs poison. All bonuses are in addition to attributes and skills.

Combat: Seven physical attack per melee or three by magic.

Damage: Punch and kick damage will vary with the supernatural P.S. attribute, but seldom do less than 1D6 M.D.

    Bite — 2D6 S.D.C.

    Body Flip — 2D6 S.D.C.

    Head Butt or a Restrained Punch — 2D6 S.D.C.

    Pincer/Stinger Attack — The demon mage has six tentacle or stinger-like appendages that gives it a great advantage in combat, parrying and striking with deadly results. A mere stab from one stinger inflicts 1D6 M.D., but as many as three can strike simultaneously, inflicting 3D6 M.D. points. Furthermore, the c'ro demon mage can inject a combatant with a powerful toxin that causes 4D6 M.D. and disorien-

tation to mega-damage creatures; −1 on all combat bonuses and lose one melee attack for the next 1D6 melee rounds — all damage and penalties are cumulative.

    Mere mortals suffer 1D6×10 S.D.C./hit point damage and must roll to save vs lethal poison. A failed roll means the character lapses into a coma; roll to save vs coma/death! Those who survive the coma/death will remain unconscious for 2D4 minutes and when the character regains consciousness he is weak and shaken; only one attack per melee and no combat bonuses for 1D6 hours!

Psionics: None.

Magic: 1D4×100+50 P.P.E.; 50% knows all level 1-5 spell magic plus three spells (GM's choice) from each levels 6-12. 25% are necromancers and have all the necromancer's powers, knows all necromancer spells and the first six levels of common spell magic as described in **Rifts Africa**, page 108. The remaining 25% are temporal wizards equal to 14 years of study and servitude (see **Rifts England**).

Appearance: A red skinned, humanoid demon with a snake's nose (slits), yellow eyes, and a pair of yellow stripes on each cheek. The skin is covered in fine, soft scales like a snake, and six stingers protrude from the back. The hands are very human looking except they are a bit longer, slender and have yellow nails. Most demon mages cover their body in a robe, gown, cape or cloak, but even such bulky coverings cannot conceal the pointed bone plates that rise up from the collar bone and shoulders.

Slave Market Value: Not applicable.

Habitat: Any place.

Enemies: Undead slayers, azverkan, and champions of good.

Allies: Other demons (lesser demons, entities, and sub-demons like gargoyles and brodkil are frequently enslaved), witches, necromancers, and evil beings of all kind.

R.C.C. Skills of the C'ro Demon Mage:

    Lore: Magic (+15%, see Rifts Triax)

    Lore: Demons & Monsters (+20%)

    Holistic Medicine (+20%)

    Streetwise (+10%)

    Concealment (+10%)

    Palming (+10%)

    Land Navigation (+10%)

    Basic Math (+30%)

    Literacy: Dragonese/Elf and Demongogain (+20%)

    Radio: Basic (+20%)

    Pilot: Two of choice (+10%)

    W.P. Sword

    W.P.: Any two of choice

    Hand to Hand: Not applicable — see combat above

R.C.C. Related Skills: Select eight other skills plus one at levels two, four, six, eight, ten and twelve.

    Communications: Any (+10%)

    Domestic: Any (+10%)

    Electrical: None

    Espionage: None

    Mechanical: None

    Medical: None other than the R.C.C. skill noted above

    Military: Any (+5%)

    Physical: None

    Pilot: Any (+10%)

    Pilot Related: Any (+10%)

    Rogue: Any (+2%)

    Science: Any (+10%)

    Technical: Any (+15%)

    Weapon Proficiencies: Any

    Wilderness: Any

Secondary Skills: None; relies on magic and natural abilities.

Standard Equipment: Varies dramatically; all will have 1D4+1 magic items (magic weapon, amulet, talisman, etc.). Demon mages are attracted to rune weapons, techno-wizard devices, magic items and bio-wizardry. Many are also familiar with some technology and may use any number of technological devices and vehicles.

Cybernetics & Bionics: None; a supernatural being.

Money: The typical adventuring lone wolf will have 1D6×10,000 in credits and/or gems and gold. Others may command a kingdom and have virtually unlimited resources.

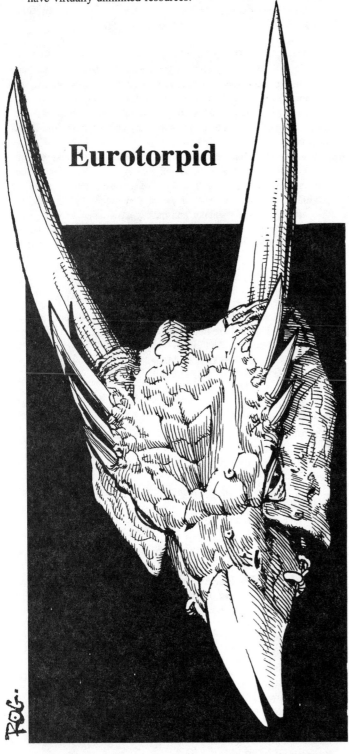

Eurotorpid

Like the Americas, a number of dinosaur-like creatures have made a reappearance in Europe. The most famous is the large, triceratops-like creature known as the eurotorpid. This lumbering herbivore is at home in the steppes of Russia and Mongolia or the grasslands and forests of Europe, grazing on grass and leaves. The full grown eurotorpid is about the size of the Indian elephant, only this mega-damage animal has heavy plates and an array of horns to protect it.

The eurotorpid typically travels in herds. A small herd will have 3D4 members while the largest will have 3D4 × 100 animals! The giant beast is very tolerant of humans and other creatures and will not attack unless they feel threatened or are attacked first. Although an animal with an intelligence roughly equal to that of a horse, the creature has psionic intuition that warns it of danger, making it impossible to catch unawares and always giving it the initiative in any confrontation. Humans and others who have no intention of endangering the great beasts are ignored and can walk through a herd and even touch the beasts without fear of being attacked. However, even the eurotorpid's tolerance has a limit, and the animal will butt, push away, stomp, charge, or throw most humanoids who get overconfident and either try to ride the animal or become too annoying. Psi-stalkers, mutant dog boys and simvan are often seen among the eurotorpid. The simvan, with their psionic link to animals, love to use the eurotorpid for riding.

Note: This creature is a dull-witted predatory animal and is not available as a player character.

Alignment: Effectively good or anarchist; grazing animal.

Attributes: I.Q.: 1D6 (animal), M.E.: 4D6, M.A.: 4D6, P.S.: 4D6+30 (equal to supernatural), P.P.: 3D6+6, P.E.: 3D6+12, P.B.: 3D6, Spd.: 6D6+30 (half that speed swimming).

Hit Points: Mega-damage creature

M.D.C. by Location:
    Legs (4) — 150 each
    Large Horns (2) — 150 each
    Underbelly — 200 (attackers are −5 to strike)
    Head — 200
    Main Body — 2D4 × 100

P.P.E.: 6D6

Horror Factor: 10

Weight: 6 to 10 tons

Size: 10 to 12 feet (3 to 3.6 m) tall and 12 to 14 feet (3.6 to 4.3 m) long.

Average Level of Experience: Not applicable.

Natural Abilities: Nightvision 100 feet (30.5 m), fair normal color vision. Extremely keen sense of smell and hearing — track by scent 65%, Swim 65%, heals twice as fast as humans and is resistant to cold, heat and fire (half damage).

Combat: 4 attacks per melee round.

Damage:
    Restrained Head-Butt — 3D6 S.D.C.
    Full Strength Head-Butt — 2D6 M.D.
    Power Head-Butt — 4D6 M.D.
    Short Charge & Ram — 5D6 M.D. counts as one attack
    Full Speed & Strength Ram — 1D6 × 10 M.D. counts as two attacks
    Gore with Horns — 4D6 M.D.
    Stomp — 1D6 M.D.
    Bite — 3D6 S.D.C.
    Kick attacks are not possible, but a ram attack has a 01-75% likelihood of knocking an opponent down (victim loses initiative and one melee attack).

Bonuses: Cannot be caught unawares (see psionics), +3 on initiative, +4 to strike, +5 to parry, +2 to dodge, +2 to roll with impact or fall, +3 to save vs horror factor, +1 to save vs magic, +4 to save vs poison, drugs and disease. All bonuses are in addition to any attribute bonuses.

Psionics: 3D6 × 10 I.S.P.; all eurotorpids possess sixth sense, empathy, and sense evil. The creature automatically senses impending danger via a sort of automatic sixth sense.

Magic: None.

Appearance: An elephant-sized, triceratops-like beast with two large horns and two rows of three smaller horns.

Slave Market Value: 10,000 to 40,000 credits; used in gladiatorial arenas and as beasts of burden pulling heavy carts. The eurotorpid can also be domesticated as a riding animal for humanoids. The simvan and psi-stalkers often use the eurotorpid as a riding animal.

Habitat: Grasslands and light forests. They are numerous in the countries once known as Russia and Mongolia.

Enemies: None per se.

Allies: None per se.

Mega-Foot Mastica

The mega-foot mastica is a giant alien scavenger who gets its name from the fact that it has two oversized hind legs, huge feet and an enormous appetite. The beast resembles a giant, mutant centipede or alien insect of some sort, but it is actually a warmblooded animal loosely akin to Earth birds. At the end of its four arms are articulated fingers with four razor sharp claws used for slicing up carcasses. Its mouth is huge and the jaw can unhinge to swallow larger chunks of food or small animals whole.

The creature feeds on carrion — eats the remains of dead animals like a vulture. Its first choice for food is meat of any kind, animal or humanoid, but it will eat anything that won't eat him first, including spoiled fish, vegetables, blood, bones and other organic edibles. Packs of the horrible creatures often flock to the site of battles to feast on the remains of the dead and dying. They have also been known to plunder graveyards and even infirmaries and hospitals (especially field hospitals).

In addition to feeding on carrion and garbage, the mega-foot mastica may also turn its attention to the weak and injured. They are infamous for attacking and trying to eat the sick, injured, young and helpless, including humans, D-bees, and livestock. Wilderness folk keep a sharp eye on little children (9 and younger), the elderly, infirm and family pets when a pack of mega-foot have been sighted in the area.

The macabre monsters are skittish and shy when alone or in pairs, but they are pack animals who instinctively gather in large groups. It is in these groups that they are at their most dangerous, showing aggressiveness and tenacity that is not present in the individual. A typical hunting pack can contain 3D4 members while a swarm or large pack can contain 3D4 × 10 hungry scavengers. However, the largest group of mega-foot are hesitant to attack healthy humans and animals, even if they outnumber them five to one. Furthermore, they give up easily if their intended prey offers too much of a fight.

Feeding Frenzy: There is a 01-65% chance that a pack of mega-foot mastica will fall into a feeding frenzy. During the frenzy they become swarming, fearless (and almost mindless) devourers pouncing on all available food. Although this can be a terrifying sight, humanoids who keep a cool head have the advantage. During the frenzy the creatures will attack any food that becomes available, including fallen mega-foot mastica, slaughtered cattle, and garbage thrown in their way. This means the beasts are easily distracted and will stop in the middle of a melee to eat anything that comes their way, sometimes fighting amongst themselves for the tiniest scraps. Better yet, the monsters lose their initiative and half their melee attacks whenever lost to the frenzy. Thus, killing a few mega-foot mastica will usually give humans an opportunity to flee or hide while the majority of the creatures stop to feed.

Note: The feeding frenzy only occurs among groups of four or more. One or two mega-foot mastica rarely attack humans or large animals, even when cornered. One or two are also easily frightened and chased away.

Most wilderness folk have adopted the practice of killing the mega-foot whenever they are encountered, especially when found in tiny groups or as lone individuals.

Note: This creature is a stupid, scavenging animal and is not available as a player character.

Alignment: Effectively anarchist or miscreant; scavenger/pack hunter.

Attributes: I.Q.: 1D4 (animal), M.E.: 1D6, M.A.: 1D6, P.S.: 3D6+20 (equal to supernatural), P.P.: 2D6+10, P.E.: 3D6+10, P.B.: 1D4, Spd.: 4D6+40 (running; half that speed climbing or swimming).

Hit Points: Mega-damage creature.

M.D.C.: 4D6+20

P.P.E.: 2D6

Horror Factor: 11 (13 for a large group/swarm)

Weight: 700 pounds (315 kg)

Size: 7 to 8 feet (2.1 to 2.4 m) tall and the flexible body is also 7 to 8 feet long.

Average Level of Experience: Not applicable.

Natural Abilities: Nightvision 100 feet (30.5 m) and keen hawk-like vision able to detect a rotting carcass a mile (1.6 km) away. Super keen sense of smell — can smell the scent of blood or decay two miles (3.2 km) away, sometimes as far as 10 miles (16 km) if carried by the wind. Track blood scent or stench of decay 80%, track by sight 45%, swim 70%, climb 60%/55%, and can leap 20 feet (6 m) high or 30 feet (9 m) lengthwise from a standing still position or double if running/loping at full speed! Bio-regenerates 2D6 M.D.C. once per minute (4 melee rounds). It is also resistant to cold and fire (half damage).

The body of the mega-foot is extremely flexible, especially at the joints of its large hind legs. Thus it can twist and turn like a pretzel in any direction or angle, including so completely backward that it faces forward again (see the illustration). It has four arms and a deceptively large mouth filled with serrated teeth.

Combat: 5 attacks per melee round. The claws can be used like paired weapons.

Damage: Restrained claw strike 4D6 S.D.C., a single hand claw strike inflicts 1D6 M.D., two simultaneous strikes 2D6 M.D., three-handed strike 3D6 M.D., or a four-handed strike 4D6 M.D. The simultaneous quadruple strike counts as one attack but the beast cannot parry or dodge his opponent's counter-attack. The bite inflicts 1D4 M.D. and the pincer located in the tail does 1D6 M.D.

A kick inflicts 2D6 M.D., a leap kick is not possible but a leaping pounce is; does 1D6 M.D. and has a 01-65% likelihood of knocking his prey down (victim loses initiative and one melee attack), plus there's a 01-55% chance of pinning an opponent with two of the arms while biting with the mouth or slashing with the other claws.

Bonuses: +1 on initiative, +3 to strike, +4 to parry, +4 to dodge (conventional). Special: +6 Automatic Dodge: The body of the mega-foot mastica is so flexible and fast that it can automatically bob and weave out of the way without the creature ever moving its huge feet! The automatic dodge does not use up a melee attack/action.

Other bonuses: +1 to roll with impact or fall, +3 to save vs horror factor, +1 to save vs magic, +10 to save vs poison, drugs and disease (can eat just about anything). All bonuses are in addition to any attributes bonuses.

Psionics: None.

Magic: None.

Appearance: A giant centipede with four arms that stands on a pair of huge, spiny, stilt-like legs and enormous feet. The body is covered in light M.D.C. plates.

Slave Market Value: 1000 or 2000 credits. They make lousy combatants in gladiatorial contests unless there are three or more and nobody likes the disgusting things.

Habitat: Anywhere. In Europe they are found primarily in the wilderness.

Enemies: Humans and D-bees exterminate the monsters whenever they are encountered. The simvan monster riders occasionally use the creatures for tracking, but have found them to be too awkward to use as riding animals and too stupid and timid (as lone animals) to use for anything else. Their light mega-damage plate armor is sometimes used to make inexpensive body armor (a full suit costs about 5000 credits and has 30 M.D.C.) and the spikes are used as needles, picks and decorations.

Allies: None; the mega-foot mastica is a wild animal.

The Stone-Claw

The stone-claw usually inhabits the ruins of ancient cities, mountains and rocky regions. The texture of the creature's dull grey hide is reminiscent of a rhinoceros, only tougher. It has large crab-like claws, a thick, short tail and a short, thick neck that ends in a pair of eyes and a maw of larger sharp teeth. The creature can stand and walk on its hind legs, like a human, or lope on all fours for maximum speed. The stone-claw is a very straight-forward fighter, usually facing its opponent and, standing on its hind legs, fights toe to toe. To this end, evolution has given the monster a belly and chest covered in hard, mega-damage plates. The knees, shoulders and crab-claws are also protected by natural plate armor. The creature's dull grey color and shape helps it blend into natural surroundings. When standing motionless, sleeping or tucked into a defensive position, the monster is easily mistaken for a large boulder.

The stone-claw is a solitary predator who hunts alone or in a small group of two to four; usually with its mate and/or offspring. The powerful, clawed beasts are fearless and hunt prey large and small, animal and humanoid. They have been known to attack gargoyles and bots twice their size and include peryton, melech, white slayers and mega-foot mastica among their favorite prey. The animal is fiercely territorial and will fight to the death to defend its lair, or when the beast or its family is threatened. The stone-claw's diet is primarily fresh meat, but it can also survive on a diet of vegetables, fruits, insects, roots, and human garbage if no other food is available.

The simvan monster riders love to use the stone-claw as an infantry attack animal, watchdog, and defender. Although the big, grey beasts make good riding animals, they are comparatively slow and ponderous.

Note: This creature is a dull-witted predatory animal and is not available as a player character.

Alignment: Effectively anarchist or miscreant; hunter.

Attributes: I.Q.: 1D6 (animal), M.E.: 2D6, M.A.: 1D6, P.S.: 3D6+30 (equal to supernatural), P.P.: 2D6+12, P.E.: 3D6+12, P.B.: 1D6, Spd.: 4D6+10 (half that speed climbing, swimming or walking on two legs).

Hit Points: Mega-damage creature.

M.D.C. by Location:
- Tail (1) — 60
- Hind Legs (2) — 110 each
- Crab-Claws (2) — 150 each
- Underbelly (covered in plates) — 200
- Head (small target; attackers are −4 to strike) — 60
- Main Body (top of the body) — 4D6×10

P.P.E.: 6D6

Horror Factor: 14

Weight: 1.5 tons

Size: 7 to 9 feet (2.1 to 2.7 m) long and 11 to 14 feet (3.3 to 4.3 m) tall when standing erect.

Average Level of Experience: Not applicable.

Natural Abilities: Nightvision 100 feet (30.5 m), fair dayvision. Extremely keen sense of smell — track by scent 75%. Swim 60%, climb 55%/50%, and can leap five feet (1.5 m) high or 10 feet (3 m) lengthwise from a standing still position; doubled when running/loping at full speed. Heals twice as fast as humans and is resistant to cold, heat and fire (half damage).

Combat: 4 attacks per melee round. The claws can be used like paired weapons.

Damage:

Restrained Claw Strike/Slap — 1D6 M.D.

Full Strength Claw Strike — 3D6 M.D.

Claw Crush/Scissor Snap — 3D6 M.D.

Power Punch/Strike — 6D6 M.D.

Bite —2D6 M.D.

Kick attacks are not possible, but a leaping pounce does 2D6 M.D. and has a 01-85% likelihood of knocking his prey down

(victim loses initiative and one melee attack), plus there's a 01-45% chance of pinning an opponent with the two claws while biting with the mouth.

Bonuses: +3 on initiative, +4 to strike, +2 to parry, +2 to dodge, +3 to roll with impact or fall, +6 to save vs horror factor, +2 to save vs magic, +2 to save vs poison, drugs and disease. All bonuses are in addition to any attributes bonuses.

Psionics: None.

Magic: None.

Appearance: A huge brute of a monster that can stand on its hind legs like a bear, has crab-claws for arms, protective body plates and a worm-like head with tiny eyes and a large mouth.

Slave Market Value: 10,000 to 20,000 credits primarily as a gladiatorial combatant. The monster is ferocious and always a crowd pleaser. Monster riders also like to use the beast as a mount.

Habitat: Ancient ruins, mountains, rocky terrain, and forests. In Europe they are found primarily in the wilderness and are rumored to be most numerous along the alps and in the country once known as Russia.

Enemies: Preys on any humanoid, animal, demon or creature who gets too close. Their mega-damage armor plates are sometimes made into shields and body armor (a full suit costs about 15,000 credits and has 100 M.D.C.).

Allies: None in nature; frequently controlled and used by the simvan monster riders who have a special affinity with most beasts.

White Slayer

The monster known as the white slayer is a demon from a Rift. It is a malevolent predator who delights in hunting and killing all lesser creatures — for pleasure as much as for food. They feed on animals and humanoids. They also like to engage in torture, play cat and mouse games, and frighten potential victims before they kill them. Although barely intelligent by human standards, the white slayer is instinctively cunning and has incredible patience. One tactic is to stalk and observe its intended prey without its knowing, making careful note of its habits and routines, then striking when least expected or the prey is at its most vulnerable. Others tactics include using the element of surprise, chasing and tiring out the prey, herding the prey into a corner or trap, and ambushing its prey. The monster often tries to catch its prey unawares by laying in wait or sneaking in close, using prowl.

When two or more are hunting in a pack, they act as a team, encircle the enemy and attack from several sides, or one acts as a decoy while the others move into better position for attack. Thankfully, white slayers seldom travel in packs larger than 1D4 + 2 members.

Note: This villain is not intended for use as a player character.

Alignment: Anarchist, diabolic or miscreant.

Attributes: I.Q.: 1D6 + 2 (animal), M.E.: 3D6 + 6, M.A.: 1D6, P.S.: 4D6 + 10 (supernatural), P.P.: 3D6 + 6, P.E.: 3D6 + 10, P.B.: 2D4, Spd.: 6D6 + 40 (running).

Hit Points: Mega-damage creature.

M.D.C.: 6D6 + 20

P.P.E.: 1D4 × 10

Horror Factor: 13

Weight: 250 pounds (113 kg)

Size: 6 to 7 feet (1.8 to 2.1 m) long; same height when standing on hind legs.

Average Level of Experience: Not applicable.

Natural Abilities: Nightvision 200 feet (61 m), keen hawk-like vision, able to see a rabbit a mile (1.6 km) away, track by sight 65%; the creature is ambidextrous, fast and can leap 20 feet (6 m) high or 30 feet (9 m) lengthwise from a standing still position or doubled running at full speed. Bio-regenerates 2D6 M.D.C. as often as once per

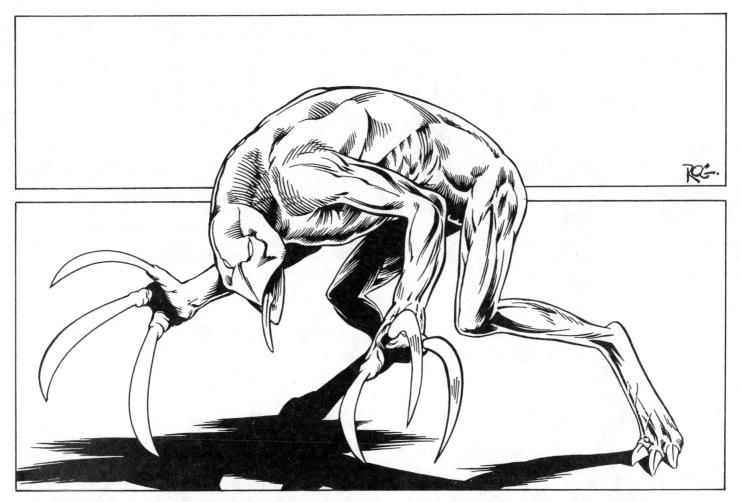

melee round, impervious to cold (no damage) and resistant to fire (half damage).

Combat: 5 attacks per melee round. The claws can be used like paired weapons.

Damage: Restrained claw strike 2D6 to 6D6 S.D.C. (usually to torture S.D.C. creatures). A single blade/claw strike 1D6 M.D., double strike 2D6 M.D., triple blade strike 3D6 M.D., power punch/claw strike 6D6 (only possible using one hand, counts as two attacks).

Both clawed hands can strike simultaneously to inflict 6D6 M.D.! The simultaneous double-handed strike counts as one attack but the white slayer cannot parry or dodge his opponent's counter-strike.

A kick does 2D6 M.D., a leap kick 4D6 M.D., and a bite does 2D6 M.D.

Bonuses: +2 on initiative, +4 to strike, +5 to parry, +3 to dodge, +3 to pull punch, +3 to roll with impact or fall, +6 to save vs horror factor, +2 to save vs magic, +2 to save vs poison, drugs and disease. All bonuses are in addition to attributes and skills.

Psionics: Special: Senses fear: a limited form of empathy enabling the slayer to sense when its prey is scared; I.S.P. cost and limitations the same as empathy. Other psionic powers include detect psionics, and sense magic. $2D4 \times 10$ I.S.P.

Magic: None.

Appearance: A demonic predator that resembles both man and animal. Its hairless flesh is stark white, but its eyes are a bright emerald green. Its rear legs are like those of an animal, while its arms are more like those of a humanoid, except that its three fingers have long, sickle shaped claws the length of a short sword. The head is inhuman and has a beak-like mouth that is as sharp as a razor blade. Its long, pale green tongue is used to lap up the blood of its prey.

Slave Market Value: 150,000 to 300,000 credits; they make dynamic combatants in gladiatorial contests.

Habitat: Forests and jungles, including the Black Forest, but they are especially fond of the northern forests and frozen tundras of Russia and Scandinavia. Their white skin lets them blend into the snow and makes them all the more dangerous. Rumor suggests some white slayers found their way to China.

Enemies: All weaker beings, particularly psi-stalkers, simvan, and humans. Although an animalistic predator, the demonic white slayer cannot be controlled by the simvan monster riders. However, the simvan's empathic powers can touch and influence the white slayer, clouding the beast's judgement and senses: −2 on initiative, −1 attack per melee and all combat skills are half when facing a simvan monster rider.

Allies: None per se, although they can associate with demons, powerful sorcerers and supernatural beings.

R.C.C. Skills (limited):
Streetwise (+6%)
Land Navigation (+20%)
Wilderness Survival (+20%)
Identify Plants & Fruits (+30%)
Track: Animals (+30%)
Track: Humanoids (+20%)
Swim (+10%)
Climb (+10%)
Prowl (+5%)
Speaks Demongogian and Gobblely at 75% efficiency. Sentences are usually short and simple — seldom more than phrases like, "Now you die," or "Don't be afraid. It will hurt only for a minute."

R.C.C. Related Skills: None.

Secondary Skills: None

Money & Equipment: This hunter and murderer has little need for possessions but may collect things that humanoids and demons consider valuable to prove its equality.

Cybernetics & Bionics: Not applicable; a supernatural being.

Gene-Splicers

Gene-splicers are aliens from another planet who seem to have mastered the secrets of eugenics.

The DNA molecule is the blueprint for the entire living animal. By examining the DNA blueprint, the gene-splicer can learn the creature's evolutionary history, as well as his physical and mental strengths, weaknesses and potential. Once the blueprint is understood and all the building blocks have been identified, the aliens can rearrange the blocks to make changes and adjustments to the original design. They manipulate and rearrange the genetic building blocks of living DNA like an architect designing and constructing a building. The process is much more complex and time consuming than it may sound, but that's the basic idea.

Theoretically, genetic manipulation and reconstruction can help put an end to most sicknesses and disease, eradicate genetic aberrations, and negate the effects of old age. Furthermore, life forms could be tweaked and adjusted beyond their current level of evolution to create superhumans without the need of cybernetics, M.O.M. implants, drugs or magic augmentation. The trick is making the proper changes on the zillions of DNA molecules that make up the human body. If changed properly, the aliens can make an instant and permanent alteration to living creatures. This is the secret and the power held by the gene-splicers, and with it, the very secrets of life and creation!

Genetic Reconstruction & The Human Blueprint

Through genetic reconstruction, the gene-splicers are able to move the building blocks of life around to make a completely new and different structure! They can do little things like change the color of a character's eyes, hair or skin, grow new hair (by removing/fixing the gene for baldness), make the nose or ears smaller or larger, rounded or pointed, even add inches to one's height, take 20 years off one's appearance and eliminate genetic weaknesses in the body that might cause alzheimer, cancer or arthritis all in an afternoon. Little miracles to the maniacal aliens.

Genetic changes can be an improvement or a disaster. The cruel aliens are just as likely to knock the building blocks apart or build strange, monstrous structures as they are to instil beneficial ones. Sometimes they do strange and terrible things just because they can. Like a spiteful and mischevious child, gene-splicers may make outlandish, humorous (to them), or detrimental changes without regard for the subject of the experiment. Genetic reconstruction is often performed to satisfy their own interests, curiosity, sadistic amusement or whims. The changes may be made to study strengths, evolutionary alternatives, to examine weaknesses or adaptability, or done as a lark.

Many gene-splicers simply enjoy inflicting and studying physical and mental trauma. The entire record of evolution is recorded on each DNA molecule. Records that can be re-created if one knows how — and the gene-splicers do know how. Thus, they can turn back the passage of time and explore every step of human evolution. They can nudge and rearrange the building blocks to explore evolutionary paths never taken. To see how man might have developed under a different set of circumstances. The diabolical aliens can turn a genius into a gibbering monkey or muscle-bound Neanderthal. The changes produced through genetic reconstruction are not just physical but can affect mental, psionic, and behavior/instincts as well. Then there's the sociological, anthropological and psychological elements to consider. How will the creature react to his new body? How will those around him respond? Will he become a leader or slave? How will a superior being (or inferior mutant) react to the world around him and the world to him? Will he be accepted, chastised, hunted, worshiped, feared or destroyed? What happens if there is more than one? And so on. All things that fascinate the coldhearted gene-slicers.

Whether there is any rhyme or reason to their insane creations, experiments and acts of torture is unknown (there doesn't seem to be any). They do, however, exhibit some interesting trends and habits. Gene-splicers seem fascinated by human beings, human D-bees and primates, and spend a vast amount of time experimenting on them. Like Mindwerks, they often abduct or lure a subject into their clutches, work their scientific magic on them and release them. Sometimes the subject of experimentation is part of a long term study. In these cases, the character is observed, periodically recaptured, subjected to genetic adjustments (or dramatic changes), and released again. Just as frequently, test subjects are altered and released, allowed to go on their merry way, never to be bothered by the aliens again.

Gene-splicers have shown similar interest in brodkil and, to a lesser degree, gargoyles. For whatever reason, they have altered a thousand brodkil in the same way. This is extremely unusual because as a rule, gene-splicers rarely create more than a couple dozen of the same (or similar) creature. In many cases, their creations are one-of-a-kind studies in living flesh and blood. Humans call these mutants *Monster Brodkil*, because they are even larger, uglier, and more powerful, and have four to six arms, a prehensile tail and a pair of huge, gargoyle-like wings. At first glance, all of these monster brodkil seem the same, but even here there are notable variations. Some are covered in spines or lumps while others are not. Some have more slender builds and are taller, while others are squat and thickly muscled. Some have heightened intelligence while others are simple-minded Neanderthals.

Why the gene-splicers have created so many monster brodkil is yet another one of the mysteries that surround them. Rumors have suggested one of the brodkil chieftains made a pact with them, but one must wonder what a brodkil might have to offer beings such as they. Normally, gene-splicers don't take any interest in the life, politics or events unfolding around them. They have never been known to help people, although they do take sides in conflicts for various (selfish) reasons. It's possible these brodkil have somehow captured the favor of the gene-splicers, but it's more likely to be some twisted experiment or behavioral study.

Such complete mastery over the genetic structure is virtually unheard of in the Megaverse! In the hands of some other race, such knowledge might have led to incredible achievements and benefits for all intelligent life. Instead, the gene-splicers are maleficent beings who use their incredible knowledge to create monsters and misery.

Gene-splicing

When one looks at all the myriad possibilities, there are millions of variations that can be explored! Add in gene-splicing, and the blending of one completely different life form with another, and the possibilities are virtually endless.

Gene-splicing is used to alter the genetic structure of one creature by combining it with several traits from two or three completely different animals. The "splicing" process allows the aliens to bond different animal parts into one monstrosity. Genetic reconstruction of the DNA code means there is no risk of the body rejecting any of its new parts or traits. The results can be staggering, combining incongruous and normally incompatible elements that defy natural evolution.

One of the frightening things about these genetic modifications its that because they are done on the most fundamental genetic level, frequently they can be passed on to offspring. Of course, the gene-splicer controls whether or not such "improvements" or "new variables" are hereditary or not. The high-tech wizards can make a creation compatible or incompatible with his own (original) species or compatible or not with other creations like himself. Unfortunately for the victims of many gene-splicing experiments, they are one-of-a-kind creations and often completely alien.

Game Master Notes:

How to use a Gene-Splicer

One might think of gene-splicers as a custom-design Monsters Factory. Using them as a story element, the G.M. can devise "one-of-a-kind" mutants and monsters, creating alternatives to monsters from the Rifts. This can be useful in keeping players on their toes and guessing when an unknown monster steps around the corner. Or they can be thrown for a curve when a familiar looking D-bee or monster demonstrates some unusual power or ability.

The gene-splicer is definitely restricted to non-player characters (NPCs). As arch-villains, they offer virtually limitless possibilities. BEWARE! Going crazy with the possibilities can unbalance your game or turn it into a monster-fest. Neither is desirable.

Some Considerations

1. Remember, Gene-splicers should be used sparingly and in ways that are twisted and dangerous. They aren't benevolent beings, so they aren't going to create superhumans for the betterment of mankind. Nor are they likely to save a brilliant leader or hero from old age or disease unless it was to turn him or her into a monster.

2. Remember, not all monsters are ugly or alien looking. Evil is a state of mind and a way of life.

3. Remember, gene-splices don't create monsters out of thin air, they usually kidnap humans and D-bees and transform them into something superhuman and usually ugly and monstrous.

4. They have a twisted sense of humor and often turn heroes into grotesque monsters and monsters into beautiful or at least more attractive looking beings.

5. The creations of Gene-splicer monsters can be responsible for random acts of violence and intervention that could have little, medium level or high level consequences to a particular person, place or event. A village could be ravaged (or saved) by a gene-splicer creation. And when it's done it moves on to reap more trouble or invades and tries to hold on to its conquest.

6. A gene-splicer creation could become a major hero, crook, misunderstood villain, an arch-villain, predator, slave, minion or just about anything. Whether or not a genetically reconstructed character is available as a player characters (and what his powers and penalties may be) is left entirely to the discretion of the Game Master.

7. G.M.'s, always think about the creations you allow in the game either as NPCs or player characters.

8. Gene-splicers can also make clones.

9. People can't usually tell the difference between a gene-splicer creation and a monster from a Rift.

10. A player character or NPC hero could be forever altered (good and/or bad changes) as the result of a gene-splicer's experiment. Don't bee too vicious. Show some compassion.

11. Monsters created from earth life forms have an advantage because they don't have to adapt to a strange new world. They already know the lay of the land and should be able to understand the language(s), are familiar with existing technology, laws, customs, routines, and so on. This strange familiarity can add to the mystery, suspense and tragedy of encounters with such beings.

For example: A terrible monster is stalking the countryside. Those who have seen it report that it is hideous and definitely not human. Yet the creature knows how to operate hover vehicles, knows secret passwords or locations known only to local villagers (or a select few) and seems to know patterns of activities such as police patrols (and resources?). Furthermore, when it leaped out of the shadows to attack poor Mary, it seemed to recognize her and for some inexplicable reason, bolted into the woods without harming a hair on her head.

As the adventure unfolds, it turns out the monster is young Robert, Mary's fiance (or brother, father, uncle, friend, sister, mother, etc.) who disappeared about six months ago. Now we learn that he has been transformed into a predatory beast by a gene-splicer. As a monster, he functions more on instinct than intellect and many of his memories as a human are gone (or not), but he recognized Mary and was able to control his hunger for human blood and stopped himself from hurting her. Now the player characters must hunt him down and stop his rampage/killing spree. Will they be able to reason with him or must the beast be slain? Is it all a misunderstanding (there's another monster, and Bob was only trying to protect or warn his old girlfriend, but can no longer speak or didn't get the chance before other villagers attacked him, forcing him to flee)?

A twist might be the old revenge angle: Why are all of Adam Harley's old enemies being slaughtered? Because Adam is the monster and is extracting revenge against those he didn't like and anybody who gets in his way.

Another story idea might be the misunderstood monsters. The character looks frightening and evokes fear and loathing even though it didn't do anything. It may even be falsely accused of crimes it never committed and has the heart of a Palladin and only wants to be left alone or find somebody (the player group?) to accept him as a friend.

Some Limitations

1. There are only a dozen gene-splicers on Rifts Earth and perhaps not many more throughout the Megaverse. Presently, those dozen aliens are limiting their research to the countries once known as Germany, Austria, Poland and Czechoslovakia. They are not found anywhere else in the world!

The largest group of gene-splicers arrived about ten years ago. Their base of operation is in the Black Forest, nestled in the comparative safety of the Tree of Darkness. They also have access to one spaceship (mobile laboratory). A pair of gene-splicers have been working from their spaceship mainly in Poland and Czechoslavokia for almost 200 years. They were the first gene-splicers to arrive on Rifts Earth and their experiments are likely to have contributed to some of the legends about Mindwerks.

2. Although they can alter and evolve animals (i.e. create Dog Boys or monstrous predatory versions of regular animals) they usually spend most of their energy mutating humans, humanoids and other intelligent life forms. One can only presume that the aliens get greater sadistic pleasure transforming creatures who will understand what horrors have befallen them and what their future may hold.

3. Remember, gene-splicers are evil and they are motivated by cruelty and evilness. They like to inflict misery on others through genetic reconstruction. They will seldom do anything to help anybody.

4. The creations of gene-splicers are usually monstrous or deliberately flawed in some way. Remember, the majority are nothing more than genetic experiments. Like all experiment, some are more successful than others.

5. It takes 4D4 weeks to perform major genetic reconstruction, sometimes longer. However, simple genetic grafts, splicing and minor alterations can be accomplished in 6D6 hours.

6. Gene-splicers can quickly become hated and hunted monsters themselves. Many communities will try to find and destroy them, or at least chase them away. Atlantean Undead Slayers and Azverkan will consider the aliens to be a plague that needs to be eradicated from existence.

7. Gene-splicers NEVER share their secrets! The Splugorth would pay or do just about anything to possess even a fraction of the gene-splicers' knowledge of genetic reconstruction, but it will NEVER happen. Note: Very little physical data can be found on the gene-splicers' computers or spaceships. Much of it is locked away in their memory (total recall) and they are impervious to psionic probes.

8. They rarely uses cybernetics, bionics or any kind of mechanical augmentation in their creations. Thus, borgs, bots, and androids will not be selected for genetic experimentation.

9. Energy beings, alien intelligences and most, true supernatural beings and creatures of magic cannot be genetically altered.

10. Lost limbs cannot (as a rule) be genetically regrown. However, new limbs of all kinds can be "gene-spliced" onto an individual from other creatures or clones.

The following are just a few notable traits/changes that the gene-splicers can instill on humans and human-like D-bees.

- Customize living creatures to have specific traits, attributes and powers.
- Reduce aging. Doubles the average life expectancy and the character always looks reasonably youthful.
- Stop aging. Actually the aging process is so dramatically reduced that he seems to have stopped aging entirely. Add 2D6×100 years to the character's normal life expectancy.
- Increase human height up to an additional six feet (1.8 m).
- Decrease normal human height by up to four feet (1.2 m).
- Increase human intelligence up to 30 but roll for one random insanity.
- Increase human aggression: +3 on initiative, +3 to strike and parry, +2 to save vs horror factor, +4D6 S.D.C.; tends to be hyper, short tempered, suspicious of others, competitive, loves combat and physical contests. Level of concentration is reduced; −10% on skill performance and may have trouble sleeping.
- Instinctive hunter/predator: Likes to hunt and kill. Automatically gets the hunting and prowl skill, +2 on initiative, +3 to strike, plus one additional attack/action per melee. Likes to eat raw meat and the taste of blood and may be a cannibal (01-50% chance).
- Add 2D4 psionic powers from any of the three lesser categories to minor psionics and double I.S.P.; add 3D4 psionic powers from any of the three lesser categories or four super psi-power to major psionics and double I.S.P.; or give ALL psionic powers to mind melters or mind bleeders, and double I.S.P.
- Double the I.S.P., range and damage of a burster's powers.
- Create the genetic equivalent of the following O.C.C.s:
  Burster, dog boy, crazy or juicer without artificial implants or drugs.
- Add one to four arms, tail (prehensile or not), wings and the capability to fly (may mean hollow bones and different size), horns, and others. Can also change physical features.

Note: Even gene-splicers make mistakes and cause physical or mental aberrations which may include strange sided-effects, powers, insanity and physical deformity — G.M.'s option.

Gene-Splicers

Gene-splicers can accurately be considered demons, although they are not supernatural beings. They regard themselves to be a higher (the highest?) life form in the Megaverse and show a total disregard (sometimes complete disdain) for life in general. They are coldhearted, cruel and evil beings who are always dispassionate, aloof and menacing.

Talking to a gene-splicer is like talking to a rock. They never answer questions, ignore insults, and brush away or destroy intruders in the same way a human might brush away an annoying insect. A gene-splicer doesn't care about a person's problems, whether it be a toothache or a life and death struggle against demons. Empires can rise and fall around them, the gene-splicer doesn't care. He is concerned only with his work (Whatever that may be. They are always lost to their own secret agenda, presumably something beyond human comprehension).

Legends & Rumors: Where the gene-splicers come from or how many exist is part of the mystery surrounding them. Even among the Splugorth, the gene-splicer is known only as a creature of myth and

legend. Lord Splynncryth has never met one and he thought they had perished 50,000 years ago. Presumably their numbers are quite small, but then, nobody knows.

One of the rumors popular among non-humans is that the entire human race is the creation of the gene-splicers — a dumb animal snatched out of the jungle by aliens that had a few choice genes rearranged to change and advance its evolution, and then let loose to see what happens. Now, the aliens have returned to examine their handiwork. Thankfully, this rumor is not likely to be true, but it does make a person wonder.

The Gene-Splicers — An NPC villain

Note: The gene-splicer is NOT intended for use as a player character. They are maniacal villains.

Alignment: Selfish or evil; usually anarchist, miscreant or diabolic.

Average Attributes: I.Q.: 2D6+16, M.E.: 2D6+16, M.A.: 2D6, P.S.: 2D6+16, P.P.: 2D6+16, P.E.: 2D6+16, P.B.: 2D4, Spd.: 2D6+16. They themselves have been genetically re-engineered, with only a small degree of desired randomness.

Average Life Span: 1200+2D6×100 years.

Hit Points: 3D4×10+40, S.D.C.: 1D4×100

M.D.C.: 75 from light body armor robe, plus force field from sphere.

P.P.E.: 6D6, but possess no natural magic powers.

Horror Factor: 11

Weight: 260 to 300 pounds (117 to 135 kg)

Size: 7 feet tall (2.1 m).

Average Level of Experience for NPCs: 1D6+6; use the dragon's experience table for determining additional experience.

Insanity: Obsessed with genetic experimentation and study. 80% are extremely sadistic and indifferent toward all other life forms (pathological). The lives of others has little meaning to these coldhearted fiends.

Natural Abilities: Perfect 20/20 color vision, nightvision 90 feet (27.4 m), see the invisible, ambidextrous, resistant to fatigue (half normal), impervious to disease, impervious to mind control, and impervious to psionic probes: telepathy, empathy, and mind bond unless deliberately allowed.

Bonuses (Natural): Lightning reflexes and agility. +4 on initiative, +2 to strike, parry and roll with impact or fall, +3 to pull punch, +8 to save vs horror factor, +8 to save vs symbiotic union and control, +8 to save vs magic illusions, +4 to save vs all other forms of magic. Impervious to supernatural and psionic possession, impervious to the bite and gaze of vampires (cannot be turned into vampires). All bonuses are in addition to attributes and skills bonuses!

Combat & Attacks Per Melee Round (natural): Five melee attacks/actions per melee, plus one additional attack/melee action at levels four, eight, and 12. Paired weapons and targeting skills are automatic.

Damage: Hand to hand is equal to any human or by weapon.

Psionics: All sensitive, healing and super. I.S.P. is M.E. times 10, plus 10 points per level of experience.

Magic: None.

Appearance: Tall, thin humanoids with long, slender fingers. The eyes and hair are dark, and their complexion is a pasty yellow-white. Most are over a 1000 years old and look to be the equivalent of a 50 year old human. Those who look to be 70 or older are over 2000 years old and those who have a youthful appearance are only around 500 years old.

Slave Market Value: Not applicable.

Habitat: Any place.

Enemies: None/all

Allies: None

Skills of Note: Gene-splicers have a high intellect, superior total recall, centuries of education and studies, and an analytical and inquisitive mind. They know entire skill categories: All communication skills at 80%, all electrical at 80%, all mechanical at 80%, all medical at 98%, all science at 98%, all computer skills at 98%, all pilot related skill at 98% and pilot: spaceship and hover vehicles at 98%, W.P. energy rifle, W.P. knife, and W.P. archery/targeting.

Secondary Skills (G.M.'s option): The character can know six secondary skills plus three additional secondary skills at levels 8, 12 and 16. No bonuses other than I.Q. are applicable. Selections can be made from: Domestic, espionage, military, physical, pilot, rogue, technical, weapon proficiencies or wilderness.

Standard Equipment:

1. Omni-sphere: Described later.
2. Protective robe: 75 M.D.C.; lightweight: 15 pounds (6.8 kg); language translator and mini-computer built into the collar (both are back-up systems to the multi-communications helmet).
3. Multi-communications helmet: Includes a long- and short-range radio (can monitor and play 10 channels simultaneously), mini-computer and cryptography program, radio scrambling capabilities, radar detection, bio-comp self-monitoring system and language translator. Plus a special telepathic and radio com-link to the omni-sphere.
4. Surgical sensor glove: This is a tight fitting glove made out of a strong-as-steel ceramic. It has nano-systems that gives it all the features/capabilities of the Triax medical sensor hand described in **World Book Five: Triax & the NGR**, page 153. Plus, the two fingers have scalpel sharp, retractable fingernails/blades and two laser scalpels. A concealed compartment holds IRMSS and RMK nano-bots.
5. Multi-dimensional lab-spaceship: Described later. Most elder gene-splicers, pairs or groups will have one ship.
6. Other items: Just about any equipment or weapon available to the NGR, Mindwerks or Splugorth is available to the gene-splicer.

Cybernetics & Bionics: None as a rule, uses genetic manipulation and gene-splicing to "enhance" their abilities and replace injured limbs.

Note: Most gene-splicers have 1D4 clones in storage. These clones have blank minds and are created exclusively to serve as replacement parts and bodies for their gene-splicer creator.

Omni-Sphere
(aka Floating Eye or Omni-Bot)

The omni-sphere is an all-purpose robot helper and defender. A typical gene-splicer will be accompanied by 2D4 of these bots at any given time. On the spaceship he can command as many as 50! They are designed to serve the gene-splicer's every need including ship operation, gene-splicing, research and defense. However, their top priority is to protect and defend the gene-splicer.

Class: Robot Drone — Artificial intelligence.
M.D.C. by Location:
* Optics Eye — 50
* Retractable Force Field Transmitter (1; rear) — 15
* Retractable Laser Antennas (2) — 15 each
* Retractable Arms (2) — 25 each
Force Field (self or other) — 200

** Main body — 80
* Items marked by a single asterisk are tiny and difficult to strike. The attacker must make a "called" shot and even then he is −5 to strike.

** Destroying the main body destroys the bot.

Speed: Antigravity: Hover stationary or at speeds up to 200 mph (321.8 km) maximum. Underwater (max. speed 90 mph/144 km) and space capable.

Statistical Data:
Size: Slightly larger than a basketball. About 1 foot, 4 inches (0.41 m) in diameter.
Weight: 50 pounds (22.6 kg)
Power System: Nuclear

Weapon Systems

Note: Six hand to hand attacks/actions per melee round.

1. **Retractable Lasers (2):** This item is used as both a tool and a weapon. It can extend one foot (0.3 m) and can rotate 360 degrees.
Primary Purpose: Defense
Secondary Purpose: Tool
S.D.C. Damage: In increments from 1D6 to 10D6 S.D.C.
Mega-Damage: Four Settings: 1D6 M.D., 2D6 M.D., 4D6 M.D. or a maximum of $1D4 \times 10 + 8$ M.D. if both lasers are fired simultaneously at the same target (counts as one melee attack).
Maximum Range: 2000 feet (610 m)
Rate of Fire: Six times per melee round.
Payload: Effectively unlimited.
2. **Retractable Arms (2):** The retractable/extendable arm has three different "hand" attachments: Claw, scalpel blade or laser scalpel.
Primary Purpose: Defense
Damage: 1D6 S.D.C.
Maximum Range: About two foot (0.6 m) reach.
Rate of Fire: Six hand to hand attacks/actions per melee.
3. **Features of Note:**
Force Field Generator: A force field of 200 M.D.C. can be generated around itself, or the gene-splicer, or divided between both. Its top priority is to protect the gene-splicer and it will sacrifice itself in an instant to save him. Regenerates one point a minute or 60 per hour. To project a force field around the gene-slicer the bot must be within 60 feet (18 m). **Note:** As many as ten omni)spheres can simultaneous transmit their force field (or some part of it) around the gene splicer with an accumulative effect; from 10 M.D.C. points to 2000!

Camouflage System: Same as the GSS ship (self only). Used as an observation/reconnaissance ball.

Stealth System: Same as the spaceship; completely silent.

Sensors: Range of multi-optics, radar, sound detection, motion detection: (60 ft/18 m), radio communication and other.

Language Translator and artificial voice synthesizer.

Skill Programs (standard): All communication skills, all electrical, all mechanical, all medical, all pilot related skills, and all computer skills at 94%, plus all math, navigation and pilot: spaceship at 98%.

Advanced Artificial Intelligence: In addition to skills, the omni-bot can learn and make subjective decisions similar to a human. However, these decision making powers are usually fairly basic. I.Q. is equal to 15.

GSS Spaceship

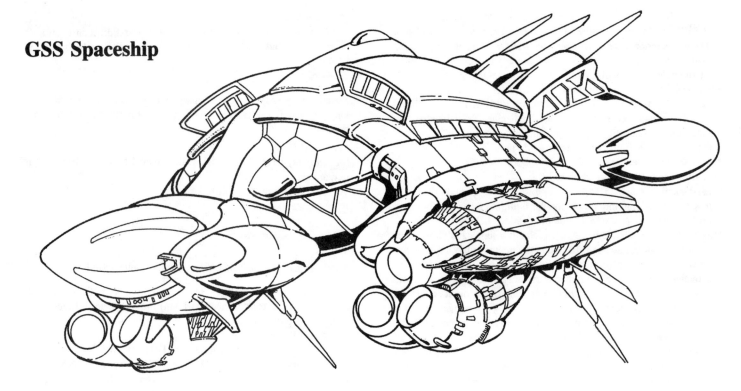

The GSS spaceship functions as a mobile base of operations for the gene-splicers. Some gene-splicers have commanded and lived in one of these ships for centuries.

The bridge & navigation are located in the front of the ship. The front section can detach and function as a smaller mobile unit or escape pod. 550 M.D.C. (no independent force field generator), maximum speed: Mach 12, space and sea capable (any depth), +4 to dodge.

The medical facilities include three gene-splicing and operating rooms, four laboratories, cloning lab (large), and cryogeneics storage bay with a room-size freezer for specimens and 12 humanoid size tubes for preserving and transporting living humanoid test subjects.

Living quarters (8) are simple. A 10×20 foot room with a work station (three computers, split-screen wall monitor, communications display and internal systems display), shelf for specimens, personal items and souvenirs, bed, lounge chair, small table and cryogenic storage chamber for long periods of space and dimensional travel (suspended animation; chamber has 200 M.D.C. and emergency release/alarm). Lighting is in the ceilings.

Other areas: Containment bay with six prison-bar style jail cells with a cot, waste disposal unit, and manacles in the floor and on the wall (80 M.D.C. each). Storage bay: A large cargo area for non-perishable specimens and supplies. Engineering, mechanics bay, communications, emergency life support, radar cloaking system, force field defenses, weapons and similar systems are all automated, with easy access by the gene-splicers and omni-spheres.

Note: All rooms are sealed air-tight and sanitized to avoid contamination; mainly to protect specimens and test subjects. Each also has its own environmental control systems; again, mainly for alien life forms.

GSS Spaceship

Class: Transdimensional environmental lab and habitat ship.
Crew: As many as a dozen gene-splicers can live comfortably in one of these ships, but most have only one to three occupants, plus 144 omni-bots. A dozen passengers (not specimens) can be accommodated comfortably. Some gene-splicers have 1D4 pets or slaves created from genetic experiments.

M.D.C. by Location:
Bridge/Forward Section (a separate vessel) — 550
Tri-Forward Thrusters (6; 2 pair, sides) — 150 each
Forward Main Thrusters (2; sides) — 600 each
Top Thrusters (2) — 200 each
Rear Center Thrusters (3) — 150 each
Rear Main Thrusters (2) — 500 each
Rear Side Thrusters (2) — 150 each
Inner Hatches (many) — 100 each
Outer Hatches (8) —200 each
Reinforced Bridge Area — 200
Force Field — 1400
* Main body — 3500

* Destroying the main body will wreck the ship and cause it to crash. 1D6×10% of the internal systems and rooms may survive and remain operational but the ship will never fly again or be spaceworthy without incredible amounts of time consuming and costly repairs.

Destroying the main body does not damage the bridge section, which is also a detachable spaceship. The forward bridge section can detach and fly away as a separate vessel before the main ship crashes.

Speed: In an atmosphere it can hover stationary or attain a speed of up to Mach 12! No limit regarding the altitude and can blast into space if so desired.

In outer space it can travel at .16 the speed of light and has a space warp system that enables it to *skip* 1D4×100,000 light years in 1D6 hours. The space warp can be performed a maximum of once every 12 hours, but its recommended safe use is once per every six days.

Underwater, maximum speed is 300 mph (482 km).

Statistical Data:
Height: 180 feet (54.8 m), overall
Length: 480 feet (146 m), overall (the forward bridge section is about 120 feet/36.5 m long)
Width: 240 feet (73 m), overall, main body is about half that width.
Weight: 450,000 tons
Power System: Nuclear and a limited antigravity system (not fully developed).

Weapon Systems

The weapon systems of the GSS spaceship are limited. Gene-splicers always try to avoid detection, let alone engage in armed conflicts. In most situations, they will try to escape and return later, unnoticed, to continue their work. They're not cowards, they just don't see any reason to waste their time fighting annoying inferior creatures. In fact, if the indigenous life forms are too annoying and/or unpredictably violent, the aliens are likely to leave in search for a quieter environment more conducive to their research.

1. Forward Laser Battery (bridge section):

Primary Purpose: Defense

Mega-Damage: Three Settings: $1D6 \times 10$ M.D., $1D4 \times 100$ M.D. or $1D6 \times 100$ M.D. (maximum is $1D4 \times 100$ when detached from the main ship)

Maximum Range: 6000 feet (1828 m)

Rate of Fire: Six times per melee round.

Payload: Effectively unlimited.

2. Concealed Missile Launchers: Concealed in each of the wing sections of the forward main thrusters is a missile launcher.

Primary Purpose: Defense

Mega-Damage: Varies with missile type. Can fire medium- and long-range missiles.

Maximum Range: Varies with missile type

Rate of Fire: One at a time or volleys of two or four.

Standard Payload: 96 total; 48 per launcher.

3. Features of Note:

Force Field Generator: 1400 M.D.C., regenerates at a rate of 200 points per hour.

Automated Repair System: Most internal systems and machinery have an automatic repair and maintenance system.

Radar Cloaking: The GSS is invisible to all forms of radar and sonar while the cloaking devise is on.

It is also covered in a material the make it invisible to both 01-70% likelihood of being invisible to radar or sonar even when the cloaking system is turned off. Trackers should roll every 1D6 minutes to see if they still have a reading.

Camouflage System: An energy field that makes the exterior of the ship changes color in patterns to reflect and blend in with its surroundings. It is virtually invisible in the sky and underwater. 01-75% prowl/hide when on land.

Stealth System: When traveling under Mach One, the ship is completely silent.

Sensors: Full long-range optics, radar, and sensor systems. There are numerous sensor clusters concealed all over the ship's hull, including close-range motion detectors (200 ft/61 m range).

Self Destruct Mechanism: The subsequent explosion completely destroys the spaceship (only scrap metal is salvageable) and inflicts $1D6 \times 10,000$ M.D. to a 1000 foot (305 m) radius! The small, detachable bridge ship only does $1D4 \times 1000$ M.D. to a 200 foot (61 m) radius.

Omni-Spheres: Standard compliment is 144, but only 10 to 50 are usually activated at any one time.

Three Headed Wolf

The three headed wolf, also known as the Tri-Wolf, is a genetically improved and gene-spliced canine predator. The genetically reconstructed animal is smarter (low human intelligence), larger, faster, and more cunning. The three heads are the result of gene-splicing. As a natural pack animal, they cooperate well with each other and regard the smartest to be their leader. The other two are submissive to the leader and seldom squabble. In fact, the three quickly learn to function as an extension of each other.

The tri-wolf can use its superior intellect and powers to take command of small to large packs of normal wolves or wild dogs. The normal wolves will follow their leader's actions and show increased aggression and much less fear toward man.

Note: This intelligent wolf is intended to be an NPC villain, but it can be used as an optional player character if it's okay with the Game Master. Player characters are likely to be of a good or selfish alignment. The Tri-Wolf cannot talk (although some may have empathic or telepathic powers) but have developed a greater range of barks, growls, grunts and whines, including growls that sound like the words yes, no, give, stop and die!

Alignment: Any, but typically anarchist, aberrant, or miscreant.

Horror Factor: 12

Size: 5 to 6 feet (1.5 to 1.8 m) long and stands about three to four feet (0.9 to 1.2 m) tall.

Weight: 100 to 200 pounds (45 to 90 kg).

Typical Attributes: I.Q.: 1D4+3, M.E.: 2D6+10, M.A.: 2D6+10, P.S.: 2D6+20, P.P.: 2D6+10, P.E. 2D6+20, P.B.: 3D6, Spd. 4D6+25.

Mega-Damage Creature: 6D6+6 main body and each head has 12 M.D.C. points each.

P.P.E.: 6D6

Average Level of Experience: 1D4 for NPCs, player characters should start at level one.

Combat Data: Four hand to hand attacks/actions per melee or three psionic.

Bonuses: +3 on initiative, difficult to surprise or sneak-up on from behind, +5 to strike, +3 to parry and +6 to dodge, +3 to pull punch/bite, +3 to roll with impact or fall, +5 to save vs horror factor, +2 to save vs psionic attack, +1 to save vs magic, +2 to save vs poison and disease.

Damage: Restrained claw strike 1D6 S.D.C., full strength claw strike 2D6 M.D., restrained bite 4D6 S.D.C., full strength bite 1D6 M.D. per each head; leap/pounce attack does 1D6 S.D.C. and has a 01-55% chance of knocking an opponent down (victim loses initiative and

one melee attack — counts at two melee attacks). The pounce attack also has a 01-50% chance of pinning the opponent, enabling the wolf to continue his attack by biting. Typically around 3D6 M.D. for punches and kicks; varies with physical strength. Tail whips do 2D4 M.D.

Natural Abilities: Exceptional senses of hearing, sight, and smell; track by smell 65%, track blood scent 85%, recognize a specific person by scent 50%, and leap 15 feet (4.6 m) high or lengthwise (double when it has a running start).

Magic Powers: None.

Monster Brodkil

70

Psionics: The tri-wolf is considered a minor psionic. The creature has three psionic attacks per melee (one per head). Each head has 3D6+12 I.S.P. All three can see the invisible, presence sense, sense evil, sense magic and sixth sense. Each head can also select one psionic power from any of the three lesser categories.

R.C.C. Skills: Hunting, track: animals, track: humans, detect ambush, prowl, swim, climb, wilderness survival, land navigation, basic math, sniper (lay in wait and then pounce), and understands three languages of choice — all skills start at 40% and increase 5% per level of experience.

Secondary Skills: Select two at levels 2, 5, 9, and 13. Selections can be made from the categories of domestic, espionage, technical and wilderness. All start at first level proficiency.

Bionics: None to start, tend to avoid them.

Note: Only 26 tri-wolves were originally created, but they can reproduce, giving birth to 1D4 pups. A mature female gives birth once a year. They mate for life.

Monster Brodkil

The monster brodkil is the creation of the gene-splicers living at the Tree of Darkness. They created about 1000 of these humanoids and have made it possible for them to mate and bear one offspring (with the same traits) annually. Most differences among these monsters are mainly cosmetic. Some may look more intimidating or weird than others but their abilities don't change that much. However, there is a range of variation which is reflected in the random attributes and other physical features. Only the rare exception (2%) has one or two incredibly high attributes (2D6 points above the norm listed).

Note: This character can be an NPC villain or optional player character. Player characters are likely to be of a good or selfish alignment. They are considered rogues or traitors to the Brodkil Empire if they associate with humans and other enemies of the Empire.

Alignment: Any, but typically selfish or evil.

Horror Factor: 12

Size: Approximately 8+1D4 feet (2.7+ meters).

Weight: 400 to 600 pounds (180 to 270 kg)

Typical Attributes: I.Q.: 2D6+3, M.E.: 2D6+6, M.A.: 2D6+2, P.S.: 4D6+20, P.P.: 3D6+6, P.E. 3D6+10, P.B.: 1D6, Spd. 4D6+20; supernatural strength and endurance.

P.P.E.: 2D4×10, **I.S.P.:** None

Mega-Damage Creature: Main Body: 2D6×10+200 (about 20% have an additional 2D6×10 M.D.C.). Wings have 52 M.D.C. each.

Combat Data: Eight attacks per melee. +4 on initiative, +4 to strike, +4 to parry and +6 to dodge, +2 to save vs psionics and +2 to save vs magic, +3 to save vs poison and disease. All bonuses are in addition to attribute bonuses.

Average Damage: Varies with physical strength; typically around 3D6 M.D. for punches and kicks. Tail whips do 2D4 M.D.

Natural Abilities: All have M.D.C. bodies, huge dragon-like wings (can fly at a speed factor of 6D6+40), prowl 40%, turn invisible at will, bio-regenerate 2D6 M.D.C. per hour and are impervious to normal fire and cold.

Approximately 50% of the monster brodkil have four arms, the other 50% have six arms (add another one melee attack). Of these, 60% have a prehensile tail (add another melee attack); all have wings and can fly.

Magic Powers: None.

Psionics: None.

Skills of Note: Climbing, tracking, intelligence, radio: basic, three languages of choice, two wilderness skills of choice, W.P. knife, sword, W.P. energy rifle and two of choice. Game Masters may add 1D6 skills from the categories of weapon proficiencies, communications, technical, domestic, and wilderness (no bonuses).

Bionics: None to start; brodkil have no supernatural, psionic, or magic powers, so they can benefit from bionic weapons and implants without ill effect, other than losing the ability to turn invisible.

Weapons: Favorite weapons include energy rifles, rail guns, vibro-blades, Kittani plasma weapons, bionics, and magic weapons. They also use binoculars and optical enhancements.

The Black Forest

The Black Forest (Schwarzwald in German) is located in a mountainous and hilly region along the Alps. Many of the trees are ancient, 400 to 600 years old. The forest gets its name from the great number of conifer trees (pines and spruce) that dominate the forest (95%; entirely coniferous in higher elevations). From a distance the coniferous trees of the Black Forest look dark green, especially as a backdrop rising behind the lighter green leaves of the mixed forest at lower elevations.

Before the Coming of the Rifts, the Black Forest area was limited to the southwestern corner of Germany, following the Rhein River along the border of France from about Ettlingen and Baden-Baden to the south along the curving Rhein and along the border of Switzerland to about Trossingen. The Black Forest of Rifts Earth covers a much larger land area. It starts with the traditional southwest corner along the French and Swiss Alps starting at the Rhein and stretches eastward beyond Lake Constance, along the Austrian border, covering the pre-Rifts communities of Tuttlingen, Ravensburg, and Wangen; ending about 10 miles (16 km) west of Wangen and south of Memmingen. From the southwest corner it extends north just short of Karlsruhe and covers pre-Rifts locations once known as Baden-Baden, Offenburg, and Freiburg.

The Black Forest has always been a place of legend and lore regarding magic, faeries, gnomes, spirits and ghosts. If the local legends and superstitions of Rifts Earth are to be believed, the forest is overcrowded with every known demon and monster to ever pass through a Rift; from vampires to Splugorth. Truth be told, the forest is a vast woodland wilderness. Although inhabited by dangerous beings, creatures of magic and predatory beasts from beyond the Rifts, a monster is *not* lurking behind every shadow in the forest. There are many lovely and serene places and pockets where humans are very safe. In fact, there are dozens of tiny human and D-bee villages nestled in the Black Forest and surrounding wilderness. Hunters, trappers, and the occasional band of gypsies also frequent the woods. Ironically, the same frightening tales that keep most humans away also keep away *most* gargoyles, brodkil, demons and other monsters and D-bees. Even the Splugorth and their minions usually steer clear of the Black Forest. As for vampires, they avoid the place because faeries, sprites, nymphs, and drakins (the semi-intelligent Luck Bird common to all of Germany and Poland) hate vampires and destroy them or chase them away whenever they are encountered.

Faerie Folk of the Black Forest

In the world of Rifts, the Black Forest has become both an enchanted and haunted place. It is home to about every type of faerie folk known to man. One can find hundreds of faeries and/or sprites playing in the flowers, darting through the branches of trees, picking berries, chasing dragonflies or drinking morning dew. Although beautiful and graceful

is usually enchanted and will impart temporary or permanent magic powers or curses on any who eat or drink them. To anger, embarrass, or harm a faerie is to evoke the wrath of that faerie and all his kin. A flock of angry faeries have been known to chase away an adult dragon!

Faeries, sprites, pixies, brownies and leprechauns are likely to inhabit areas where one finds a mound of grass covered earth or hill surrounded by a ring of flowers or mushrooms, under or around giant boulders, ancient trees or beautiful glens/glades.

The most dangerous places will be in and around eerie looking trees, swamps, slow moving streams, polluted waters, dead or foreboding looking portions of woodlands, and other places that have a nasty or frightening atmosphere to them. It is here that the cruel faerie folk and poltergeists are most likely to be found. Creatures such as goblins, cobblers, bogies, pucks, spriggans, toad stools, kinnie ger (feline predator), and kelpies (aquatic demon horses) are likely inhabitants at such locations. Fortunately, the evil faerie folk are far less numerous than the gentler folk — for every bogie, toadstool or puck, there are 10 faeries, sprites or pixies.

Other Forest Inhabitants

The Black Forest also harbors bands of psi-stalkers, simvan, and the occasional adventurer, groups or small tribes of ogres, orcs, wolfen, brodkil, lycanmorphs, srrynn, dragons, and some D-bees.

Notable wildlife includes deer, elk, wild boar, the brown bear, foxes, wolves, wild dogs, the lynx (mountain lion; tigers are found in Russia and Asia), martens, capercaillie (cock, similar to wild turkey), drakins, eurotorpids, mega-foot mastica, and the occasional stone claw monster and white slayer demon, among others.

The gryphon, peryton, dragondactyl and harpy roost among the cliffs and mountain forests of the Alps and the branches of the evil Millennium Tree, but they hunt in the forests and along the rivers, lakes and ocean coastline. **Note:** See the first **Rifts Conversion Book** for descriptions and information about faerie folk, ogres, trolls, drakin, peryton, demons and many other creatures mentioned in this section.

The Tree of Darkness

An Evil Millennium Tree

Without a doubt, the single most frightening feature of the Black Forest is the Tree of Darkness, a gargantuan Millennium Tree that challenges the peaks of the Alps in height.

Erin Tarn had this to say (excerpted from her journal):

"I could not believe my eyes when I saw this monstrous tree. My visits to several Trees of Life in England had been a calming, beautiful experience that touched my soul. The time I spent with the druids, at one tree in particular, is one of the great moments in my life. But this … thing was a nightmare. An abomination.

"Even from a distance I could make out the misshapened husk silhouetted against the Alps and the setting sun. I have heard that evil alchemists and bio-wizards have been able to corrupt and pervert the enchantment contained in the magic branches of a Tree of Life, but not an entire tree! Yet before my eyes loomed an entire Millennium Tree that had become a force for evil.

"The Tree of Darkness towers almost 2000 feet (610 m) tall. I believe that makes it the largest in the world. Unlike the traditional Tree of Life, green with leaves and beautiful to behold, this tree was barren and the trunk and branches twisted and gnarled. Huge limbs that resembled giant clawed hands or monstrous, spiked tentacles clawed at the heavens. Thorny barbs protrude from branches and tumorous growths

creatures, the denizens of faerie are alien creatures with little true understanding about, or concern for, humans or any big people. Consequently, their games, pranks and parties can be deadly. Faerie food

blistered the trunk. Many of the hollows and nodules were misshapened and resembled great gaping mouths, faces, or spiny seed pods. One such face looked like a snarling dragon, another a demonic wild bore while others looked like ghostly apparitions howling at the sky; all were ugly and menacing.

"The only leaves are found at the very top of the tree, cascading down one side like emerald locks of hair hanging around the giant face of a tortured woman. The woman's head is arched back, staring toward the heavens with an agonized expression. Two large branches resembling hands are raised skyward, making the woman of the tree seem to be beseeching the gods above — though what her silent pleading eyes might be saying was lost upon me. We were forced to keep our distance because the Tree of Darkness attracts the forces of evil. Consequently, the area around the tree is rife with demons, entities and monsters. Furthermore, I'm told that each of the gaping maws of tree's trunk are dimensional portals, each leading to a different demonic realm.

"As we stood surrounded in the quiet splendor of the Black Forest studying the horrific edifice in the distance, my mind drifted back to Wormwood. The Tree of Darkness reminded me of the crawling towers and the living cities. Buildings molded from the living planet, their shape dictated by the good or evil inhabitants who dominated the land. In the demon haunted lands of Wormwood, great tree-like towers with spikes and spines and gaping maws marred the land. So many of the same images seem present on the Tree of Darkness that it sent shivers up and down my spine. It saddens me to say it, but I found Wormwood to be a sad, depressing place. I was glad to leave it and thankful that my planet was nothing of the kind. Yet here I stood before a monolith of evil that harkened back to the demon cities of Wormwood. For the first time, I truly fear that Earth could become like the demon haunted wastelands of the living planet. I must also wonder if the Millennium Trees and Wormwood don't share some common origin or kinship. I wonder too if the branches of this tree possess magic energy and whether that magic is given to the forces of evil cradled in its body.

"My thoughts shift to ponder what incredible force of evil had the power to corrupt and deform a fabled Tree of Life. Other Millennium Trees grow amidst incredible evil, yet none of them have taken on the grotesque features or evil disposition that this one has. What makes this tree, or more to the point, this place so different that it could mutate such a primordial force of good? I think back to the days before the Great Cataclysm. To ancient Germany and a man named Faust. Could this be the root of evil?

"The Tree of Darkness grows in the soil where the ancient city of Staufen once stood. According to legend, Staufen was the place where the legendary alchemist Doctor Faustus (also known simply as Faust) worked and perished. The old pre-Rifts stories tell how Doctor Faustus' lust for knowledge enticed him to make a pact with the devil. Empowered by the pact, Doctor Faustus could bring supernatural forces to Earth and make them teach him the secrets of alchemy and the universe. Could this area, which has always been covered in ley lines, have been a gateway to other worlds even then? Did some alien intelligence gain control of that mystic force and use it for evil? I suspect the answer is yes. As I recall the legend, Faust finally began to recognize the evil to which he had given himself and regretted making the pact. He realized that the price he paid for the knowledge he sought was too high, so he plotted to break the pact. The devil laughed and proclaimed what was done could not be undone. Faustus resorted to trickery to sever the pact but the ploy failed and Doctor Faustus suffered the wrath of his demonic benefactor and was consumed by an explosion that shook the city, set it ablaze, and filled the air with the stench of sulfur.

Could the evil forces foolishly unleashed by Doctor Faustus so long ago, have permeated the land? Is it their evil essence what has tainted the great tree and turned it into something monstrous? Is the tree a willing participant to evil or enslaved by it? Does the tortured woman with her outstretched arms mock the heavens or plead to it for her release? I fear we may never know."

From the Journal of Erin Tarn — Winter 103 P.A.

A Place of Evil

Most creatures of a good alignment and a thread of intelligence don't come within 50 miles (80 km) of the Tree of Darkness. A 20 mile (32 km) radius around the great tree is perpetually covered in mist or fog and populated by a host of supernatural monsters and evil creatures. Psychics can feel the presence of supernatural evil the moment they step inside the fog ring. As psychic characters approach the Tree of Darkness, the essence of supernatural evil becomes stronger. This feeling is not limited to the great tree, but is also felt all around. Psi-stalkers, dog boys and other characters sensitive to such emanations will feel uneasy and tense. Horses, dogs and animals sensitive to psychic impressions are jumpy and frightened.

Just about any monsters imaginable can suddenly appear in the fog to challenge or attack travelers, good or evil. Banshees, poltergeists, tectonic entities, and petal things are counted among the inhabitants of the fog bank. **Note:** Visibility within the fog is poor, reducing the range and clarity of all types of vision by 75% (a human can see about 100 feet/30.5 m ahead).

Various creatures seem to have laid claim to specific portions of the mountainous tree. Among the weave of snaking roots at the base of the tree, which covers a five mile (8 km) radius, are tribes of goblins (estimated 3000 total), orcs (estimated at 1600), and hundreds of bogies, pucks, toadstools, boogie-men, grave ghouls, poltergeists, haunting entities, and the occasional tectonic entity, banshee, boschala, dar'ota, dimensional ghoul, gremlin, malignous, and demon. Predatory monsters include melech, cockatrice, dragondactyls, peryton, and the mutant creations of gene-splicers. See **Rifts Conversion Book (one)** for the description of most of these beings.

A cluster of spiky towers on a branch about half way up the tree is one of the domains of the **gene-splicers**. Eight different splicers, their creations and minions inhabit this small community; about 240 people in all. The small, unspectacular oval opening above the base of the branch leads to the gene-splicers' homeworld.

Harpies, syphon entities, the occasional rogue gargoyle, cockatrice, waternix, za, hawrk D-bee, and other winged creatures may inhabit the lower branches. Peryton, gryphon, giant clamp-mouthed dragonflies, flash beetles, yll-tree climbers, and dragondactyls roost among the branches of the tree. Evil druids and practitioners of magic are also present.

A handful of evil sphinxes, dragon wolves, air elementals and dragons inhabit the highest branches. An adult nightstalker known as **Knife Wind** (9th level, miscreant), an adult fire dragon who calls himself **Hellfire** (12th level shifter and spell caster, miscreant), an ancient great horned dragon known as **Shyrclee** (16th level ley line walker, 6th level herbologist, miscreant), a sphinx known as **Madcat** (9th level, diabolic) and a temporal raider known as **Antiquity** (14th level, anarchist) are among the most notable and powerful inhabitants of the tree.

Note: Most gargoyles, brodkil, simvan, lycanmorphs, faeries, sprites and humans avoid the evil tree and the Black Forest in general.

Dimensional Portals

Over 50 ley lines intersect at the base of the evil Millennium Tree. It is believed that the stone-claw, lycanmorph, white slayer, srrynn, and c'ro demon mage have come to Earth via one of these portals.

The largest opening near the base of the tree is said to function like a stone pyramid and can send a character anyplace on Earth where there's a stone pyramid, Millennium Tree, or open dimensional Rift. It can also create a Rift to any place known to the Rift creator, drawing on the ambient energy of the intersecting ley lines and the tree itself. Some forgotten creatures (spriggans perhaps) have built a stone bridge and road leading from one of the tall hills into the maw of this great opening. Taking this road will allow visitors to avoid the monsters that

live among the roots and fog, but does not guarantee safe passage. Peryton and other flying menaces frequently swoop down to snare prey from the bridge (there is no protective cover on the bridge). Furthermore, inside the cavernous opening lives a seven headed hydra who doesn't appreciate visitors (01-50% chance that the hydra is inside rather than gone hunting). Scores of rock crawlers, mega-foot mastica and a handful of erta also inhabit the cavern. Thus, one must carefully time his use of the dimensional portal and be careful of other inhabitants and dangerous visitors. **Note:** There is only one way in and out of the giant cavern.

To reach the other-dimensional portals the character must be able to fly or climb the evil tree. Flying is considerably faster, but not necessarily safer. Airborne characters are easy targets for any number of predators and once one spots prey and attacks, others are sure to take notice. Likewise, villains hidden within the branches, nooks and crannies of the Tree of Darkness can spot flyers a mile away and prepare for an attack or hide long before the flyers arrive. Aerial targets are easy to shoot down and prepare against.

Climbing the tree helps prevent easy targeting and identification, but the climbers have little or no idea of what lies ahead, or in wait, for them. Encounters with local inhabitants and other visitors are likely. Furthermore, the act of climbing the vast surface of the tree can be a difficult and exhausting task akin to scaling a mountain. Most of the portals to other worlds are 1200 to 1600 feet (366 to 488 m) high and the leaves and smaller branches suitable for magic wands and staves are at the very top.

Known portals to other worlds:

1. The maw with vaguely negroid features has a branch that appears to be a long, curving tongue that leads to the demon city of **Lalibela** in the mountains of Ethiopia and/or to a living planet known as **Wormwood**; see **Rifts Dimension Book One: Wormwood** for details.

2. The short, thick branch that ends with the snarling head of a demonic serpent is a dimensional portal to **Asgard**. The portal places dimensional travelers near the lair of the Midgard serpent! **Note:** See **Rifts Conversion Book Two: Pantheons of the Megaverse** for details about Asgard (and the pantheon of Brahma and other gods).

3. One of the giant, tumorous knots resembles a demonic elephant with four spikes on its head. Entering through the right eye will teleport the character to the **African Congo**. Entering the left eye will send the character to the **jungles of India** near Nagpur. Entering the mouth under the trunk will send the character to the jungle and mountainous dimension inhabited by the **Pantheon of Brahma**, the Gods of India, and populated by the Asuras (demons).

4. An opening that resembles a moaning spirit leads to **Phase World**.

5. A portal that resembles a dragon's head leads to the **Palladium World**.

6. A portal that resembles a demon with two tiny horns leads to the demon world of **Dyval**.

7. A tiny opening, barely large enough for a human to fit through, is connected with demon-ridden **Xibalba** and the temple at **Copan**, on the Yucatan Peninsula — werebeast and demon territory (see **Rifts: Vampire Kingdoms**).

8. An opening covered by a mesh screen of branches is a time hole. This dimensional pocket is used by a number of beings — G.M. decides whether anybody is home or arrives (and how he/they react to intruders) while the character(s) is still there.

Note: There are at least a dozen other openings that lead to other dimensions or which can be used to open a Rift to another world. Such a Rift might lead to the worlds dominated by gargoyles or other demons, xiticix, Splugorth, Naruni, Kittani, True Atlanteans, any D-bee race, or to an alien wilderness, Earth's past or a parallel Earth in a different dimension, or just about anywhere. The possibilities are virtually endless. Explore them carefully.

The Powers of the Evil Millennium Tree

The Tree of Darkness has all the same powers, abilities and "gifts of magic" as any normal Millennium Tree (see **Rifts England**, pages 9-21). The main difference is that the Evil Millennium Tree grants these "gifts" more sparingly and gives them only to evil beings to use against the innocent and good. The vile tree may summon thunderstorms, dense fog, or ley line storms to thwart people struggling to survive. It will use its empathy and vision to warn monsters of danger at the hands of heroes or the NGR, and heal murderers and destroyers so that they may reap more carnage. Evil practitioners of magic, blood druids and demonic menaces are given deadly magic wands and staves to help them in their evil pursuits. Meanwhile, characters of good alignments are abused and tormented.

Powers of Darkness

In addition to the powers of a normal Millennium Tree the Tree of Darkness can perform the following.

1. Nightmares (rather than helpful visions or warnings): The same basic principle as the vision, except the tree instills visions of being hunted, tortured and slain in horrible ways. Affects only characters of a good or selfish alignment.

2. Reveal (rather than camouflage): The tree can create fingers of the wind, howling wind, change wind direction, or create a globe of daylight to reveal the hiding place of good characters (or the tree's enemies) to evil creatures, predators and defenders.

3. Leaf: Blanket of pain (rather than healing): A giant leaf from a normal Millennium Tree can be used to magically heal. A leaf from the evil tree prevents wounds from healing, broken bones do not mend, and illness persists without relief. The following penalties also apply when covered by the cursed leaf: −15% to save vs coma/death, −4 to save vs poison, drugs and disease, and −3 to save vs possession. This leaf can affect a character of any alignment.

4. Power to Hurt (rather than heal): A good Millennium Tree can instantly heal, the evil tree emits an aura that reduces the healing capability of good characters by half and they are −2 to save vs poison, disease and possession. Even healing potions and salves are only half as effective on good characters while within the tree's area of influence; anywhere on the tree, within 200 feet/61 meters of the tree, or wherever the tree's shadow falls.

5. Spoil food and water: Same as the magic spell except the tree can affect 100 times more than a first level wizard. Wherever the tree's shadow falls, food is spoiled (unless the tree desires otherwise). Used mainly against characters of a good alignment and those it does not like.

6. Control over storms, ley line storms and ley line energy is usually used against the tree's enemies and good characters.

Wands and Staves of Darkness

In addition, the Tree of Darkness can create the following specific items. **Note:** Most wands (85%) created by the Tree of Darkness are cursed, but it's up to the tree whether or not it curses a wand or staff. Any characters of a good alignment who touches a cursed item will suffer the following spells equal to a 10th level spell caster (roll percentile): 01-25 Luck curse, 26-50 sickness, 51-75 minor curse, 76-00 curse phobia.

Some specific staves and wands:

1. Staff of Death: A withered rod eaten by worms and bugs. It possesses the usual features common to Millennium staves and inflicts the following: 4D6 M.D. but burns characters of a good alignment, inflicting an additional 2D6 M.D. It can also cast six spells per day from the following selection: Agony, life drain, sickness, wisps of confusion, turn dead and animate and control dead.

2. Staff or Wand of Monstrosity: A burl covered staff or scepter-like wand that has a hideous, screaming face at one end. The rod has all the usual features common to Millennium rods plus bestows the following powers upon its owner up to four times a day: Superhuman strength, superhuman speed, eyes of the wolf, invulnerability, and metamorphosis: superior (all are roughly equal to a 10th level spell strength). All five spells engage simultaneously. The first four empowers the user of the staff, the last temporarily changes him into a hideous looking monster (horror factor 13). Duration of powers: 10 minutes, but the duration of the metamorphosis is 30 minutes. The Tree of Darkness is cruel even to those it helps. Note: The staff can inflict 1D6 M.D. when used as a weapon.

3. Staff or Wand of Malignancy: A staff or wand that appears to have a mass of worms at one end (really roots). The rod has all the usual features common to Millennium rods plus enables the owner to repel animals at will. A total of ten spells can be cast per 24 hours. Available spells include: summon and control rodents, spoil, minor curse, turn dead, death trance, trance, compulsion, calling, befuddle and mask of deceit. Note: The wand can only cast five spells per day.

4. Arrow or Javelin of Doom (even rarer than wands and staves): Basically a shaft of wood shaped like an arrow or javelin that can be fired from a bow or thrown; +2 to strike. The rod inflicts only one point of damage to its target (S.D.C. to S.D.C. beings or one mega-damage point to M.D.C. creatures) and returns to its owner (the return uses up one melee attack). The rod also inflicts the following magic on any living creature it strikes: Speed of the snail and befuddle equal to a 10th level spell!

5. Corrupted Wands and Staves: See page 21 of **Rifts England**.

Regional Highlights

Other Places of Note in and around the Black Forest

Some of the **ancient roadways** have been uncovered by various beings for a number of reasons. These roads include sections of the old Autobahn which runs along the northern border of the forest.

The ruins of old French nuclear power plants can be found in the territory once dominated by the ancient French Empire near the German and Swiss borders.

Lake Constance is located on the border of Switzerland and Germany, near Austria and the ancient ruins of Zurich, Switzerland. Lake Constance is a giant mountain lake, the biggest in the territory, and has always been famous for its extremely clear water. The territory around the lake was once a resort area for the wealthy who'd visit from around the world. Today it is the domain of faeries and a handful of small simvan, human and D-bee communities; mostly fishermen, hunters and woodsmen. Some wine vineyards are located to the north of the lake and some farm communities are located at the northern edge of the forest near **Ravensburg** and around the surviving communities of **Biberach** and **Memmingen**.

Zurich, Switzerland, survived the Coming of the Rifts but was destroyed by the gargoyles 127 years ago. It remains a gargoyle city with hundreds of gargoyles and thousands of gurgoyles living in the crumbling ruins.

North Baden

A dozen hot springs are scattered in the mountains and hills known as North Baden (pronounced Bod en). The springs are regarded as holy or sacred places and are usually located along or near ley lines.

The hot springs of North Baden are renowned for their healing properties. A person who spends 20 minutes in the soothing waters, three times a day, will find his wounds, injuries or illnesses are healed at twice the normal rate. Plus characters are +10% to save vs coma/death, +2 to save vs poison and disease, and +1 to save vs possession. Waters from the spring have the same effect on vampires as "holy" water and inflicts double M.D.C. when used against the undead. Druids, herbologists and alchemists insist the waters add to the potency of their teas and elixirs. Those who use the waters in their healing potions and teas will see an additional 1D6 S.D.C./M.D.C./hit points added to the potion's power to heal. However, a character can drink gallons of the water or swim in the natural pools for hours without any additional healing or side-effects. In fact, drinking too much of the water is likely to cause an upset stomach.

Unfortunately, profiteers and scoundrels have seized control of eight of the 12 known hot springs. They guard the springs closely and sell the healing waters (and bathing access) only to those who can afford it. Three 20 minute bath sessions can cost anywhere from 100 to 1000 credits depending on the villain who controls the spring. An ounce of the water commonly costs 25 to 50 credits, sometimes more.

A couple of the springs' owners will allow local villagers to use the healing waters once or twice a week at about a quarter of the normal fee, provided they don't disturb the wealthy patrons. Most hot spring owners believe giving the locals inexpensive and occasionally free access to the water helps to keep the natives from getting restless.

Many of the communities around the springs have become small, fortified, resort towns that cater to adventurers, practitioners of magic, healers, and the wealthy (often regardless of race or political alliance). These places frequently offer other amenities and services, such as fine food, beer and wine, dancing, gambling, fortune telling, body-chop-shops, and a variety of specialty shops and other services.

Blancenhaus is a gargoyle controlled encampment south of most of the others. It services only gargoyles and allies. Those not allowed to use the waters, including local villagers, adventurers and gypsies, are killed on the spot (unless they are sneaky enough to avoid detection). Approximately 12 gargoyles, 200 gurgoyles, 200 D-bee warriors, one super bot and 24 G-20 avenger combat bots are stationed at the spring. An additional 2D6×100 other members of the Gargoyle Empire may be present at any time.

Free Springs. There are only four springs not controlled by a monster of one kind or another (whether it be a greedy human or slobbering troll). None of these locations charge for the use of the water although donations are never turned down. **Life Springs** is controlled by human supremacists who allow all humans, including gypsies and travelers, to use their waters free of charge. However, no D-bees are allowed under any circumstance. **Marxburg** is another and run in a similar fashion.

Only two locations welcome people of all races (with the possible exception of gargoyles and brodkil). One is the fortified city of **Pure Water**, controlled by well meaning humans. It is under the protection of three Undead Slayers and a band of 10 knights (4th to 10th level). The other is **White Springs.** Famous to wilderness folk because it is controlled by a large community of druids (200 and their families) and practitioners of magic (about a dozen herbalists, four alchemists, and 25 men of magic and their families). At White Springs, no person is turned away because of his race or political affiliations. It is also known to gypsies and wilderness folk as a place of healing, magic and learning. Magic potions, teas, and herbs of all kinds can be acquired at White Springs.

South Baden

Hot springs are also found farther south, closer to the French, Swiss and Austrian borders, not more than 40 miles (64 km) from the evil Millennium Tree. These springs are cursed and only heal people of an evil or anarchist alignment and at four times the normal rate of healing! Worse, the damned waters reduce the healing of any good character immersed in them (the healing process takes twice as long). The water of South Baden has a bitter, sulfuric taste and a slightly yellow tint. Gargoyles, brodkil and other monsters lay claim to most of these springs.

Freiburg

Freiburg means "free city" and it remains a free haven for D-bees trying to build a life in Germany. It is the largest city in the Black Forest, currently harboring nearly 300,000 D-bees. The majority of its inhabitants are enemies of the Gargoyle Empire and will fight to keep the New German Republic free. In fact, many wish they could be citizens of the NGR and live anywhere in the nation. Most are craftsmen, wine and beer makers and farmers who simply wish to live quiet, peaceful and productive lives. They are left unmolested by the NGR because they live in the Black Forest and have never caused the nation any problems.

So far the gargoyles have also left them alone too, but they are in constant danger from rogue troops, bandits, supernatural marauders and demons looking for trouble. To advance the fall of the evil Empire, the people of Freiburg regularly hide enemies and fugitives wanted by the gargoyles. They also sabotage gargoyle supply lines and secretly supply the NGR with intelligence data regarding enemy activity in the Black Forest and along the southwestern border.

A dozen tiny D-bee villages are scattered around Freiburg and along the Rhine River which runs through the Black Forest. The population of these villages seldom exceeds 400.

Munich

About 75 miles (120 km) northwest of the Black Forest is the city of **Munich**. The city has kept much of its pre-Rifts charm and is one of the historic districts of Germany, with many ancient, pre-Rifts churches, cathedrals, the Olympic Park (used for the 1972 Olympics) and other buildings. It is a vacation paradise billed as "a big city with old world charm." As a result, it has hundreds of restaurants, taverns and cafes, as well as book and video stores, theaters, museums, several parks, and charming shops of all kinds. Munich is famous for its beer and beer mugs, but also offers a fine selection of wine. See **Triax & The NGRs** pages 11-12, for more details.

The NGR military has a strong presence in Munich. Soldiers in body armor ride hovercycles, or use jet packs, X-60 Flankers and X-535 Hunters patrol the streets and try to squelch gang and criminal activity. A small military base with about 1200 armored troops is located ten miles (16 km) north of the city. It's important to keep the NGR's third largest Triax industrial complex safe from the enemy.

Victor Lazlo's underground organization is also based in Munich.

Victor Lazlo

True Name: Victor Charles Lazlo; professor of parapsychology, he is also a latent psychic (see **Beyond the Supernatural RPG**).

Alignment: Scrupulous

Attributes: I.Q.: 14, M.E.: 19, M.A.: 19, P.S.: 17, P.P.: 11, P.E.: 14, P.B.: 10, Spd.: 11

Hit Points: 71 H.P. and 47 S.D.C.

M.D.C.: Triax environmental body armor: 80 M.D.C.; **P.P.E.:** 19

O.C.C.: Parapsychologist; roughly equal to a rogue scientist.

Level of Experience: 12th level rogue scientist/parapsychologist.

Natural Abilities: A natural leader; intelligent, compassionate, resourceful and strong willed. He also has a curious nature and an analytical mind.

Psionic Powers: They haven't manifested themselves often enough to be considered "powers" that are available at will. Instead, they tend to automatically engage during periods of stress or danger, particularly sense magic, speed reading, mind block and impervious to cold (Victor rarely notices when they occur). He also gets "hunches" and the occasional dream warning, both of which are aspects of clairvoyance. The most overt and least often occurring psi-power is see the invisible. Victor also uses meditation to relax. **I.S.P.:** 123 points.

Magic Knowledge: Victor is not a practitioner of magic but does have a reasonable understanding about the fundamentals of how magic, spells, and ley lines work. He can read magic runes and symbols, recognize magic wards and circles (86%) and can read scrolls and perform ritual magic as long as he has comprehensive instructions (94%). His training also gives him some special abilities:

- Recognize real psychic powers; 98%. He can also determine what degree of power and the type of psychic the character is; 66%.
- Recognize mind control and whether it is the result of possession, psionics, magic, hypnosis or drugs; 98%.
- Recognize psionic and techno-wizard devices; 66%.
- Recognize real rune weapons; 98%.

Combat abilities: Hand to hand: basic (11th level proficiency).

Combat/Attacks Per Melee Round: Four

Bonuses (includes all bonuses): +3 on initiative, +1 to strike, +4 to parry, +5 to dodge, +4 to roll with impact, +4 to pull punch, +2 to S.D.C. damage, critical strike on unmodified 19 or 20, kick attack (1D6 S.D.C.), and judo style body throw/flip (1D6 damage and victim loses initiative and one melee attack). +3 to save vs psionic attack, +3 to save vs horror factor, +2 to save vs magic and poison, +3 to save vs mind altering drugs and potions, +2 to save vs possession, and +8% to save vs coma/death.

Skills of Note: Basic and advanced math, computer operation, biology, psychology, anthropology, parapsychology (including a fundamental knowledge of magic and psychic powers and how they work), research, photography, lore: demons & monsters 90%, lore: geomancy/ley lines 90%, radio: basic, radio: scramblers, He speaks and is literate in American, French and Spanish, all at 98%

He also speaks Gobblely and Euro, can read sensory equipment, perform first aid, swim, climb, run, wrestle, as well as horsemanship, pilot automobile, pilot power armor (Ulti-max and Hopper), all at 80%. He also has W.P. knife, W.P. automatic pistol, and W.P. energy rifle, all at 5th level proficiency. **Note:** See **Beyond the Supernatural** for the 20th Century skills or wing it.

Appearance: A human male who looks to be in his early forties, but is actually 55 years old. He should be 63 but is the victim of space and time anomalies. He stands 5 ft, 11 inches (1.79 m) tall, and has a full head of white hair.

Technology: As a man of science, Victor has always loved and used technology. He is fascinated by the advances of Rifts Earth and has adapted well to the use of high-tech computers, weapons and equipment.

Special vehicles: Pilots a stolen Ulti-max!

Equipment of Note: Basic articles of clothing, backpack, specimen containers, utility belt, box of a 100 pairs of surgical gloves, two air filters, one environmental helmet with gas mask, portable video camera with 50 video discs, still camera and tripod with 100 discs of film (36 exposures each), portable computer, pocket computer, portable bio-scan, laser distancer, pocket scrambler, portable language translator, pocket flashlight, medical kit, all nano-robot medical systems, a lighter, PDD pocket digital disc audio player and recorder (with 24 one inch discs), two pair of hand-held communicators, and a multi-optics band.

Weapons: Silver cross, six wooden stakes and mallet, survival knife (1D6 damage), pocket Swiss army knife (1 point of damage as a weapon), shotgun (7D6 S.D.C.), .45 automatic pistol with 144 teflon armor piercing rounds (6D6 S.D.C.) and 48 rounds of same but the bullets are silver coated. Triax laser scalpel, Triax-30 ion pulse rifle (2D6 or 6D6 M.D., 2000 ft/610 m range; dozen 50 shot clips), and a TX-11 sniper rifle (3D6 M.D.; 1600 ft/488 m range).

Body Armor: Fully armed X-1000 Ulti-max power armor with 309 M.D.C. left on the main body. He also has a Triax T-21 Terrain Hopper suit of power armor as a back-up suit. Can wear any type of armor and use most types of power armor at fifth level proficiency.

Cybernetics: Gyro-compass, dosimeter/radiation detector and amplified hearing (bonuses have been added to combat bonus section).

Money: He has accumulated a reasonable amount of money to continue his crusade to help D-Bees in the NGR underground. He has 1D6 × 10,000 credits with him and has approximately 500,000 credits back at his base in Germany.

Alliances & Allies: Victor Lazlo has a lot of friends and connections in and around the New German Republic, especially among D-bees, city rats, and subversive organizations. He is friends with Lo Fung (a chiang-ku dragon) and has become friends with Erin Tarn and heroes active in the area.

Victor is wanted by the NGR for subversive acts against the government because he helps D-bees and associates with gypsies, criminals, non-humans and other subversives. Any encounter with NGR troops means a 01-50% chance that somebody will recognize him or his stolen Ulti-max and try to make an arrest. This can only mean trouble for all involved. Characters who protect Lazlo are considered to be his dupes, criminals or fellow subversives.

Northwest Germany & Triax

German Industry and the heart of the New German Republic is located in the northwest portion of the country at such cities as Frankfurt-am-Main, Heidelberg, Dusseldorf, Bonn, Essen, Ruhr, Koln and others.

Northeastern Germany

Much of the northeast suffered considerable damage from the Great Cataclysm and repeated sieges by the brodkil, gargoyles and other monsters. Once great cities like **Berlin** and **Hamburg** are ruins, populated by peasants, vagabonds and D-bees.

Dresden is a squalid military and industrial town near the border of Poland. Its troops and citizens have a reputation for corruption, black marketeering, and playing fast and loose with laws, rules, and regulations.

The Gargoyle Offensive in Western Germany

The Gargoyle Empire is building a new front along the southwestern border of Germany and near the old French and Luxembourg borders. It is here that the so-called Gargoyle Super Bot has made its appearance (although a few have also been sighted in the Brodkil Empire as well). A total of 11 have been accounted for, but the total number may be as much as two times higher. The presence of the giant bots is disturbing but the least of the NGR's concerns. An estimated 500,000 gargoyles and their minions have gathered along this new offensive line, with another estimated million troops advancing to join them from the south.

All indications would suggest a major offensive is about to be launched. This has prompted the evacuation of scores of human villages and border towns that fall in the most likely path of attack. The NGR has increased reconnaissance along the border, dispatched two armored divisions to strategic border locations (including 40 of its new X-5000 Devastators and a wing of X-2700 Dragonwings) and has placed all troops on yellow alert. They have also deployed 200 new gargoyle EIR drones, androids, and EIC cyborgs to infiltrate the enemy. In addition, the NGR has sent two prototype Mobile Infantry Strike Bases to the area (only three exist).

Gurgoyle G-40 Super Bot

The super bot is a gigantic robot vehicle that has only recently been introduced by the gargoyles. Like the G-30 Wrecker, this robot vehicle resembles the gargoyle, complete with wings and horns. However the wings do not provide the bot with the ability to fly, but offer great armor protection from rear assaults. A powerful microwave saturation beam is fired at ground troops from blasters in the chests. However, the bot is very slow and has limited weapon capabilities. The real danger it presents is that it has so much M.D.C. that it will be difficult to stop. The advancing assault of this mountain of a robot can only serve to boost the morale of gargoyle troops.

Exclusive to the Gargoyle Empire

Model: G-40 Super Bot

Class: Strategic Armor Military Assault Robot

Crew: One gurgoyle pilot, a gunner and a gargoylite supervisor.

Note: Only the gurgoyles (usually supervised by a gargoylite) pilot the giant robot vehicle.

M.D.C. by Location:

    Chest Microwave Weapons (2) — 150 each
    * Energy Ball and Chain (2) — 170 each
    * Energy Ball and Chain Cable (2) — 75 each
    Wings (2) — 400 each
    Shoulders/Upper Arms (2) — 300 each
    Forearms (2) — 200 each
    * Hands (2) — 100 each
    Legs (2) — 500 each
    * Sensor & Communications Array (2; horns) — 80 each
    Head Pilot Compartment — 600
    Reinforced Pilot's Compartment — 50
    **Main Body — 2550

* All items marked with a single asterisk are small and/or difficult targets to hit. An attacker can only hit one when he makes a *called shot*, but even then he is −2 to strike.

Destroying the head reveals the inner pilot's compartment. Another 50 M.D.C. to the pilot's compartment immobilizes the giant robot.

** Depleting the M.D.C. of the main body will destroy the bot!

Speed

Running: 35 mph (56 km) maximum.

Leaping: Not possible.

Flying: Not possible.

Statistical Data

Height: 50 feet (15 m) from head to toe.

Width: 27 feet (8.2 m) or 35 feet (10.7 m) with wings extended.

Length: 20 feet (6 m)

Weight: 90 tons

Physical Strength: Equal to a P.S. 60

Cargo: Small area

Power System: Nuclear, average energy life is 10 years.

Black Market Cost: Not available.

Weapon Systems

Note: Total number of attacks per melee round is 10.

1. Ion Finger Blasters (8): Located in each of the bot's fingers (thumbs excluded) is a powerful ion blaster. The bot points and shoots.

Primary Purpose: Assault

Mega-Damage: 2D6 from a single finger blast, 4D6 M.D. two fingers, 6D6 M.D. three fingers, 1D4 × 10 + 8 from four fingers or 2D4 × 10 + 8 from a full four finger blast from both hands simultaneously! Simultaneous blasts count as one melee attack regardless of the number of firing finger blasters. + 3 to strike when taking careful aim with one or two fingers, no bonus to strike when using three or four fingers or both hands.

Range: 2000 feet (610 m)

Rate of Fire: Equal to the total number of melee round attacks.

Payload: Effectively unlimited.

2. **Microwave Beam Weapons (2):** Located in the chest of the giant bot are two large mounts. Both are pointed slightly downward and fire wide-beam microwave blasts. Directional fins inside the firing housing direct the angle of the beam (downward in a 45 degree arc of fire). The weapon is designed to literally fry ground troops.

Primary Purpose: Anti-Personnel

Mega-Damage: 4D6 M.D. to everything in the blast radius, plus unprotected S.D.C. plants and animals wither and die, and there is a 01-63% chance of combustible materials bursting into flame (spreading fire can cause more destruction). Metal power armor and bots will sparkle from the energy and communication and sensor systems may be temporarily disrupted (01-50% chance) for 1D4 minutes. Furthermore, the shielding in standard mega-damage body armor, especially ceramic, plastic and padded types, is not sufficient to shield against this type of attack and the wearer suffers 1D6 S.D.C. damage per blast.

Area Affected: Each beam, usually fired simultaneously (counts as one attack), covers an area 30 feet (9 m) in diameter. Everything in the blast radius suffers damage.

Range: 200 feet (61 m)

Rate of Fire: Equal to the total number of melee round attacks.

Payload: Effectively unlimited.

3. **Concealed Mini-Missile Launchers (2):** The two plates on the robot's hips slide up to fire mini-missiles. These are also usually operated by the gunner.

Primary Purpose: Anti-Aircraft and Anti-Power Armor

Missile Type: Any mini-missile can be used, but standard issue is armor piercing (1D4×10 M.D.) or plasma (1D6×10 M.D.). Fragmentation is seldom used by these anti-armor units.

Mega-Damage: Varies with missile type.

Range: Usually about a mile (1.6 km).

Rate of Fire: One at a time or volleys of two, three or four.

Payload: 48 total; 24 in each hip launcher.

4. **Retractable Energy Ball and Chain (2):** The ball-shaped nodules in the forearms are energy spheres attached to a long, extendable and retractable cable and function like giant balls and chains. They are larger versions of the weapon used by the G-30 Wrecker.

This energy weapon releases a charge that temporarily short-circuits the nervous system whenever it strikes an opponent with either the ball or the energized cable. The powerful electrical jolt the weapon delivers is especially effective against supernatural beings. Striking unarmored humans will kill them. Unarmored mega-damage creatures may be stunned. Those in body armor or power armor may have a temporary system failure.

Mega-Damage: 1D4×10 M.D. per strike. This weapon is an M.D.C. structure and can be used to parry M.D. attacks from robots and power armor.

Stun Penalties for Mega-Damage Creatures: Using this weapon against mega-damage beings such as demons and dragons inflicts the same amounts of mega-damage and double damage to beings who are vulnerable to electricity. The jolt will cause the victim to lose initiative and one melee action/attack per each strike of the ball. Furthermore, the creature will be momentarily dazed for the rest of that melee and is −2 to strike, parry, and dodge.

Characters in power armor or environmental body armor suffer damage and there is a 01-40% chance of targeting, radar or communication systems getting temporarily knocked out for 1D6 minutes. However, the character inside the armor is grounded and insulated so he is impervious to being dazed or electrified.

Robot vehicles only suffer mega-damage from the hits.

Save vs Being Dazed: 16 or higher. The character must save each time he or she is struck. A successful save means the victim of the attack is NOT dazed and suffers no penalties.

Bonuses for the Attacker: +3 to strike and parry using this item.

5. **Hand to Hand Combat:** Rather than use a weapon, the pilot can engage in mega-damage hand to hand combat. The gurgoyle is a supernatural creature, so a normal punch or kick from one will inflict mega-damage. However, inside the robot, the pilot must rely on the mechanical strengths and abilities of the robot, instead of his own.

Bonuses: A total of 10 attacks per melee round, +3 to strike from punches, +4 to parry, +2 to roll with impact, and +2 to pull punch.

Penalties: The robot's movements are slow and usually telegraphed, giving alert opponents the opportunity to dodge. Attacks marked with an asterisk are −3 to strike when the target is 15 feet (4.6 m) tall or smaller; if under 5 feet (1.5 m), the penalty is −6 to strike.

Restrained Punch — 1D6 M.D.

Full Strength Punch — 1D6×10 M.D.

* Power Punch — 2D6×10 M.D., but counts as two melee attacks.

Crush/Squeeze or Tear — 1D4×10 M.D.

* Kick — 1D6×10 M.D. (−3 to strike small targets)

Leap Kick — Not possible

* Stomp — 1D6×10 M.D.

Body Slam/Ram — 1D6×10 M.D.

Body Throw — 6D6 M.D.

Head Butt — 6D6 M.D.

6. **Sensors & Systems of Note:** Fundamentally, all the *basic* items as found in human robots, only simpler.

NGR Mobile Infantry Strike Base

The Mobile Infantry Strike Base, nicknamed the "Misfit," is the latest creation from Triax Industries. The Misfit is an impressive instrument of destruction, but many have questioned its effectiveness in the field of combat. Opponents of its costly manufacture argue that the vehicle is slow, ponderous and limited in its scope. It is only truly effective against massive enemy offensives and then only if there has been sufficient advanced warning. Proponents for the production of a dozen Misfits (only three prototypes have been produced), insist that such massive enemy offensives are likely and will almost always be telegraphed in advance by troop build-ups. The mobile base would serve to provide troop support, cover, heavy artillery and tactical strikes. The gargoyle offensive along the western border will be the NGR's opportunity to field the vehicle.

The giant vehicle is actually five armored vehicles in one. The four smaller vehicles help pull the command center with its giant particle beam acceleration cannon. They also provide artillery support and troop transportation. At any point during combat, one or all of the four smaller vehicles can detach from the command section and engage the enemy as separate units. The following description is broken down into the three major components of the armored assault vehicle: the forward troop carriers (2), the rear artillery troop carriers (2), and the command center. **Note:** All three prototypes have been moved toward the mounting gargoyle offensive.

Command Center and Main Cannon (1)

Model Type: X-MISB-01 Component A

Class: Armored Infantry Assault & Troop Transport Vehicle.

Crew: 80 (plus 20 medical personnel): A commander, a second in command, two pilots, two co-pilots, 10 communications officer, 10 field mechanics, 12 gunners, 6 reserve gunners, 12 power armor commandos, 6 robot soldiers, 6 intelligence officers, and 12 soldiers.

Mobile hospital section: 6 doctors, 2 cyber-docs, 12 nurses; accommodates 48 injured.

The vehicle is not intended to be a troop carrier but can accommodate one company (40 troops).

M.D.C. by Location:

Main Cannon (1) — 800
Secondary Laser Cannon (1; top rear) — 250
Secondary Ion Cannon (1; side) — 250
* Main Cannon Sensors (2; next to ion cannon) — 150 each
* Forward Sensor Array (1; below the ion cannon) — 150
Missile Launcher Pyramid Housing (1; center) — 350
Rear Multi-Turret (1) — 220
* Mini-Turrets (3) — 50 each
* Forward Laser Turrets (2) — 150 each
Forward Ion Cannons (2; belly guns) — 150 each
Forward Command Section — 600
Communications Section (middle) — 250
Rear Landing Platforms (2) — 300 each
Giant Wheels (16) — 150 each
** Main Body — 2100

* A single asterisk indicates small or difficult targets to hit. They can only be struck when an attacker makes a *called shot*, and even then the character is −3 to strike (the sensor array is −2). Destroying both the main cannon sensors eliminates all long-range targeting and radar.

** Depleting the M.D.C. of the main body will shut the weapon down completely, making it useless.

Statistical Data

Speed: 12 mph (19 km) maximum when separated from the four other units. 35 mph (56 km) when pulled by all four unit vehicles (23 mph/36.8 km when pulled by two).
Height: 70 feet (21.3 m) with the forward cannon level.
Width: 60 feet (18.3 m)
Length: 170 feet (51.8 m)
Weight: 80,000 tons
Power System: Nuclear, average energy life is 20 years.
Black Market Cost: Not available

Weapon Systems

1. Main Super PBA Cannon (1): The huge cannon is an accelerated particle beam cannon of unprecedented range and power.

The housing underneath it is an independent sensor, radar and targeting array. Mounted on the sides of the cannon, clustered with it, are two cannon-like appendages, but they are really long-range sensor and communication systems. The cannon can only point forward but can fire up and down in a 90 degree arc of fire.
Primary Purpose: Assault
Secondary Purpose: Anti-Aircraft & Gargoyles
Mega-Damage: 3D6×100 M.D. per single full power blast!
Maximum Effective Range: 10,000 feet (3050 m)
Rate of Fire: Once per melee round (needs about 10 seconds to recycle).
Payload: Effectively unlimited
Special Feature: Independent coordinated targeting: +3 to strike.
Note: After ten shots, roll for a system failure (01-50%) for each subsequent shot. A system failure means the gun cannot fire that melee round.

2. Secondary Super Laser Cannon (1): Mounted on the top, back section of the main gun. It can rotate 360 degrees and point up and down in a 60 degree arc of fire.
Primary Purpose: Assault
Secondary Purpose: Anti-Aircraft & Gargoyles
Mega-Damage: 1D6×10 M.D. per single full power blast or 2D6×10 M.D. per double pulse blast.
Maximum Effective Range: 8000 feet (2438 m)
Rate of Fire: Equal to the number of combined hand to hand attacks of the gunner (usually 4-8).
Payload: Effectively unlimited
Special Feature: Independent coordinated targeting: +3 to strike.

3. Secondary Super Ion Cannon (1): Mounted on the back, this big gun swings down, over the right shoulder, to fire. It can fire in any position, including while locked in the stowed position.
Primary Purpose: Anti-Armor
Secondary Purpose: Anti-Personnel
Mega-Damage of Ion Cannon: 2D4×10 M.D. per blast
Maximum Effective Range: 4000 feet (1200 m)
Rate of Fire: Equal to the number of combined hand to hand attacks of the gunner (usually 4-8).
Cannon Payload: Effectively unlimited.
Special Feature: Independent coordinated targeting: +3 to strike.

4. Long-Range Missile Launcher Bay (1; six missile silos): The triangular, pyramid shaped wedge in the center of the command center is the missile bay.
Primary Purpose: Assault
Missile Type: Any long-range missile can be used, but standard military issue is proton torpedoes (4D6×10 M.D.), nuclear multi-warhead (4D6×10 M.D.) or heavy plasma (3D6×10 M.D.). All are smart bombs and are +5 to strike.
Mega-Damage: Varies with missile type.
Range: Usually about 1000+ miles (1640+ km).
Rate of Fire: One at a time or in volleys of two, four or six.
Payload: 48 missiles.

5. Forward Double-Barreled Laser Turrets (2): The turrets are designed to counter ground troops and can rotate 90 degrees up and down. One or both guns can be fired.
Primary Purpose: Assault
Secondary Purpose: Defense
Mega-Damage: 3D6 M.D. per single blast or 1D4×10 M.D. per dual simultaneous blast.
Rate of Fire: Equal to number of combined hand to hand attacks of the gunner (usually 4-6).
Maximum Effective Range: 4000 feet (1200 m)
Payload: Effectively unlimited.

6. Ion Belly Guns (2): The double-barreled ion blasters are designed to counter ground troops and can rotate 90 degrees up and down. One or both guns can be fired simultaneously.
Primary Purpose: Assault
Secondary Purpose: Defense
Mega-Damage: 4D6 M.D. per single blast or 1D4×10+8 M.D. per dual simultaneous blast.
Rate of Fire: Equal to number of combined hand to hand attacks of the gunner (usually 4-6).
Maximum Effective Range: 2000 feet (610 m)
Payload: Effectively unlimited.

7. Mini Double-Barreled Laser Turrets (3): Three mini-turrets are mounted on the side of the hospital wing. They are intended for self defense. Each can rotate 180 degrees and fire in a 90 degree arc. Each works independent of the other.
Primary Purpose: Defense
Secondary Purpose: Anti-missile
Mega-Damage: 2D6 M.D. per single blast or 4D6 M.D. per dual simultaneous blast per turret.
Rate of Fire: Equal to number of combined hand to hand attacks of the gunner (usually 4-6).
Maximum Effective Range: 2000 feet (610 m)
Payload: Effectively unlimited

8. Rear Multi-Turret (1): This is a rear defense and assault weapon with three heavy laser cannons and a mini-missile launcher. It can rotate 360 degrees and shoot in a 90 degree arc of fire.
Primary Purpose: Defense
Secondary Purpose: Anti-missile
Mega-Damage: Lasers: 4D6 M.D. per single blast, 1D4×10+8 M.D. per double blast or 2D4×10 M.D. per simultaneous triple blast. Mini-missiles: Varies with missile type.

Rate of Fire: Equal to number of combined hand to hand attacks of the gunner (usually 4-6).

Maximum Effective Range: Lasers 4000 feet (1200 m). Missiles usually about a mile (1.6 km).

Payload: The lasers are effectively unlimited. Mini-missiles are limited to 24.

9. Sensor Systems Note: The most advanced optic, sensory and radio systems plus all other features common to most robots and military vehicles.

Forward Troop Carriers (2; identical)

Model Type: X-MISB-01 Component B
Class: Armored Infantry Assault & Troop Transport Vehicle.
Crew: 11: Pilot, co-pilot, three communications officer, four gunners and two reserve gunners.

The vehicle carries two companies of soldiers in body armor or DV-12 Dyna bots (80 troops) or one company (40 troops) in smallish

power armor suits like the T-31 Super Trooper, X-10A Predator, or basic X-535 Jager.

M.D.C. by Location:

Main Laser Turret (1; rear) — 250
High-Powered Ion Cannon Turrets (2; side) — 150
* Mini-Missile Launchers (3) — 80 each
* High-Powered Headlights (4; front) — 10 each
* Entry Hatches (5) — 120 each
** Main Body — 1200
Reinforced Pilot's Compartment — 150

    * A single asterisk indicates small or difficult targets to hit. They can only be struck when an attacker makes a *called shot*, and even then the character is −3 to strike.

    ** Depleting the M.D.C. of the main body will shut the vehicle down completely, making it useless.

Statistical Data:

Speed: 45 mph (72 km) maximum when separated from the command center. 35 mph (56 km) when pulling the command center with all four component units.
Height: 20 feet (6 m)
Width: 30 feet (9 m)
Length: 80 feet (24.4 m)
Weight: 10,000 tons
Power System: Nuclear, average energy life is 20 years.
Black Market Cost: Not available

Weapon Systems

1. **Double-Barreled Laser Turret (1):** The turret is an all-purpose assault weapon. It can rotate 180 degrees side to side and the guns can move up and down in a 90 degree arc of fire. One or both guns can be fired.

Primary Purpose: Assault
Secondary Purpose: Defense
Mega-Damage: 1D4 × 10 M.D. per single blast or 2D4 × 10 M.D. per dual simultaneous blast.
Rate of Fire: Equal to number of combined hand to hand attacks of the gunner (usually 4-6).

Maximum Effective Range: 4000 feet (1200 m)

Payload: Effectively unlimited.

2. Ion Turrets (2): The double-barreled ion turrets are designed to inflict heavy damage to ground troops. Each can rotate 360 degrees and shoot in an up and down 180 degree arc. One or both guns can be fired simultaneously.

Primary Purpose: Assault

Secondary Purpose: Defense

Mega-Damage: 4D6 M.D. per single blast or 1D4×10+8 M.D. per dual simultaneous blast.

Rate of Fire: Equal to number of combined hand to hand attacks of the gunner (usually 4-6).

Maximum Effective Range: 3000 feet (914 m)

Payload: Effectively unlimited.

3. Mini-Missile Launchers (3): On the side of the vehicle are three mini-missile launchers.

Primary Purpose: Anti-Missile and Flying Monsters

Secondary Purpose: Anti-Personnel

Missile Type: Any mini-missile can be used, but standard issue is armor piercing (1D4×10 M.D.) or plasma (1D6×10). Fragmentation and/or tear gas may be used for anti-personnel operations.

Mega-Damage: Varies with missile type.

Range: Usually about a mile (1.6 km).

Rate of Fire: One at a time or in volleys of 2, 3 or 6.

Payload: 90 total; 30 in each launcher compartment.

4. Sensor Systems Note: All of the most advanced optic, sensory and radio equipment, plus all other features common to most robots.

Artillery Troop Carriers (2; identical)

Model Type: X-MISB-01 Component C

Class: Armored Infantry Assault & Troop Transport Vehicle.

Crew: 12: Pilot, co-pilot, three communications officers, four gunners and three reserve gunners.

The vehicle can carry two companies of soldiers in body armor or DV-12 Dyna bots (80 troops) or one company (40 troops) in smallish power armor suits like the T-31 Super Trooper, X-10A Predator, or basic X-535 Jager or about 20 of the larger power armor or robot units.

M.D.C. by Location:

Main Laser Turret & Missile Launcher (1; front) — 250

High-Powered Ion Cannon Turrets (2; side) — 150 each

Multi-Missile & Laser Turret (1) — 500

* High-Powered Infrared Searchlight (1; front) — 20

* Entry Hatches (4) — 150 each

** Main Body — 1400

Reinforced Pilot's Compartment — 150

   * A single asterisk indicates small or difficult targets to hit. They can only be struck when an attacker makes a *called shot*, and even then the character is −3 to strike.

   ** Depleting the M.D.C. of the main body will shut the vehicle down completely, making it useless.

Statistical Data:

Speed: 37 mph (59 km) maximum when separated from the command center. 35 mph (56 km) when pulling the command center with all four component units.

Height: 20 feet (6 m)

Width: 30 feet (9 m)

Length: 95 feet (27.4 m)

Weight: 15,000 tons fully loaded

Power System: Nuclear, average energy life is 20 years.

Black Market Cost: Not available

Weapon Systems

1. Double-Barreled Laser Turret & Missile Launcher (1): The turret is an all-purpose assault weapon. It can rotate 180 degrees side to side and the guns can move up and down in a 180 degree arc of fire. One or both of the laser guns can be fired. Above the laser cannons are two mini-missile launch tubes.

Primary Purpose: Assault

Secondary Purpose: Defense

Mega-Damage: Laser: 1D4×10 M.D. per single blast or 2D4×10 M.D. per dual simultaneous blast. Mini-missiles: Varies with type.

Rate of Fire: Equal to number of combined hand to hand attacks of the gunner (usually 4-6). Mini-missiles can be launched one at a time or in volleys of two.

Maximum Effective Range: Lasers 4000 feet (1200 m). Missiles usually about a mile (1.6 km).

Payload: Effectively unlimited for the laser. Mini-missiles: 24 total (12 per each launch tube).

2. Ion Turrets (2): The double barreled ion turrets are designed to inflict heavy damage to ground troops. These turrets are a different design than the one on the forward vehicle but are the same guns. The barrels can turn side to side in an 80 degree sweep and shoot up and down in a 30 degree arc. One or both guns can be fired simultaneously.

Primary Purpose: Assault

Secondary Purpose: Defense

Mega-Damage: 4D6 M.D. per single blast or 1D4×10+8 M.D. per dual simultaneous blast.

Rate of Fire: Equal to number of combined hand to hand attacks (of the gunner (usually 4-6).

Maximum Effective Range: 3000 feet (914 m)

Payload: Effectively unlimited.

3. Multi Missile Launcher & Laser System (1): On the side of the vehicle are two missile launchers and a laser.

   * Medium-Range Missile Launcher (1): The large drum is a medium-range missile launcher (210 M.D.C.).

Primary Purpose: Anti-Armor

Secondary Purpose: Anti-Aircraft

Missile Type: Any medium-range missile can be used, but standard military issue is armor piercing (2D4×10 M.D.; multi-warhead whenever possible) or plasma (2D6×10). All missiles are +3 to strike.

Mega-Damage: Varies with missile type.

Range: Usually about 40+ miles (64+ km).

Rate of Fire: One at a time or in volleys of two or four.

Payload: 33 missiles

   * Mini-Missile Launcher (1): Mounted under the heavy armored laser cannon (80 M.D.C.).

Primary Purpose: Anti-Missile and Flying Monsters

Secondary Purpose: Anti-Personnel

Missile Type: Any mini-missile can be used, but standard issue is armor piercing (1D4×10 M.D.) or plasma (1D6×10). Fragmentation and/or tear gas may be used for anti-personnel operations.

Mega-Damage: Varies with missile type.

Range: Usually about a mile (1.6 km).

Rate of Fire: One at a time or in volleys of 2, 3 or 6.

Payload: 21 mini-missiles.

   * Heavy Armored Laser Cannon (1): It can rotate 180 degrees side to side and the gun can move up and down in a 180 degree arc of fire (210 M.D.C.).

Primary Purpose: Anti-Missile & Anti-Aircraft

Secondary Purpose: Defense

Mega-Damage: 1D4×10 M.D. per single blast.

Rate of Fire: Equal to number of combined hand to hand attacks of the gunner (usually 4-6).

Maximum Effective Range: 4000 feet (1200 m)

Payload: Effectively unlimited for the laser.

4. Sensor Systems Note: All of the most advanced optic, sensory and radio equipment, plus all other features common to most robots.

The Kingdom of Tarnow

And the Mystery of the Tarnow Crystal

The Kingdom of Tarnow (also known as New Tarnow) is one of the few truly independent human strongholds in Poland. Although it trades with other kingdoms and cities, it is completely self reliant — unlike Wroclaw and Poznan, both of which rely on the New German Republic for trade and protection. What makes Tarnow all the more outstanding is that it rests at the heart of the Brodkil Empire! This is all possible thanks to the mystical **Tarnow Crystal**, perhaps more internationally known as the legendary *Philosopher's Stone*. It is the Tarnow Crystal's amazing powers to transmute base metal into gold, silver and, most importantly, into mega-damage metal that gives the Kingdom of Tarnow much of its power and wealth.

The Legends of the Tarnow Crystal

The Tarnow Crystal is an ancient artifact that dates back to pre-Rifts 12th Century. It is called the "Tarnow" (pronounced Tar-nuve) Crystal because it was first discovered in the city of Tarnow in Poland during the age of alchemy. The later myths regarding the fabled "Philosopher's Stone" are almost certainly inspired by tales of the Tarnow Crystal that spread to Germany and other parts of Europe.

It is not known whether the crystal was somehow created or simply, unearthed one day. Modern practitioners of magic speculate that the famous crystal is the creation of alien bio-wizardry. They insist that it is probably some sort of *rune* weapon or is at least related to rune magic. They also suggest that if this is true, the stone was probably lost by a dimensional traveler visiting ancient Earth, perhaps a True Atlantean or dragon. They reason this, since there is no evidence that any human, with the possible exception of the infamous Doctor Faustus and Ancient Atlanteans, ever possessed the knowledge to create such a powerful magic item.

According to ancient legend, the stone was a large crystal, the size of grapefruit, that shone with its own inner light. The crystal was entrusted to a Polish noble, who was hiding in the Ukraine, to protect it from the Tatars (nomadic Mongolians) when they invaded that country. He kept the gem safely hidden in a hollowed out gourd placed in the corner of his vegetable shed. The noble charged his heirs with a sworn oath to keep the crystal safe. Hence, this duty was passed down from generation to generation. Those charged with the crystal's safekeeping never used it, for they were warned of its strangely beguiling powers.

Several hundred years passed before the crystal was brought to Krakow where it was presented to the king of Poland. However, the mystic stone was stolen by an alchemist shortly after it was placed in the king's keeping. The mage didn't understand its powers and his misuse of its magic caused a great fire that burned down half the city of Krakow. The disaster that killed the foolish alchemist and destroyed half the city was only the beginning of a legacy of evil. The Tarnow Crystal passed through many hands due to theft, treachery and murder, but was finally recovered a few years later.

The king assigned his best scientists to unravel the secrets of the Tarnow Crystal and to harness its power. Legends credit the crystal with many feats of magic. The most famous was the transmutation of lead into gold. However, the wise king saw that the magic could not be controlled and that it had been tainted with evil (perhaps it had always been evil). He noted with great consternation that the enchanted crystal had a corrupting influence on his scientists. Good, loyal men who he once trusted with his life, now showed uncharacteristic pettiness, avarice, paranoia and backstabbing.

One night, while alone with the crystal, the king could feel its evil touch caressing his soul and filling him with a lust for conquest and power. Afraid that the Tarnow Crystal might fill his heart with dark desires that would plunge his nation into war, he decided to destroy it! Fearful of what dangerous forces he might unleash if it was shattered, he carried it to the deepest, most turbulent part of the river and threw it into the cleansing waters. People searched and dredged the river for centuries, but the magic crystal was never seen again. At least not before the Great Cataclysm.

One can only presume that the Tarnow Crystal had been buried on the river floor until the eruption of the ley lines, earthquakes, floods or other disasters dislodged it. The new legends claim that a peasant fisherman found the stone in the belly of a large fish the man's wife was preparing for dinner. The woman polished the crystal and the family gathered around to examine it. Not knowing anything about gems, they guessed the crystal might be a giant diamond worth a king's ransom in gold. One of the children held the stone in hand, touched a large iron cauldron, and announced that he guessed the "diamond" was so valuable that it would fill the kettle to the brim with gold. With that statement a spark of pulsating light appeared in the crystal and the iron cauldron turned into gold! Terrified, the fisherman and his wife threw the crystal into the cauldron and carried it to King Peter Wojtyla. The rest is as they say, history. The family was handsomely rewarded and the king has learned to harness the power of the Tarnow Crystal (an easier task in the magic rich environment of Rifts Earth). He has used it to keep his people safe and make his kingdom strong.

The Tarnow Crystal

The Tarnow Crystal appears to be some sort of a rune-type creation. Presumably, the secrets to making such a device are lost even to powerful beings such as the Splugorth. It is possible that the gem is an incredibly ancient creation of the *Old Ones,* super-powerful alien intelligences once common to the *Palladium World and dimension.* This seems a likely possibility because locked inside the amber gem is an evil, alien intelligence! Not just a fragment of an intelligence's life essence, but an entire being who is roughly the equivalent of a Splugorth!!

Statistical Data

Alignment: Diabolic

Attributes of Note: I.Q. 25, M.A. 27, M.E. 30

Description: A golden yellow colored, many facetted crystal with the appearance and texture of amber. Normal amber is a stone-like, fossilized resin originating from tree sap. Although rock hard, it is rarely cut into facets because it lacks the natural brilliance of gem stones. However, the Tarnow Crystal shines with an inner light that seems to radiate from its center. The stone is roughly the size of a softball or grapefruit; a bit smaller than the ancient legends suggest.

The Glow: The crystal glows with an inner light from the heart of the crystal. When the dormant stone is first discovered, the glow is barely a spark deep within it. As the bond between the stone and its owner grows (over years and through corruption toward evil) the light grows brighter. The more time spent together and the greater the degree of corruption, the brighter the crystal glows. At its maximum level of power, the light is equal to an intense globe of daylight. The light emanating from the stone can become so bright that one cannot look at its center and the stone must be covered. This blinding light occurs when the crystal has completely corrupted its owner, making him diabolic evil.

M.D.C. of the Crystal: 2000 M.D.C. (2000 S.D.C. in magic poor environments), plus it automatically regenerates from damage at a rate of 1D6×100 per minute. This makes it very difficult to destroy. The regeneration process is beyond the control of the alien intelligence trapped inside and who would like to see his prison destroyed (but can do nothing to promote it).

While trapped inside the amber crystal, the thing within is impervious to all outside forces, including psionic probes and attacks.
Psionic Powers: While trapped in the crystal, its psionic powers are limited to empathy, telepathy, object read, sixth sense, total recall, mind block auto-defense, and group mind block. However, it may not let its owner know the full extent of these powers, particularly group mind block, object read, and sixth sense.

The stone uses its psionic powers to push people to do selfish and evil things. The saying "Absolute power corrupts absolutely" may originate from the legends of the Tarnow Crystal.
The Evil Within: The alien intelligence imprisoned inside the crystal cannot make even the slightest suggestion that his owner destroy its amber prison. Nor can it aid in its destruction or take a passive position, allowing itself to be destroyed. In fact, the monster must do everything in its power to survive and defend itself as the Tarnow Crystal — such is the curse of its imprisonment. Consequently, the crystal suggests secrecy and discretion on the part of its owner — manipulating him and events from behind the scenes. To protect itself, the mystic stone preys on its owner's insecurities, pointing out that others, especially enemies, will covet its power and try to steal it away.

If the crystal prison is destroyed, the malignant force contained inside will be unleashed! Hopefully this will never happen, but if it does, the Megaverse will become a more dangerous place.

The thing inside the crystal is about 25% more powerful than most modern day alien intelligences. It can be created using the rules described in **Rifts Conversion Book (one)**, pages 205 and 206, with the following modifications: Horror factor is 17, add another 2D6 × 10,000 points to the M.D.C. and it bio-regenerates 1D6 × 100 M.D.C. per minute (rather than the usual 1D6 × 10). Psionic powers: All sensitive powers and 10 super psionic powers of choice. Magic knowledge includes all spells, levels 1-3, plus all those available as the Tarnow Crystal, with the exception of transmuting pure metals (that power is lost).

The Powers of the Tarnow Crystal

Note: To access any of the crystal's powers, including spells, saving throws, bonuses, and transmutation, the Tarnow Crystal's owner must have the stone in his possession (in hand or on his person) or be within telepathic range (typically 10 to 20 feet/3 to 6 meters).

1. Communication with the Crystal: The crystal communicates with its owner via empathy for the first six months. Then after the two are more familiar with each other, they communicate through telepathy. Range is limited to touch or 10 feet (3 m).

2. Transmutation of Metal: This is the Tarnow Crystal's most famous power. Although the legends focus on the crystal's ability to change lead into gold, it possesses greater abilities than that. Any pure/natural metal can be transformed into any other pure metal, meaning lead, iron, zinc, and the others could be turned into silver or gold, while silver or gold can be transformed into iron or lead, and so on. The magic crystal can also turn ordinary pure metals into mega-damage structures (see the following description).

Limitations:
- "Pure" metals are limited to iron, lead, aluminum, zinc, nickel, copper, silver, gold and platinum. It does not include alloys such as pewter, bronze, brass, and steel.
- The material must be a pure base metal (95% purity rating). Once transformed from one type of material into another, that particular metal cannot be changed again — the transformation is permanent and unalterable even by the Tarnow Crystal.
- As much as two tons of base metal can be transformed daily! Note that only one third as much can be transformed into precious metals such as gold, silver and platinum. If the crystal refuses to cooperate, as little as one quarter the full amount is transformed.

3. S.D.C. to M.D.C.: An even more incredible feat of transmutation is changing any of the base "S.D.C." metals into mega-damage material! The material's normal S.D.C. is transformed into M.D.C. points. Thus, if a suit of body armor has 100 S.D.C. it now has 100 M.D.C. A vehicle with 600 S.D.C. is transformed to have 600 M.D.C.! This is actually more valuable than turning lead into gold because it enables the crystal's owner to make S.D.C. vehicles, armor, and materials and transform them into mega-damage items!

Limitations:
- The S.D.C. material must be a pure base metal (95% purity rating). Only the pure metal is transformed, any metal alloys, synthetic metal, plastic, ceramic or wood are unaltered. However, the various pure metals can be combined in the construction of the object.
- Once transformed the item cannot be changed in any way again.
- Mega-damage material cannot be transformed into S.D.C. material.
- The M.D.C. transformation is possible only on Earth and similarly magic rich environments. Otherwise transmutation is limited to S.D.C. materials.
- As much as two tons can be transformed into M.D.C. material daily, unless the crystal refuses to cooperate. Under such circumstances as little as one-third the full amount is transformed.
- After the character has owned the crystal for six years, the amount of material that can be transformed tripples.

4. An increase of power: The longer one owns and uses the Tarnow Crystal (and the more evil he becomes), the more powerful the magic offered by the crystal. As the owner becomes increasingly powerful, evil and dependent on the crystal, the brighter it glows.
Bonuses: All bonuses are cumulative.
- After the first three months the owner feels stronger, healthier, and bold; +1 on initiative, +1 to parry, +1 to roll with impact or fall, +2 to save vs disease, +2 to P.S., +1D6 to spd attribute and +2D6 to S.D.C.
- After a year of regular use and contact, the character is +1 to strike, +1 on initiative, +1 on all saving throws, +2 to save vs horror factor, +2 points to P.S. attribute, and adds +2D6 to S.D.C.
- After three years, the character gets another +1 on initiative, +1 to strike, +1 to on all saving throws, +2 to save vs horror factor, +10% to save vs coma and death, +1D6 to spd attribute and +2D6 to S.D.C.
- When the character becomes a diabolic alignment (or has owned the crystal for six years if he was miscreant or diabolic to begin with), add +1 to all combat bonuses, +1 to all saving throws, and +1 attack per melee round.

Increased Telepathic/Empathic Range: Double the range of communication between the owner and the Tarnow Crystal when the character has owned it for six years and again when the character becomes diabolic.

Spell Strength: At the beginning, spells are cast at 2nd level potency. After a year or a change in alignment, whichever comes first, the spell strength increases to the equivalent of fourth level. With each subsequent year and/or alignment change, the spell strength increases by two.

Conditions of spell power: Characters of a good or unprincipled alignment never exceed a maximum spell strength of 4th level. Anarchist and aberrant evil: 6th level, Miscreant: 8th level. Only diabolic evil characters can cast spells equal to a 10th level practitioner of magic.

Paranoia and/or Megalomania: As the union between the crystal and its owner increases, the stone encourages paranoia and breeds distrust and suspicion. After a year or two, the crystal owner will regard not only his enemies with suspicion but his friends as well. He will believe that all around him are jealous and would like to see him fail. In most cases, after five or ten years, he'll also believe that all intelligent beings, from peasant to demi-god, covet his precious gem and will do anything to get it.

In some cases, the feeling of paranoia is comparatively minor, but the owner begins to believe he is invincible. This inevitably leads to acts of aggression, intolerance, arrogance and indifference. Decisions become impetuous and rash, often needlessly endangering the lives of others. However, the character's megalomania prevents him from seeing the truth or accepting it from others. In fact, he is likely to consider the most well intentioned and constructive criticism as verbal condemnation and betrayal!

5. Impart knowledge of alchemy and science: The owner gets an additional bonus of +10% on all science and medical skills he or she may already know.

6. Mystic knowledge and spells of transformation: The crystal can provide the owner with the following skills/knowledge, but these are applicable only when linked directly to the stone; i.e. has it on his person or is within telepathic range. Lore: magic, lore: demons and monsters, holistic medicine, herbology, chemistry, chemistry: analytical and ley line walker abilities numbers 1-4 (see **Rifts RPG**, page 83), all at a skill proficiency of 80%.

Magic spells available to the crystal's owner: Fool's gold, water to wine, negate poison, mute, blind, trance, domination, compulsion, cure illness, purification, spoil, sickness, tongues, breathe without air, reduce self, charismatic aura, Eyes of Thoth, Eyes of the wolf, superhuman strength, superhuman speed, invulnerability, swim as a fish (superior), fly as the eagle, and metamorphosis: animal and human.

Note: All the spells cause a transformation or change of some kind. See number four for the level of power/spell strength available. The owner/crystal user doesn't actually need to know how to cast spells, because the crystal channels through him to cast its magic. The owner of the crystal can access the spells only when he is holding the stone or within psionic communication range and the crystal allows it. The force inside the Tarnow Crystal does have some degree of control over itself and can limit the number of spells available to its owner by half. Likewise, the crystal can elect to teach a practitioner of magic any of the spells it knows, but has no obligation to do so and cannot be forced to teach anything.

7. Summon spirits/beings from other worlds. The Tarnow Crystal can summon a number of supernatural beings. The problem is it can't necessarily control them or send them back from where they came. For example, it can open Rifts, but can't close them. The crystal owner doesn't actually need to know how to cast spells, because the crystal channels through him to cast its magic.

Magic spells related to summoning: Commune with spirits, summon (but not control) animals, summon entity, summon shadow beast, summon lesser being, mystic portal, dimensional portal (open Rift), and protection circle: simple and superior.

8. Elemental Magic: Globe of daylight, globe of silence, see the invisible, levitation, fingers of wind, heavy breathing, chameleon, ignite fire, fuel flame, fire bolt, fire ball, circle of flame, and call lightning. The owner/crystal user doesn't actually need to know how to cast spells, because the crystal channels through him to cast its magic. The owner of the crystal can access the spells only when he is holding the stone or within psionic communication range and the crystal allows it.

9. Aura of Protection: After a year or more, the Tarnow Crystal provides its owner with an aura of M.D.C. protection that effectively transforms the character into a mega-damage being. The character gets 100 M.D.C. per every year he has been linked to the crystal (maximum is 2000 points). M.D.C. is restored at a rate of 1D6×10 every ten minutes. King Peter of Tarnow has 900 M.D.C. The stone must be on the person of its owner or within psionic range to sustain the M.D.C. aura. Of course, after a few years, most owners won't part with the crystal, even for a moment, and keep it on them at all times.

The Corruption

Since the crystal can turn base metals into gold and silver, the temptation of wealth becomes a moot point — the owner of the stone can make as much gold as he or she desires. Consequently, the evil force inside the crystal corrupts its owner with dreams of power (usually through conquest), respect (usually through fear) and fame (usually a reputation for strength, viciousness and cruelty).

The process is slow and insidious and usually fans the flames of discontent, hatred and desire. The result of this in a good character is uncharacteristic pettiness, selfishness, and aggressiveness. Within six months to a year, the character's alignment will drop to the next lowest classification. The passage of each subsequent year will see similar changes for the worse (i.e. principled to scrupulous; scrupulous to unprincipled; unprincipled to anarchist; anarchist to aberrant or miscreant and finally to diabolic). When the character finally becomes diabolic evil, the process of corruption is complete.

The only way to stop the corruption process is to get rid of the Tarnow Crystal. Lost alignments can be regained by trying to be a better person, but this can take years or even decades of dedicated effort and hard work to accomplish.

Characters who are evil to begin with are more easily tempted and corrupted, because they are already foul creatures given to excess, selfishness and dark desires.

Note: It is important to understand the corruption of the crystal's owner is not mind control. The crystal cannot force a person to do anything. Instead, through the telepathic and empathic link between the owner and the stone, the crystal encourages acts of retribution and fuels already existing emotions to ignite hate, anger, and cruelty. These sentiments are encouraged in as positive and spontaneous a light as possible. For example: When a hated opponent is defeated in battle, the crystal owner will be flooded with feelings of hate and a desire to slay his enemy. Some, perhaps even most, of these emotions are his to begin with — a normal reaction to the heat of the moment. Normally, the character may be able to suppress these emotions and do what is right (and in accordance to his or her alignment). What the Tarnow Crystal does is contribute to the base feelings and entice the character to act upon them. This is accomplished by sending thoughts like, "He's responsible for the murder of hundreds of people. Kill him! He deserves to die! If you don't, he'll kill again!! He's an animal. This is justice! Do it!!" Another tactic is to prey on insecurities, "They're laughing at you. You're nothing to them. They despise you (or think you're a coward, child, fool, sissy, fill in the blank). Show them different. Prove you're a man (or no coward, child, etc.). Wipe those smiles off their faces." This can lead to acts of retribution, violence and cruelty, as well as murder, torture, rape, theft, blackmail, etc. Thanks to the evil crystal, such action will be justified in the mind of the perpetrator and is all part of the turning to evil. Just because a person can justify something doesn't mean their actions are just, moral or acceptable; such is the way to selfishness and evil.

King Peter Wojtyla
Ruler of Tarnow

King Peter is a handsome, dark haired, 29 year old man. He is the oldest of three brothers, all born of royal lineage. He took the throne when he was 17, after his father was slain defending the city against a band of marauding brodkil. Young King Wojtyla proved to be wise beyond his years and has led his people well and faithfully. He has earned a reputation for being compassionate, just, and honorable. He is loved by his family and the people of New Tarnow.

The king welcomes both humans and non-humans to his kingdom, provided they swear their eternal allegiance to the king and country. Unlike many mixed communities, D-bees live under the same laws and

True Name: Peter Michael Wojtyla; prefers to be called King Peter rather than King Wojtyla.

Alignment: He started out with a principled alignment, slipped to scrupulous, and is currently unprincipled. Under the right set of circumstance he will become anarchist. It is only a matter of 1D4 years afterward that he'll become miscreant and soon after, diabolic.

Attributes: I.Q.: 14, M.E.: 23, M.A.: 22, P.S.: 21 (including the boost from the crystal), P.P.: 14, P.E.: 17, P.B.: 15, Spd.: 18

Hit Points: 50 H.P. and 45 S.D.C. (including the bonuses from the crystal)

M.D.C.: 900 M.D.C. from the aura of protection provided by the crystal, but he's never tested the extent of this protection and suspects it stops at around 400 M.D.C. points.

P.P.E.: 9

O.C.C.: King and Knight of Tarnow

Level of Experience: 7th level

Natural Abilities: A natural, charismatic leader and intelligent with an inventive, analytical mind and high mental endurance.

Disposition: He has become increasingly cocky and vindictive toward the Gargoyle and Brodkil Empires. He was a good guy but the crystal corrupts and makes its owner selfish and potentially evil. Still, he is basically a good person who continues to do what's best for his people, regardless of his personal feelings (unprincipled alignment). But how long will that last?

Psionic Powers: None, other than his link with the Tarnow crystal; 20 foot (6 m) range.

Magic Knowledge: None, other than a general knowledge of lore and the powers provided through the crystal.

Combat abilities: Hand to hand expert (7th level proficiency).

Combat/Attacks Per Melee Round: Three; hand to hand expert.

Bonuses (includes all bonuses): +3 on initiative, +4 to strike, +4 to parry, +3 to dodge, +4 to roll with impact, +2 to pull punch, +6 to S.D.C. damage, critical strike on unmodified 18, 19 or 20, kick attack (1D6 S.D.C.), and paired weapons. +5 to save vs psionic attack, +4 to save vs disease, +4 to save vs horror factor, +3 to save vs magic and poison, +2 to save vs possession. Includes all applicable crystal bonuses.

Skills of Note: Basic and advanced math, literacy: Euro 90%, speaks traditional Polish, Euro, Spanish, and Gobblely, all at 90%, computer operation 98%, anthropology 70%, lore: demons & monsters 75%, lore: magic 70%, radio: basic 98%, radio: scramblers 90%, navigation 95%, dance 90%, swimming 98%, pilot sailboat 98%, pilot hydrofoils 98%, pilot hover vehicles 98%, pilot robots and power armor, robot combat: basic, W.P. sword, W.P. energy pistol, and W.P. energy rifle.

Appearance: A handsome male with collar length, dark brown hair, long (mutton chops) sideburns and hazel eyes. He stands six feet (1.8 m) tall and has a confident, noble aura about him. He seems menacing only when angry and during combat.

Weapons & Equipment of Note: King Peter has the full resources of the Tarnow Kingdom and the Tarnow Crystal at his disposal. The Crystal is always at his side, kept in a pouch that hangs at his waist. The king also carries his father's holy sword (monsters slayer does 2D6+6 S.D.C. to humans or 4D6+12 to supernatural monsters, and can restore 2D6 hit points six times a day), a TX-20 laser pistol (2D6 M.D.) and a Triax-30 ion pulse rifle (2D6 or 6D6 M.D., 2000 ft/610 m range; 50 shot clip). He can also pilot any Tarnow power armor or bots.

He wears a silver cross and chain around his neck, likes tall boots, gloves and capes. He often wears light mega-damage ceremonial armor (30 M.D.C.).

Cybernetics: None.

Money: Billions! He has the resources of the Tarnow Kingdom and the Tarnow Stone at his fingertips. He can lay his hands on 1D6 × 100,000 universal credits and 3D4 × 10 million in gold at a moment's notice.

receive the same treatment as humans. This true justice has attracted millions of non-humans to the Kingdom in numbers that threaten to surpass the human population.

King Peter has used the magic stone for nine years. Through the power of the Tarnow Crystal he has made the city of New Tarnow the heart of the increasingly powerful kingdom. Thanks to the magic crystal, New Tarnow now makes weapons, body armor, vehicles and fortifications out of pure metals such as iron, aluminum, zinc, etc., and magically transforms them into mega-damage structures. An incredible resource that no power on the planet can match!

The wise and cunning use of the Tarnow Crystal has brought the people of New Tarnow prosperity and freedom, and has earned the king fame, glory and the loving devotion of his people. For the first seven years of owning the crystal, the independent and strong-willed youth had successfully persevered over the relentless dark urgings of the crystal (King Peter has proven to be one of the most defiant owners the crystal has ever encountered). Sadly, it appears that the persuasive powers of the dreaded crystal have finally won the battle of wills. In the last year, King Peter has become increasingly intolerant of the monster races and speaks regularly of the death of his father, extracting revenge, and waging war. He has also become more arrogant, aggressive and a bit paranoid. The crystal never leaves his sight and glows with a new radiance.

Alliances & Allies: The Tarnow Kingdom has a friendly relationship with dozens of neighboring human and D-bee communities. He considers the NGR and the kingdoms of Poznan and Wroclaw to be basically friendly, but there is no formal relationship between them and Tarnow — the king (and most of his people) prefer to stay completely unaffiliated with the NGR. The king and the people of Tarnow do feel a bit of resentment toward the NGR, whom they believe think of themselves as superior to them. Of course, the NGR has nothing to do with Tarnow because the kingdom associates openly with D-bees. The NGR respects Tarnow's dangerous predicament, being located in the heart of Brodkil territory and respects their military power and ingenuity. The forces at the NGR are only now hearing rumors about the Tarnow Crystal.

Enemies: Gargoyles, brodkil, simvan, gene-splicers and most supernatural beings. The gargoyles of the Empire have mixed feelings about the kingdom and the Tarnow Crystal. For the most part they consider it to be the brodkil's problem. The Brodkil Empire fears the magic crystal and have decided to leave the Kingdom of Tarnow alone, at least for the moment. The Brodkil Empire will launch an all-out attack only if the Tarnow Kingdom strikes first. The outcome of such a war will be bloody with huge numbers of casualties on both sides, but in the end, the brodkil are most likely to win from sheer force of numbers.

Notes about the Wojtyla Family

Matthew Wojtyla is the second oldest brother, age 25, anarchist alignment. He is the only other person to have been allowed to use the Tarnow Crystal, although not in recent years. He has not fallen prey to its corrupting powers, but it gave him a taste of power that he enjoyed and would like to have again. He is a hot head and warmonger who encourages the king to wage war against the Brodkil Empire. He is completely loyal to his brother, the king, and will never raise his hand against him in any way. However, should he someday become king and/or get control of the Tarnow Crystal, he will fall easy prey to its corrupting influence.

Stanley "Stashu" Wojtyla is the youngest, age 19, principled alignment. He serves as a calming and rational influence on the king and is completely against war. This has evoked the disdain of his brother Matthew. Young Stashu also sees his beloved eldest brother changing and continues to point out his observations and concerns to him. Stashu is the only person whose criticisms are never viewed negatively by the king and helps him to keep his perspective (and current unprincipled alignment). If Stashu is killed it will send King Peter over the brink into the anarchist alignment and the angry king will seek bloody retribution.

Uncle Dominic Wojtyla is an old warrior and counsel to the king; age 56, unprincipled alignment. He has mixed feelings about going to war and has, for the present, suggested continuing to build up defenses and manufacture more mega-damage war machines. He is also concerned about the changes he sees in his nephew, but has kept them to himself. At this point, he has attributed the change in Peter to becoming more hardened with age. The uncle doesn't want to accept the truth that the crystal is evil because he believes it is absolutely necessary to the survival of the kingdom. He may be right, but the price may be greater than he imagines.

New Tarnow

New Tarnow is the capital city of the Tarnow Kingdom. The city itself is currently home to 3.6 million human inhabitants and 2.4 million D-bees, and continues to grow. It is the birthplace and home of King Peter and the royal family.

New Tarnow is an industrial city with technology roughly equal to the early 21st Century. The capabilities of most of its factories are limited to the manufacturing of S.D.C. products, which was a serious problem until the discovery of the Tarnow Crystal. The city now produces ordinary S.D.C. body armor, power armor, vehicles, building materials and so on from S.D.C. materials, all of which are infinitely cheaper, faster and easier to make than mega-damage items, and magically turn them into mega-damage items! This has made the kingdom rich and powerful.

They can create enough silver and gold to purchase many of the resources and materials they don't have and they also trade a number of mega-damage products (mainly armor, boats and building materials) to other human and friendly D-bee communities.

Old Tarnow

The original city was laid to waste by the brodkil generations ago. The survivors salvaged what they could and built the city of New Tarnow about 30 miles (48 km) west of the old city and closer to the Wisla River. In recent years, settlers have begun to rebuild the ancient city. Approximately 100,000 people (60% human) live there. The tech level is 19th century; mostly farmers and vagabond settlers. Gypsies also frequent this community.

The Vistula River

King Peter has used the blending of magic and technology to seize control of the Vistula River. The kingdom completely dominates the river for a hundred miles in both directions. Its speed boats, ships and underwater power armor troops, salvage teams and fishermen keep the riverway safe and profitable. The river runs south ending just before the border of old Czechoslovakia and to the north and into the Baltic Sea. From the sea, oceangoing vessels can reach Germany, Scandinavia, up around Denmark and into the Atlantic Ocean and sail to any place in the world (barring trouble from pirates, monsters, and violent storms).

Port Tarnow sits on the banks of the Vistula about 15 miles (24 km) due west of New Tarnow. It is a major city in its own right with a population of 354,000 humans and 237,000 D-bees. The city manufactures ships, speed boats and power armor magically transformed into mega-damage structures. Port Tarnow also serves as the Command Center of the Tarnow Navy which keeps the waterway free and safe from the brodkil and others.

Kielce sits on the bank across the river and 20 miles (32 km) northwest of Port Tarnow. It has a population of about 320,000 divided evenly between humans and D-bees. Its main industries are lumber, fishing and light manufacturing.

Rzeszow is a large, but comparatively poor community of farmers, raisers of livestock, and hunters/trappers. Most of the houses are made of wood, except for ten churches made of stone and a large, metal mega-damage bunker/fallout shelter (which is also used for meetings and dances). Few buildings stand higher than two stories tall.

Visitors will find the city to be a simple backwoods community that harkens back to the early 1930's. Half the streets are dirt roads but the overall city is clean and well kept. The people are friendly and generous toward humans and human-looking D-bees (the more monstrous are viewed with suspicion and a certain amount of disdain). Rooms for rent are often in private homes and are small but cozy. Home cooked meals are delicious and local craftsmen offer excellent leather goods, quilts, and down-filled clothing. Prices for everything are inexpensive. King Peter has stationed a platoon of men composed of 10 TC-R3, 10 TC-R5 and 20 power armor troops in the city of Rzeszow and two others to patrol its farmlands. Rzeszow is too important an agricultural community to fall into the hands of the enemy.

Approximately 150,000 people live in Rzeszow (90% are human), with another 50,000+ (60% human) in the surrounding farmlands. There are hundreds of tiny, privately owned farms. Many have been farmed by the same families for hundreds of years.

A **score of other towns and villages** can be found along the river in the area controlled by Tarnow. Most are fishing villages and farm communities with populations that range from a few hundred to several thousand (2D4 × 1000 maximum).

Likewise, a hundred small villages can be found throughout the Tarnow Kingdom. Most are farm communities that seldom have a population above 2000 (2D6 × 100).

The Army of Tarnow

The Tarnow army is one of the most powerful in Europe (see the descriptions of bots, armors and vehicles that follow this section). The gargoyles and brodkil learned about the incredible magic crystal and the Army of Tarnow the hard way. Two years ago, the Brodkil Empire launched three unsuccessful assaults against the kingdom. In each case, the brodkil suffered great losses, while Tarnow was virtually unscathed. The first two times, the enemy didn't know what hit them. King Peter had kept the Tarnow Crystal a secret and had quietly built himself a mega-damage army complete with armored troops, battleships and tanks. The Brodkil's intelligence reports showed New Tarnow to be an easy target, armed mainly with S.D.C. weapons and defenses.

The first attack force was completely unprepared and was obliterated — no survivors. The second, larger assault force met with the same fate. The third attack saw an entire division sent against the kingdom. Included among its troops were gargoyles, gurgoyles, simvan, and Mindwerks borgs and crazies. The attackers made a good stand and lost only 45% of the troops before retreating. Mindwerks spies learned about the magic crystal a few months later. A gargoyle strike force and a half dozen assassins have since failed to slay the king and capture the crystal. **Note:** The success of his army and the unsuccessful attempts on his life have made the king bold and hungry for revenge.

King Peter has also hired an ancient thunder lizard called Karl the Defender (his real name is K'rrel, anarchist alignment, 11th level, 8000 M.D.C.) and a platoon of NGR defectors turned mercenaries armed with stolen Triax Dragonwings (4), Super Hunters (8), Dyna-Maxes (8), Predators (8) and Flankers (12). The dragon and the mercs are paid a hefty fee in gold transmuted by the Tarnow Crystal.

The War Machines of the Tarnow Kingdom

Most of the robots and power armor created by the Tarnow Kingdom look clunky and primitive compared to the sleek and powerful designs of Triax or the Coalition. That's because Tarnow's level of technology is less advanced and most items are created first as S.D.C. structures out of such unlikely materials as aluminum, zinc and nickel (as well as iron and others metal). The machines are built and later magically transformed into M.D.C. structures by the Tarnow Crystal. This means that a typical mega-damage Tarnow suit of power armor, robot, and vehicle is 50% to 80% lighter and costs 75% less than Triax or any other arms manufacturer. The lightness adds to the speed and mobility of the machine or armor — so even clunky bots are as mobile and effective as the Triax creations. The low cost means they are easier to mass produce and are more expendable than most mega-damage creations.

The Tarnow Kingdom sometimes sells and trades its robots to other friendly or loosely allied communities and mercenaries. After all, the secrets of its manufacturing can't be duplicated and most of the robot technology is known and older than Triax's. The King may also give armor and vehicles to worthy adventurers and heroes as a reward for their efforts to defend the kingdom.

Approximately one-third of the giant robots and vehicles are hidden at the bottom of the Vistula River, which often catches invaders by surprise.

Note: Only a fraction of the S.D.C. material that makes up armor, robots, and vehicles is transformed into M.D.C. material.

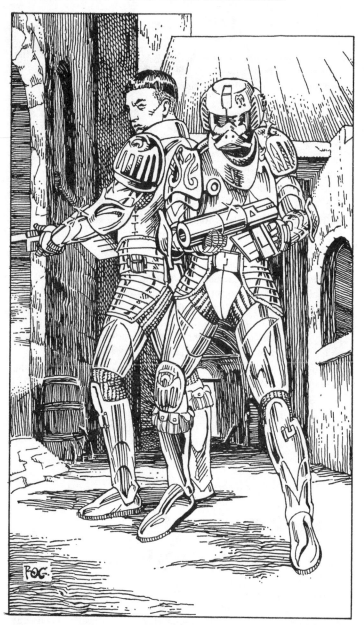

Tarnow Body Armor

The following are some of the most basic types of Tarnow armor. Precious metals such as gold and silver tend to be heavy and softer and offer less S.D.C./M.D.C. protection. The lighter metals are less dense and have a flimsier structure with less S.D.C./M.D.C., but the heavier metals like iron, while strong, are also heavy and cumbersome, Consequently, the best armor will use a combination of metal in its design.

"Pure" metals suitable for mega-damage transmutation are limited to iron, lead, aluminum, zinc, nickel, copper, silver, gold and platinum. It does not include alloys such as pewter, bronze, brass, and steel.

Non-Environmental Chain Mail

Ancient style chain mail made by hand or machine from S.D.C. metals and transformed into M.D.C. material. These are full suits that cover the entire body and include a chain shirt, gauntlets, pants, and skirt, over padding, plus an M.D.C. helmet, goggles, and an air filter. A gas mask and oxygen tank costs an extra 500 credits. **Note:** Availability for most Tarnow body armor, power armor and vehicles is fair to poor.

Mega-Damage Aluminum & Zinc Chain Mail:
- M.D.C.: 25
- Weight: 5 pounds (2.3 kg)
- Excellent mobility; no prowl penalty
- Cost: 8,000 to 10,000 credits; varies depending on the seller and availability.

Mega-Damage Copper and/or Nickel Chain Mail:
- M.D.C.: 40
- Weight: 15 pounds (6.8 kg)
- Good mobility; −5% prowl penalty
- Cost: 12,000 to 16,000 credits; varies depending on the seller and availability.

Mega-Damage Iron Chain Mail:
- M.D.C.: 55
- Weight: 40 pounds (18 kg)
- Poor to fair mobility; −15% prowl penalty and reduce spd by 10%.
- Cost: 18,000 to 25,000 credits; varies depending on the seller and availability.

Mega-Damage Iron, Nickel & Aluminum Composite:
- M.D.C.: 50
- Weight: 25 pounds (11 kg)
- Fair mobility; −10% prowl penalty
- Cost: 20,000 to 30,000 credits; varies depending on the seller and availability.

Non-Environmental Plate Armor

The following plate armors are mega-damage variations of the ancient style suit of armor like those worn by the knights of old. Modern technology has made the suit of armor more comfortable, and joints more flexible (often covered with M.D.C. chain mail). The helmet is typically more modern looking, with a tinted visor and a built-in air filter. An oxygen tank costs an extra 500 credits. An internal cooling, temperature control and circulation system costs an additional 10,000 credits.

Mega-Damage Aluminum & Zinc Plate:
- M.D.C.: 35
- Weight: 15 pounds (6.8 kg)
- Fair to good mobility; −10% prowl penalty
- Cost: 9,000 to 12,000 credits; varies depending on the seller and availability.

Mega-Damage Copper and/or Nickel Plate:
- M.D.C.: 65
- Weight: 32 pounds (14.4 kg)
- Fair mobility; −15% prowl penalty and reduce spd by 10%.
- Cost: 18,000 to 25,000 credits; varies depending on the seller and availability.

Mega-Damage Iron Plate:
- M.D.C.: 110
- Weight: 50 pounds (22.5 kg)
- Poor mobility; −25% prowl penalty and reduce spd by 30%.
- Cost: 18,000 to 25,000 credits; varies depending on the seller and availability.

Mega-Damage Iron, Nickel & Aluminum Composite Plate:
- M.D.C.: 80
- Weight: 40 pounds (18 kg)
- Fair mobility; −15% prowl penalty and reduce spd by 20%
- Cost: 25,000 to 35,000 credits; varies depending on the seller and availability.

Mega-Damage Iron & Nickel Plate & Chain:

- M.D.C.: 70
- Weight: 35 pounds (15.7 kg)
- Fair mobility; −15% prowl penalty
- Cost: 20,000 to 25,000 credits; varies depending on the seller and availability.

Environmental Body Armor

Mega-Damage Iron, Nickel & Aluminum Composite:

- M.D.C.: 80
- Weight: 40 pounds (18 kg)
- Fair mobility; −15% prowl penalty and reduce spd by 10%.
- This suit is a complete, sealed, environmental battle suit with all the modern features common to such armor, including radiation proofing, built-in radio, air circulation, temperature control, oxygen supply, and so on.
- Cost: 30,000 to 50,000 credits; varies depending on the seller and availability.

Royal Mega-Damage EVA Body Armor:

- M.D.C.: 90; a combination of iron, nickel and copper with silver detailing and emblems.
- Weight: 40 pounds (18 kg)

- Fair mobility; −15% prowl penalty and reduce spd by 10%.
- This suit is a complete, sealed, environmental battle suit with all the modern features common to such armor, including radiation proofing, built-in radio, air circulation, temperature control, oxygen supply, and so on.
- Black market Cost: 35,000 to 50,000 credits; varies depending on the seller and availability.

Sting-Ray Power Armor

The sting-ray power armor suit is the smallest and most slender of Tarnow's robotic creations. It offers the wearer enhanced strength, endurance, speed and full environmental capabilities. This exo-skeleton

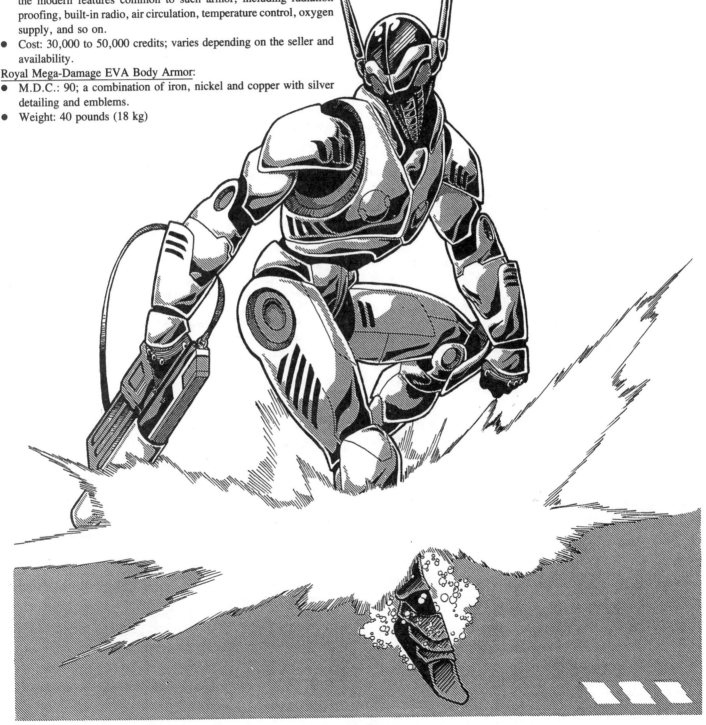

functions as an augmentation and deep sea suit designed with underwater exploration and salvage in mind, as well as combat. It is inspired by Triax designs and has all the standard feature of most power armor suits.

Small, concealed jets in the feet, legs and back help to give the suit greater control in the water. However, theses small jets are not large enough or powerful enough to attain flight or great speeds. A jet pack can be attached for flight. Similarly, a propulsion system can be used underwater to increase speed and maneuverability. As usual, the sting-ray is made out of various S.D.C. metals and later, magically transformed in to a mega-damage suit.

Sting-Ray: Part of the Tarnow Kingdom's Defense Force
Model Type: TC-A6
Class: Strategic Military Environmental Exo-Skeleton
Crew: One
M.D.C. by Location:

* Rear Jets (2; back) — 25 each
* Sensor Antennas (2) — 10 each
* Head — 70
** Main Body — 200

* All items marked with a single asterisk are small, difficult targets to hit. The attacker must make a called shot to strike and even then the character is −3 to hit.

Destroying the head/helmet has a 1-70% chance of knocking the pilot unconscious. If destroyed, the pilot has two problems. One, no power armor combat bonuses to strike, parry and dodge. Two, the human head is now vulnerable to attack.

** Depleting the M.D.C. of the main body will shut the armor down completely, making it useless. Destroying an aerial jet pack or underwater propulsion unit will prevent flight or fast water travel.

Speed
Running: 45 mph (72 km)
Leaping: The character can leap 15 feet (4.6 m) high or lengthwise from a stationary position; double when from a running start.
Flying: Possible only with the aid of a jet pack. Almost all kinds are suitable.
Swimming: 25 mph (40 km). The act of running or swimming does tire the suit's operator, but at a fatigue rate of 20% of normal.
Underwater Propulsion: This is only possible with a special backpack that resembles a jet pack used for flying. This propulsion system enables the power armor to travel underwater like a fish at speeds of 50 mph (80 km). The propulsion unit has 30 M.D.C. and costs around 2000 to 4000 credits.
Underwater Depth: The sting-ray can withstand pressure up to 500 feet (153 m) deep. A special decompression system helps to prevent the bends.

Statistical Data
Height: Roughly 6 to 7 feet (1.8 to 2.1 m) from the top of the head to the bottom of the feet.
Width: 3 feet (0.9 m)
Length: 2.5 feet (0.76 m)
Weight: 130 lbs (58 kg)
Physical Strength: Equal to a P.S. 25
Cargo: None
Weapon Systems: None. Typically Triax and Mindwerks energy rifles, pistols and rail guns are used.
Bonuses & Damage from the TC-A6 Sting-Ray
Restrained Punch — 5D6 S.D.C.
Full Strength Punch — 1D6 M.D.
Power Punch — 3D6 M.D. (counts as two attacks)
Crush, Pry or Tear — 1D6 M.D.
Kick — 2D6 M.D.
Leap Kick — 4D6 M.D. (counts as two attacks)
Body Block/Ram or Throw — 1D6 M.D.

+2 on initiative
+1 to strike
+1 to parry
+2 to dodge; +4 underwater
+2 to roll with impact
+2 to pull punch
+1 melee action/attack at levels 1, 3, 7 and 11.
Note: All combat bonuses are in addition to those of the pilot!
Power System: Nuclear, average energy life is 10 years.
Black Market Cost: 350,000 to 450,000 credits
Current stockpile: Port Tarnow: 2100, New Tarnow: 22,000, another 22,000 in storage and approximately 15,000 are dispatched throughout the kingdom with other troops, bots and vehicles. The sting-ray power armor suit is used extensively by the navy.

The Sea Star

The sea star is a deep sea power armor suit specifically designed for deep sea exploration and salvage. It can tolerate pressure at depths up to 1200 feet (365 m) and has a propulsion systems that makes it as fast as the sting-ray which is considerably smaller and lighter. Numerous directional jets only add to the behemoth's maneuverability underwater; it is considerably less formidable on dry land. The sea star is made out of lead, iron, nickel and gold which has been magically transformed into mega-damage materials.

Sea Star: Part of the Tarnow Kingdom's Navy
Model Type: TC-A12
Class: Strategic Military Environmental Exo-Skeleton
Crew: One
M.D.C. by Location:

Main Jets (4; top back) — 70 each
Hands (2) — 60 each
Arms (2) — 180 each
Legs (2) — 260 each
Feet (2; clawed) — 80 each
* Forearm Launchers (6; three per arm) — 15 each
* Chest Lasers (4) — 20 each
* Shoulder Compartments (2) — 20 each
* Maneuvering Jets (12) — 10 each
* Lights (4, on the collar of the helmet) — 5 each
* Infrared Lights (2; on helmet/head) — 5 each
* Head/Helmet — 185
** Main Body — 700

* All items marked with a single asterisk are small, difficult targets to hit. The attacker must make a called shot to strike and even then the character is −3 to hit.

Destroying the head/helmet while in shallow water (less than 200 feet/61 m) will cause the water to fill the suit. The pilot can either bring the mechanical giant to the surface or eject out of the suit and head to the surface himself. Most sea star pilots will have a mini-oxygen tank (10 minutes of air) or a bionic implant that will save them from drowning. At depths of 400 feet (122 m) or greater, the sudden change in pressure will kill the pilot.

On dry land, destroying the head/helmet has a 1-70% chance of knocking the pilot unconscious. If destroyed, the pilot has two problems. One, no power armor combat bonuses to strike, parry and dodge. Two, the human head is now vulnerable to attack.

** Depleting the M.D.C. of the main body will shut the armor down completely, making it useless. Destroying the underwater propulsion unit will force the pilot to swim, walk or sink.

Speed
Running: 20 mph (32 km) on dry land or underwater.
Leaping: Not possible.

Flying: Not possible.

Swimming: 10 mph (16 km) without propulsion (the act of swimming does not tire the suit's operator)

Underwater Propulsion: 50 mph (80 km)

Underwater Depth: The sea star can withstand pressure up to 1200 feet (365 m) deep. A special decompression system helps to prevent the pilot from getting the bends.

Statistical Data

Height: 12 feet (3.6 m)

Width: The main body is 8 feet (2.4 m) wide, but the spines make the overall width 12 feet (3.6 m)

Length: 7 feet (2.1 m)

Weight: Two tons

Physical Strength: Equal to a P.S. 35

Cargo: None

Power System: Nuclear, average energy life is 20 years.

Black Market Cost: One million credits

Current stockpile: Port Tarnow: 480, New Tarnow: 96, another 1200 in storage and approximately 1100 are in service at sea and throughout the Vistula River. The sea star power armor suit is used extensively by the navy.

Weapon Systems

1. Mini-Missile Launchers (6): Three small mini-missile launchers are mounted on each forearm. Each holds two missiles.

Primary Purpose: Assault

Secondary Purpose: Defense

Missile Type: Any mini-missile can be used but fragmentation (5D6 M.D.) and armor piercing (1D4×10 M.D.) are the standard.

Mega-Damage: Varies with missile type.

Range: Usually about a half mile (0.8 km) underwater.

Rate of Fire: One at a time or in volleys of 2 or 4.

Payload: A total of 12 mini-missiles; two in each launcher, three launchers per arm.

2. Chest Lasers (4): Four short-range, low intensity lasers are built into the chest of the sea star. Each can point in a 90 degree arc.

Primary Purpose: Defense

Mega-Damage: 1D6 from one laser, 2D6 from two simultaneous blasts, 3D6 M.D from three blasts or 4D6 M.D. from all four fired at the same time at the same target.

Rate of Fire: Equal to the number of combined hand to hand attacks of the pilot (typically 5-7).

Maximum Effective Range Underwater: 600 feet (183 m)

Payload: Effectively unlimited.

3. Shoulder Compartments (2): On each shoulder is a compartment that can hold tools, explosives, or specimens. In a military situation, the compartment may contain one or two fusion blocks used to sabotage bridges and vehicles.

4. Harpoons and Rail Guns and giant-sized energy weapons can also be used. All weapons will have half their normal range and strike bonuses.

5. Hand to Hand Combat: Rather than use a weapon, the pilot can engage in mega-damage hand to hand combat.

Bonuses & Damage from the TC-A12 Sea Star

Restrained Punch — 6D6 M.D.

Full Strength Punch — 2D6 M.D.

Power Punch — 4D6 M.D. (counts as two attacks)

Crush, Pry or Tear — 2D4 M.D.

Kick — 2D6 M.D.

Body Block/Ram or Throw — 1D6 M.D.

+1 on initiative
+2 to strike
+2 to parry
+1 to dodge; +4 underwater
+2 to roll with impact
+2 to pull punch
+1 melee action/attack at levels 1, 4, 8, and 12.

Note: All combat bonuses are in addition to those of the pilot!

Penalty: Reduce the number of attacks and combat bonuses by half when on dry land.

6. Features & Sensors of note: All standard robot features, plus sonar, infrared spotlights (2), signal beacon, and electromagnetic adhesive pads on the feet and wrists (used to hold on to and climb the metal hulls of ships).

TC-R3 Missileer

The missileer is actually an all-purpose construction and salvage robot modified for combat. In fact, the TC-R2 is identical except that it doesn't have the shoulder missiles, grenade launchers or forearm plates. The TC-R2 is used in the construction of boats and buildings, as well as exploration and underwater salvage.

The TC-R3 is equipped with a battery of missiles and grenades. The bot is used for riot control, border defense, exploration, and underwater salvage. It is a heavier, slower robot than the TC-R5, but has greater armor, strength, and water capabilities.

Missileer: Part of the Tarnow Kingdom's Defense Force

Model Type: TC-R3

Class: Two Man Strategic Infantry Assault Robot

Crew: One (pilot) and gunner. One human-sized passenger can also be squeezed in.

M.D.C. by Location:

Shoulder Guards (2) — 110 each
Upper Arms (2) — 80 each
Lower Arms (2; plate with grenade launchers) — 200 each
Legs (2) — 150 each
Feet (2) — 60 each
Rear Jets (2) — 50 each
* Sensors (6, small canisters) — 5 each
* Hands (2) — 20 each
* Chest Headlights (4) — 3 each
* Lower Body Headlights (2) — 5 each
* Chest/head Viewport (1) — 20
* Chest Laser (1) — 20
* Head/Pilot Area — 90
Mini-Missile Launchers (1; back) — 150
Reinforced Pilot's Compartment — 50
** Main Body — 330

* All items marked with a single asterisk are small, difficult targets to hit. The attacker must make a called shot to strike and even then the character is −3 to hit.

Destroying the head will rupture the outer hull and reveal the reinforced pilot's compartment. If the six sensor units are destroyed the pilot loses all forms of optical enhancement, radar, targeting and most sensory systems. The pilot is forced to rely on short-range radar/sonar (two miles/8 km, 24 target tracking) and his own human vision and senses. Furthermore, all bot combat bonuses to strike, parry, and dodge are reduced by half and attacks per melee by one.

**Depleting the M.D.C. of the main body will shut the bot down completely, making it useless.

Speed

Running: 45 mph (72 km) maximum running or 20 mph (32 km) walking underwater on the river bed; maximum depth is 1200 feet (365 m). The TC-R3 (and R2) is also designed to travel on the surface of the water like a boat. The robot's legs fold back and up into a prone position and the two rear jets in the lower body provide the propulsion. Maximum speed is 35 mph (56 km). This same configuration and jets can be used to propel the submerged robot through water like a submarine; maximum speed is 25 mph (40 km).

Leaping: The robot can leap up to 10 feet (3 m) high or lengthwise from a running start.

Flying: None

Statistical Data

Height: 25 feet (7.6 m) from the top of the missile launchers to its toes.

Width: 15 feet (4.6 m)

Length: 12 feet (3.6 m)

Weight: 18 tons

Physical Strength: Equal to a P.S. 47

Cargo: None

Power System: Nuclear, average energy life is 20 years.

Black Market Cost: 12 million (construction cost is 2 million). The TC-R2, non-combat model (no missile launchers, grenade launchers, and forearm plates), costs 6 to 8 million.

Note: Current stockpile: Port Tarnow: 1200, New Tarnow: 600, another 600 in storage and approximately 2600 dispatched throughout the kingdom in squads and platoons.

Weapon Systems

1. Forearm Grenade Launchers (2): The two large, protective forearm plates conceal a dual launching grenade launcher. Explosive or riot control (smoke and/or stun/flash) grenades can be fired to stun, disperse and attack ground troops. The grenades also function as simple depth charges when on the water (detonate at a depth of about 300 to 400 feet/91 to 122 m below the robot).

Primary Purpose: Close-range anti-personnel and riot control.

Grenade Type: Canister style grenades — usually no mega-damage.

Stun/flash grenades are designed to disorient and confuse terrorists or criminals who are holding hostages in confined places. The flash, burning sparks and smoke should blind and startle any character without environmental armor and shielded visor. Victims of the stun/flash grenade are −8 to strike, parry and dodge, −1 on initiative and lose one melee attack/action for the next 1D4 melee rounds (15 to 60 seconds). Even those in armor should be momentarily distracted for 1D4 seconds and lose initiative.

Tear gas grenades release a gas that will instantly affect all characters without gas masks or environmental body armor. The eyes burn, sting and water profusely, making seeing clearly impossible. The gas also makes breathing difficult and irritates exposed skin. The effects last for 3D4 minutes. The 25 foot (7.6 m) cloud dissipates in about five minutes unless blown away by wind in 1D4 minutes. Victims of tear gas are −10 to strike, parry and dodge, −3 on initiative and lose one melee attack/action for each of the next 1D6 + 1 melee rounds. Those in environmental armor are completely unaffected. Note: Tear gas is usually only half as effective against brodkil, gargoyles, and some of the more powerful and alien D-bees.

Smoke grenades release a thick cloud of smoke that covers a 20 foot (6 m) radius and obscures vision. Infrared cannot penetrate a smoke cloud or be used inside a smoke cloud. Those who are not protected by environmental suits or gas masks and goggles will find it difficult to breathe and are −5 to strike, parry and dodge and −1 on initiative. Attackers firing into/through the cloud are shooting wild. Note that passive nightscopes will work in a smoke cloud.

Explosive grenades: Typically fragmentation (3D6 M.D. with a 30 ft/9 m blast radius) or plasma (5D6 M.D. with a 12 ft/3.6 m blast radius), but any type can be used.

Mega-Damage: Varies with grenade type.

Range: 35 foot (10.7 m) minimum to 250 feet (76 m) maximum.

Rate of Fire: One at a time or a volley of two or four.

Payload: A total of 80 grenades; 40 in each arm.

2. Mini-Missile Launchers (2): A pair of mini-missile launchers are mounted above each of the shoulders. Each can rotate 360 degrees.

Primary Purpose: Anti-Gargoyle, Anti-Aircraft

Secondary Purpose: Defense

Missile Type: Any mini-missile can be used; fragmentation (5D6 M.D.), armor piercing (1D4 × 10 M.D.), plasma (1D6 × 10 M.D.), smoke or stun/riot control.

Mega-Damage: Varies with missile type.

Range: Usually about a mile.

Rate of Fire: One at a time or in volleys of 2, 3, 6 or 12.

Payload: A total of 48 mini-missiles; 24 in each launcher.

3. Chest Laser (1): The laser's barrel head can point in all directions in a 90 degree arc.

Primary Purpose: Anti-personnel

Secondary Purpose: Defense

Mega-Damage: Laser: 3D6 M.D per blast

Rate of Fire: Equal to the number of combined hand to hand attacks of the pilot (typically 6-8).

Maximum Effective Range: Laser 2000 feet (1200 m)

Payload: Effectively unlimited.

4. Smoke-Dispenser (2): In the rear of each lower leg is a housing that can release a cloud of smoke. The smoke is typically used to create cover and to confuse the enemy.

Mega-Damage: None. Same effect as the smoke grenade described under number one.

Rate of Fire: Once per melee round.

Range: A smoke cloud appears around the robot.

Payload: 8 total smoke releases.

Hand to Hand Combat: Rather than use a weapon, the pilot can engage in mega-damage hand to hand combat.

Bonuses & Damage from the TC-R3 Missileer

Restrained Punch — 5D6 S.D.C.

Full Strength Punch — 1D6 M.D.

Power Punch — 2D6 M.D. (counts as two attacks)

Crush, Pry or Tear: 1D6 M.D.

Kick — 3D6 M.D.

Leap Kick — 6D6 M.D. (counts as two attacks)

Body Flip/Throw — 1D4 M.D.

Body Block/Ram — 2D6 M.D.

+2 on initiative

+2 to strike

+2 to parry

+2 to dodge

+3 to roll with impact

+4 to pull punch

+1 melee action/attack at levels 2, 4, 8, and 12.

Note: The additional attacks and combat bonuses are in addition to those of the pilot!

Features & Sensors of note: All standard robot features, plus sonar, and rear jets (2) for use in and under water.

TC-R5 Gargoyle Stopper

The TC-R5 gargoyle stopper is the most powerful of New Tarnow's robot vehicles. It is specifically designed to engage and counter gargoyles and flying enemies. To accomplish this task, an array of missiles and a huge, long range cannon are part of it its standard armaments. Like most of Tarnow's robots, the gargoyle stopper is first made out of iron and other pure metals and magically transformed into a mega-damage powerhouse by the Tarnow Crystal. This makes the giant robot vehicle comparatively easy and inexpensive to manufacture. The most expensive part of its construction is the nuclear power supply and internal electronics. The gargoyle stopper is an air tight, lead lined, full environmental vehicle that can walk underwater or survive the rigors of outer-space. The TC-R5 and all the Tarnow robot vehicles have all the standard features of any vehicle of its kind.

Gargoyle Stopper: Part of the Tarnow Kingdom's Defense Force

Model Type: TC-R5

Class: One-man Strategic Infantry Assault Robot

Crew: One (pilot), plus one human-sized passenger can be squeezed in, but it is a tight, uncomfortable fit.

M.D.C. by Location:

    Shoulder Guards (2) — 110 each

    * Rear Sensor Array (1, middle rear) — 80

    * Hands (2) — 20 each

    Arms — (2) — 100 each

    Legs (2) — 150 each

    Feet (2) — 60 each

    * Chest Headlight (1) — 2

    * Chest Viewport (1) — 10

    * Head Searchlight (1; face) — 4

    * Head Ion Blaster (1, right side) — 15

    * Chin Laser (1, lower right) — 10

    * Forearm Rail Gun (1; left) — 50

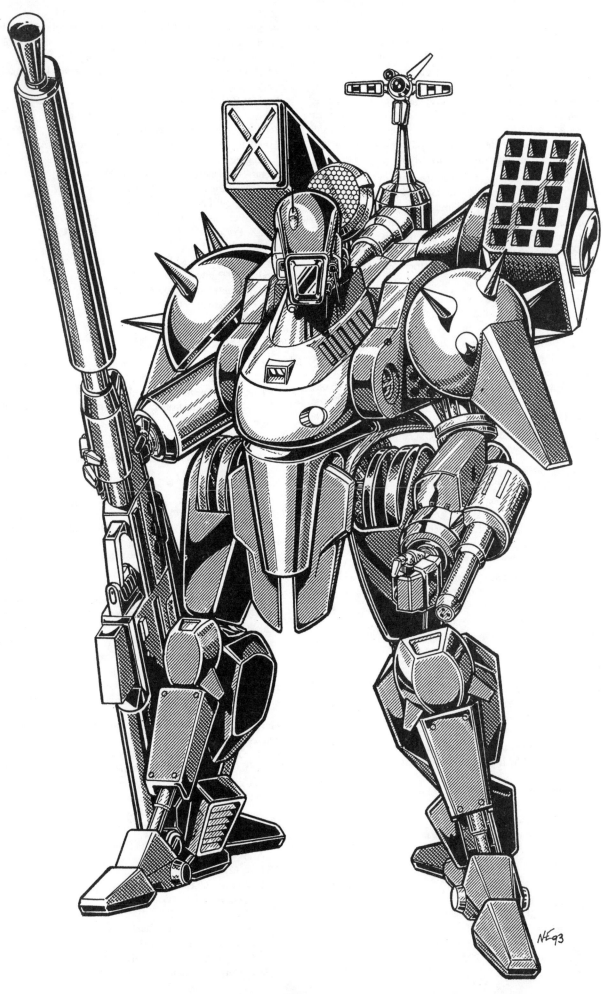

Mini-Missile Launcher (1; back) — 150
Med. Range Missile Launcher (1; back) — 100
Mega-Rifle (1; hand-held) — 150
Reinforced Pilot's Compartment — 50
** Main Body — 280

* All items marked with a single asterisk are small, difficult targets to hit. The attacker must make a called shot to strike and even then the character is −4 to hit.

Destroying the head of the robot will eliminate two of the short-range weapons, the giant searchlight and video recording capabilities. The large sensor array behind the head provides all communications and sensory capabilities. If the sensor array is destroyed the pilot loses all forms of optical enhancement, long-range radar, targeting and most sensory systems. The pilot is forced to rely on short-range radar (two miles/8 km, 24 target tracking) and his own human vision and senses. Furthermore, all bot combat bonuses to strike, parry, and dodge are reduced by half and attacks per melee by one.

**Depleting the M.D.C. of the main body will shut the bot down completely, making it useless.

Speed
Running: 60 mph (96 km) maximum. The bot can also travel underwater by walking on the river bed and has a number of maneuvering jets for additional underwater maneuvers and to rise to the surface. Maximum speed underwater is 25 mph (40 km) maximum depth is 1000 feet (305 m).
Leaping: The robot can leap up to 15 feet (4.6 m) high or 20 feet lengthwise (6 m) from a running start.
Flying: None

Statistical Data
Height: 22 feet (6.6 m) from the top of the sensor array to its toes.
Width: 13 feet (3.9 m)
Length: 8 feet (2.4 m), including the missile launch tubes.
Weight: 11 tons
Physical Strength: Equal to a P.S. 40
Cargo: None
Power System: Nuclear, average energy life is 20 years.
Black Market Cost: 20 million (construction cost is around 6 million; the most expensive of all Tarnow's creations).
Note: Current stockpile: Port Tarnow: 144, New Tarnow: 480 (three entire TC-R5 companies), another 480 in storage and approximately 640 dispatched throughout the kingdom in squads and platoons.

Weapon Systems

1. Medium-Range Missile Launcher (1): The launcher positioned behind the right shoulder is a medium-range missile launcher. It can rotate up and down 90 degrees.
Primary Purpose: Anti-Gargoyle, Anti-Aircraft
Secondary Purpose: Defense
Missile Type: Any medium-range missile can be used; typically high explosive (2D6 × 10 M.D.), armor piercing (2D4 × 10 M.D.), or plasma (2D6 × 10).
Mega-Damage: Varies with missile type.
Range: Usually about 40 miles (64 km).
Rate of Fire: One at a time or in volleys of 2, 3 or 4.
Payload: Six total

2. Mini-Missile Launcher (1): The launcher positioned behind the left shoulder is a mini-missile launcher. It can rotate up and down 360 degrees.
Primary Purpose: Anti-Gargoyle, Anti-Aircraft
Secondary Purpose: Defense
Missile Type: Any mini-missile can be used; fragmentation (5D6 M.D.), armor piercing (1D4 × 10 M.D.), plasma (1D6 × 10 M.D.), smoke or stun/riot control.

Mega-Damage: Varies with missile type.
Range: Usually about a mile (1.6 km).
Rate of Fire: One at a time or in volleys of 2 or 3.
Payload: A total of 45 mini-missiles.

3. Head Weapons (2; ion & laser): The head is a multi-purpose system with a huge searchlight covering the face, video camera and sound recording devices on the left side of the head, a laser on the right side of the chin and an ion blaster on the side of the head where an ear might be. The chin laser can move side to side and up or down by 45 degrees. The ion gun is fixed forward and shoots in whatever direction the head is turned.
Primary Purpose: Anti-personnel
Secondary Purpose: Defense
Mega-Damage: Laser: 2D6 M.D., ion blaster 4D6 M.D., or 6D6 M.D. from a simultaneous double blast from both weapons at the same target.
Rate of Fire: Equal to the number of combined hand to hand attacks of the pilot (typically 6-8).
Maximum Effective Range: Laser: 1200 feet (365 m), ion blaster: 500 feet (152 m).
Payload: Effectively unlimited.

4. Forearm Rail Gun (1): The left arm has a triple-barrel rail gun and ammo drum; just point and fire.
Primary Purpose: Anti-Gargoyles/Giants
Secondary Purpose: Anti-Personnel
Mega-Damage: A burst is 30 rounds and inflicts 6D6 M.D.; one round does 1D4 M.D.
Maximum Effective Range: 4000 feet (1200 m)
Rate of Fire: Equal to number of combined hand to hand attacks (usually 6-8). One short 30 round burst counts as one melee attack.
Payload: 3000 round drum providing 100 bursts.
Note: The weapon can also fire DU and U-rounds but must acquire them through the NGR or the black market, which is difficult.

5. Concealed Shoulder Grenade Launchers (2): Under the shoulder guard on each arm is a grenade launcher. The pilot need only to raise the arm slightly and fire; fixed forward.
Primary Purpose: Assault
Secondary Purpose: Defense
Mega-Damage: Typically fragmentation (3D6 M.D. with a 30 ft/9 m blast radius) or plasma (5D6 M.D. with a 12 ft/3.6 m blast radius), but any type can be used.
Rate of Fire: One at a time or volley of 2, 3 or five.
Maximum Effective Range: 300 feet (91 m)
Payload: Total 20; ten in launcher.

6. A Giant-Sized Energy Rifle known as the "Mega-Rifle" fires powerful, long-range laser blasts. Other hand-held weapons can be substituted.
Primary Purpose: Anti-Gargoyle and Anti-Aircraft
Secondary Purpose: Defense
Mega-Damage: 3D6 M.D. per individual blast, 6D6 M.D. per simultaneous double pulse blast.
Rate of Fire: Equal to the number of combined hand to hand attacks of the pilot (typically 6-8).
Maximum Effective Range: 8000 feet (2438 m)
Payload: 40 total. The E-clip holds 20 charges, plus the weapon has an independent energy source that has another 20 charges and recharges at a rate of five per hour.

Hand to Hand Combat: Rather than use a weapon, the pilot can engage in mega-damage hand to hand combat.
Bonuses & Damage from the TC-R5 Gargoyle Stopper
Restrained Punch — 5D6 S.D.C.
Full Strength Punch — 1D6 M.D.
Power Punch — 2D6 M.D. (counts as two attacks)
Crush, Pry or Tear — 1D4 M.D.
Kick — 2D6 M.D.

Leap Kick — 4D6 M.D. (counts as two attacks)
Body Flip/Throw — 1D4 M.D.
Body Block/Ram — 1D6 M.D.
+4 on initiative (sensor array bonus)
+4 to strike
+3 to parry
+2 to dodge
+2 to roll with impact
+2 to pull punch
+1 melee action/attack at levels 1, 2, 6, 10 and 14.

Note: The additional attacks and combat bonuses are in addition to those of the pilot!

Sensors of note: 1. Long-Range Radar: Can identify up to 100 flying targets and simultaneously track 72 at a range of 100 miles (160 km).

2. Enhanced Aerial Targeting: Tied to radar and combat computer: +4 to strike with missiles and the mega-rifle, +2 at close range.

3. Other: Full multi-optics, long- and short-range radio and video recording, broadcasting and communications, a distress homing beacon, and all standard robot features the same as Triax or Mindwerks.

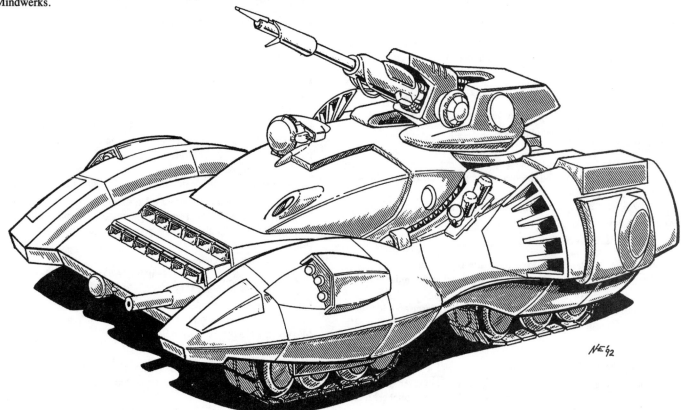

Stinger Turbo Tank

The stinger turbo tank is made from a combination of lightweight S.D.C. metals which are magically transformed into mega-damage structures. It is about as fast and easy to maneuver as a small truck. The turbo engines give that additional burst of speed whenever it is needed.

Model Type: T-322
Class: Light Assault Tank
Crew: Three: one driver, a gunner, and a commander. Can accommodate two passengers in a snug area behind the crew.
M.D.C. by Location:

   Main Laser Turret — 200
   * Mini-Missile Launchers (2) — 35 each
   * Rail Gun — 30
   * Smoke Grenade Launchers (6) — 5 each
   Turbo Thrusters (2) — 150 each

Sensor Cluster (1; mid-tank, right side) — 30
* Track Treads (2) — 80 each
Reinforced Crew Compartment — 70
** Main Body — 310

   * All items marked with a single asterisk are small, difficult targets to hit. The attacker must make a called shot to strike and even then the character is −3 to hit.

Depleting the M.D.C. of a tread will immobilize the tank until it is replaced. Replacing a tread will take 1D6×10 minutes by a trained crew (2 replacements are carried on board) or three times as long by the inexperienced. Changing the tread is only possible when the vehicle is not under attack.

   ** Depleting the M.D.C. from the main body will shut the tank down completely, rendering it useless.

Speed: Normally 65 mph (104 km) on land. When the turbo jets are activated the tank can attain a speed of 110 mph (176 km)! Buttoned

102

up, it can travel on water at speeds between 15 mph (24 km) to 30 mph (48 km) when the turbo engines are engaged!

Maximum Effective Range: 600 miles (960 km) with a full tank of gasoline or via electric motor, before needing refueling; unlimited if nuclear (10 year life).

Statistical Data:

Height: 11 feet (3.3 m)

Width: 9 feet (2.7 m)

Length: 19 feet (5.8 m)

Weight: 8 tons fully loaded!

Cargo: Minimal storage space; about four feet (1.2 m) for extra clothing, weapons, and some personal items.

Power System: Gasoline, electric or nuclear.

Black Market Cost: 2 million with gasoline engine, 2.5 million for one with an electric motor, 12+ million with nuclear engine (lifetime of 10 years).

Note: Current stockpile: Port Tarnow: 160 (one armored company), New Tarnow: 320, 288 in storage, and approximately 1920 dispatched throughout the kingdom.

Weapon Systems

1. Main Laser Turret (1): The top mounted turret can be fired by the gunner or the tank commander. The weapon consists of a heavy-duty, long range laser built into a turret that can rotate 360 degrees and has automatic targeting adjustments. The laser cannon can be raised and lowered in a 90 degree arc of fire. In vehicles without nuclear engines, the laser is powered by a rechargeable battery and has an indefinite payload.

Primary Purpose: Anti-Personnel

Secondary Purpose: Defense

Weight: 600 lbs (279 kg)

Mega-Damage: 6D6 M.D. per dual blast.

Rate of Fire: Can shoot up to six times per melee.

Effective Range: 4000 feet (1200 m)

Payload: 1000 dual blasts. Unlimited if vehicle has a nuclear engine.

2. Mini-Missile Launchers (2): A mini-missile launcher is mounted on both sides, toward the front of the tank.

Primary Purpose: Anti-Gargoyle, Anti-Aircraft

Secondary Purpose: Defense

Missile Type: Any mini-missile can be used; fragmentation (5D6 M.D.), armor piercing (1D4 × 10 M.D.), plasma (1D6 × 10 M.D.), smoke or stun/riot control.

Mega-Damage: Varies with missile type.

Range: Usually about a mile (1.6 km).

Rate of Fire: One at a time or in volleys of 2, 3, or 6.

Payload: A total of 12 mini-missiles; six in each launcher.

3. Forward Rail Gun (1): Built into the front of the tank is a rapid-fire rail gun. It is fixed forward and low to the ground because it is intended to be an anti-personnel weapon.

Primary Purpose: Anti-Personnel

Secondary Purpose: Defense

Mega-Damage: A full damage burst fires 30 rounds and inflicts 1D4 × 10 M.D. A short burst of 15 rounds does 4D6 M.D. and a single round does 1D4 M.D.

Rate of Fire: Equal to the gunner's hand to hand attacks (9 bursts).

Maximum Effective Range: 4000 feet (1200 m)

Payload: 3000 round drum and is capable of firing 100 full damage bursts (30 rounds) or 200 short bursts (15 rounds)! Reloading a drum will take about three minutes for those not trained, but a mere one minute by somebody trained in the use of power armor. A strength of 28 or higher is required to handle the drum.

4. Smoke grenades launchers (6): There are three smoke grenades and mini-launchers on each side of the tank. The grenades release a thick cloud of smoke that covers a 20 foot (6 m) radius and obscures vision. Infrared cannot penetrate a smoke cloud or be used inside a smoke cloud. Those who are not protected by environmental suits or gas masks and goggles will find it difficult to breathe and are −5 to strike, parry and dodge and −1 on initiative. Attackers firing into/through the cloud are shooting wild. Note that passive nightscopes will work in a smoke cloud.

Primary Purpose: Ground Cover

Mega-Damage: None

Range: 35 foot (10.7 m) minimum to 150 feet (46 m) maximum.

Rate of Fire: One at a time or a volley of two or three.

Payload: Six

Sensor Note: All the standard necessities are in place: short range radar (5 miles/8 km), laser targeting (+1 to strike), combat computer (+1 to strike), long range and short range radio, load speaker, radiation detector, light radiation shielding, and an environmental crew compartment with air-conditioning, heating, oxygen supply and an air purging, purification and circulation system.

Water Vessels

Sea Dart, Mini-Sub

The sea dart is a versatile multi-purpose mini-submarine. Its primary use is exploration and salvage, but it is also used for military reconnaissance, mine sweeping, sabotage, combat and military troop insertion. The large and small fan-jet propellers can tilt 180 degrees and function similarly to VTOL aircraft, giving the mini-sub greater control and versatility of movement.

Model Type: TC-B40

Class: Mini-Submarine

Crew: Two: Pilot/navigator and communications officer/sensors operator. It can also accommodate three passengers.

M.D.C. by Location:

    Torpedo Launch Tubes (3) — 25 each

    Large Thrusters (2) — 80 each

    Small Thrusters (3) — 35 each

    Mechanical Arms (2) — 70 each

    Large Claws (2) — 100 each

    Rear Fins (2) — 50 each

    Searchlights (2) — 5 each

    Reinforced Crew Compartment — 75

    ** Main Body — 225

    ** Depleting the M.D.C. of the main body will cause the boat to sink.

Speed: 70 mph (112 km) maximum; cruising speed is usually about half.

Maximum Range: Indefinite if nuclear powered (15 year life) or 800 miles (1280 km) if a fuel driven vessel; most are nuclear.

Statistical Data:

Height: 8 feet (2.4 m)

Width: 26 feet (7.9 m) from one end of the propeller arm to the other. The width of the main sub body is about six feet (1.8 m).

Length: 25 feet (7.6 m) total, including tail fins. The crew compartment is only about 10 feet (3 m) long.

Weight: 2 tons

Cargo: A small 3 × 3 foot (1 × 1 m) area.

Power System: 90% are nuclear, but some are fuel driven.

Black Market Cost: 1.5 to 4 million credits.

Weapon Systems

1. Exterior Torpedo Launch Tubes (3): Toward the rear underside of the submarine are three light torpedoes held in place by cylindrical launch tubes.

Primary Purpose: Anti-Ship and Sea Monster

Secondary Purpose: Defense

Mega-Damage: 2D4 × 10 M.D. (high explosive)

Rate of Fire: Up to three per melee round, firing one at a time or in a volley of two or three.

Effective Range: About 5 miles (8 km)

Payload: 3 total; one per launcher.

2. Mechanical Arms & Claws (2): The mechanical arms are designed mainly for salvage and exploration but can also be used for combat.

Mega-Damage: 1D6 M.D. punch or crush with claws; 2D6 M.D. power punch.

Physical Strength: Equal to a P.S. of 28.

Attacks/Actions Per Melee: Two plus those of the pilot/operator.

Hand to Hand Combat Bonuses: +2 on initiative, +3 to strike, +2 to parry, +3 to pull punch.

Effective Reach: 15 feet (4.6 km)

Special Bonuses: +3 on initiative/response, +4 to dodge, +10% on piloting skill on the successful execution of sharp turns, navigating through a tight squeeze and trick maneuvers.

Power Armor Crew: Two or more of the crew members may be clad in the sting-ray power armor and a sea star power armor unit may hitch a ride on the top or underbelly of the mini-sub.

Torpedo Speed Boat

The torpedo speed boat is a lightweight, incredibly fast, hydrofoil assault craft, designed for maneuvering down the winding Vistula river. It is used for reconnaissance, river patrol and messenger delivery, as well as for racing and pleasure. It has become a favorite among adventurers, escort services and pirates.

Model Type: TC-B20

Class: Speed Boat

Crew: Two: Pilot/navigator and communications officer/sensors operator. It can also accommodate four passengers.

M.D.C. by Location:

  Depth Charge Launchers (8) — 10 each

  Reinforced Crew Compartment — 60

  Rear Thrusters (2) — 60 each

  ** Main Body — 200

  ** Depleting the M.D.C. of the main body will cause the boat to sink.

Speed: 150 mph (240 km); although cruising speed is usually around 70 mph (112.5 km).

Maximum Range: 800 miles (1280 km); a fuel driven vessel.

Statistical Data:

Height: 10 feet (3 m)

Width: 10 feet (3 m)

Length: 35 feet (10.5 m)

Weight: 2 tons

Cargo: A small 6 × 8 foot (1.8 × 2.4 m) area.

Power System: Liquid fuel hydrofoil

Black Market Cost: 400,000 to 500,000 credits not counting the depth charges.

Weapon Systems

1. 14mm Machinegun or Laser Gun: A heavy dual machinegun loaded with explosive bullets is standard issue and can be mounted on the front or back of the boat. The main section of the gun is protected by a small metal shield. The gun is for defense to fight off pirates and power armor raiders. It can also be used to detonate enemy torpedoes. A laser can be substituted.

Primary Purpose: Anti-Vehicle and Anti-Personnel
Secondary Purpose: Defense
Mega-Damage: The machinegun: Fires 20 round bursts and does 4D6 M.D. per burst. The laser: 3D6 M.D. per blast.
Rate of Fire: Machinegun: Four bursts per melee. Laser: Equal to the gunner's hand to hand attacks per melee.
Effective Range: Machinegun: 2000 feet (610 m) or laser: 4000 feet (1200 m)
Payload: Machinegun: 2000 rounds (that's 100 bursts). Laser: 50 blasts (it takes two melee rounds to replace an energy drum).

2. **Depth Charge Launchers (8):** This weapon is used against vessels and monsters submerged under the waves or pursuit ships. A depth charge is basically a bomb that is dropped into the water, sinks and detonates when it reaches a particular depth or hits an object.

Maximum range/depth: 2000 feet (610 m) deep — automatically explodes at 2000 feet (or any depth between 200 and 2000 feet/61-610 m); damage: 2D4 × 10 M.D. (HE; high explosive); cost: 4500 credits each.

Primary Purpose: Anti-Submarine and Anti-Pursuit Ship
Secondary Purpose: Anti-Sea Monster
Mega-Damage: 2D4 × 10 M.D. per each explosive canister.
Rate of Fire: One at a time or volleys of two. A volley can be fired three times per melee round.
Effective Range: 2000 foot (610 m) maximum depth.
Payload: 8; one per launcher

3. **Special Bonuses:** +2 on initiative/response, +4 to dodge, +10% on piloting skill on the successful execution of sharp turns and trick maneuvers.

Lightning Hydrofoil Gun Ship

The lightning gun boat is a fast combat vessel used to patrol the Vistula River, protect city ports, and escort cargo ships. It uses hydrofoil propulsion for great speed and is ideal as a Coast Guard ship to deter pirates, invaders, monsters and smugglers. The boat is also well-armed, with a complement of missiles, torpedoes and long-range laser turrets. If the people of Tarnow know about anything, it's ship building.

Model Type: TC-B30
Class: Patrol Boat and Gun Ship
Crew: 7; The captain, one navigator, one communications tech, three gunners and a power armor sailor. The boat can also accommodate six additional crewmen (half are probably in sting-ray power armor) or passengers below deck.

In an emergency, the ship can be run with as few as three crew members, but only a maximum of two weapon systems can be operated and the short-handed crew is −2 on initiative and −1 to strike and dodge.

M.D.C. by Location:
Mini-Missile Launchers (4; sides) — 50 each
Depth Charge Launchers (2 bays, rear) — 55 each
Heavy Laser Turrets (3) — 150 each
Main Body: Bow/Forward Torpedo Section (2, forked) — 130 each
**Main Body: Stern/Back Section — 370

** Depleting the M.D.C. of the main body of the stern will cause the ship to sink in 1D4 minutes. Inflatable rafts (enough for twice the maximum crew) are stored in special compartments in the ship.

Destroying one of the bow appendages will reduce speed by 25% and maneuvering bonuses by half. Destroying both bow sections reduces speed by half, eliminates all maneuvering bonuses and the boat will sink in 1D4 hours.

Speed: 90 mph (144 km); cruising speed is about half.

Statistical Data:

Height: 15 feet (4.6 m)

Width: 15 feet (4.6 m)

Length: 72 feet (22 m)

Weight: 20 tons

Cargo: One 6 × 8 foot (1.8 × 2.4 m) cabin and a weapons locker containing 13 energy rifles, 24 signal flares, seven flotation vests, and a portable long-range radio with a flotation device.

Power System: Nuclear (15 year life) or liquid fuel driven (700 mile/1120 km range).

Black Market Cost: 10 to 20 million credits for a new, undamaged ship with all weapons and accessories. Does not include crew.

Weapon Systems

1. Mini-Missile Launcher (4): The two long, tubular shapes on each side of the stern are mini-missile launchers.

Primary Purpose: Anti-Ship

Secondary Purpose: Anti-Aircraft and Defense

Mega-Damage: Varies with missile type.

Rate of Fire: One at a time or volleys of two or four. Once the launcher is empty, it must be reloaded from the cargo hold, which requires two trained crewmen and takes five minutes to load a single tube.

Effective Range: About one mile (1.6 km)

Payload: 32 total; eight in each launch tube. The small cargo area can hold another 32 missiles in storage.

2. Torpedo Tubes (2): The gun ship also has twin torpedo launch tubes in each of the bow sections. A common tactic against a single foe consists of launching a combined torpedo and missile attack, trying to overwhelm the target's defenses through saturation.

Primary Purpose: Anti-Ship

Secondary Purpose: Anti-Sea Monster

Mega-Damage: 3D4 × 10 M.D. (high explosive) or 2D6 × 10 M.D. (Plasma).

Rate of Fire: Two attacks per melee round, firing one at a time or two pairs of torpedoes.

Effective Range: About 10 miles (16 km)

Payload: 12 total; six torpedoes per each launcher.

3. Depth Charge Launchers (2): This weapon is used against underwater submarines and monsters.

Primary Purpose: Anti-Ship

Secondary Purpose: Anti-Sea Monster

Mega-Damage: 2D4 × 10 M.D. — explosive canisters.

Rate of Fire: One at a time or volleys of two. A single depth charge or a pair can be launched three times per melee round.

Effective Range: 2000 foot (610 m) maximum depth.

Payload: 48 total; 24 depth charges for each launch bay.

4. **Heavy, Long-Range Laser Turrets (3):** One turret is located in the stern of the ship, while two others face the bow. Each turret can rotate 360 degrees and can be raised and lowered in a 90 degree arc of fire. Rail guns can be substituted.

Primary Purpose: Anti-Aircraft and Defense

Secondary Purpose: Anti-Ship

Mega-Damage: 4D6 per single blast or $8 + 1D4 \times 10$ M.D. per standard dual blast.

Rate of Fire: Equal to the melee round attacks of the gunner.

Effective Range: 4000 feet (1200 m)

Payload: Effectively unlimited

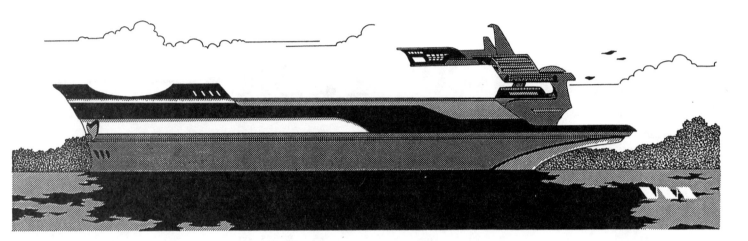

Walesa Cargo Ship

The Walesa class cargo ship is a sleek, reliable cargo hauler designed to operate on the ocean and in the considerably more shallow waters of the Vistula river.

Model Type: TC-B100

Class: Cargo Transport

Crew: Typically 25-50: Captain, first officer, two chief officers (in charge of navigation, sensors, engineering and weapon systems respectively), two medical officers, three communication technicians, 6 engineers/mechanics, a cook and two assistant cooks, and seamen. The ship can be piloted by a skeleton crew of eight, but at half efficiency.

Troop Capacity: The cargo ship typically has two sea stars and a dozen sting-ray power armor suits. In the capacity as a troop carrier the ship can carry a full company of 160 men or power armor troops and 30 tons of additional equipment. The inclusion of robots or vehicles will reduce the area available for troops.

Cargo Capacity: 110 tons

M.D.C. by Location:

  Bridge & Communications (rear) — 200
  Giant Rail Crane (1) — 500
  Missile Launchers (2) — 150 each
  Depth Charge Launchers (2) — 50 each
  * Main Body — 2600

  * Depleting the M.D.C. of the main body will cause the ship to sink in 4D6 minutes. Inflatable rafts (enough for twice the maximum crew) are stored in special compartments on the ship.

Speed: 40 mph (64 km)

Statistical Data:

Height: 50 feet (15 m)

Width: 40 feet (12 m)

Length: 150 feet (45.7 m)

Weight: 300 tons

Power System: Nuclear, with an average life of 20 years.

Black Market Cost: 70 to 80 million credits.

Weapon Systems

1. **Missile Launchers (2):** Two medium-range missile launchers are located in the stern of the ship. They are the main weapon systems of the vessel and generally intended for defensive purposes only. These auto-loading missile turrets can fire off their entire payload in a couple of minutes. The launchers are controlled from the bridge, sometimes by a single gunner/operator.

Primary Purpose: Anti-Ship and Anti-Aircraft.

Secondary Purpose: Defense

Mega-Damage: Varies with missile type. Any medium-range missile can be used.

Rate of Fire: One at a time or volleys of two.

Effective Range: 50 miles (80 km) depending on type.

Payload: 20 total; each launcher has an auto-loading magazine that holds 10 missiles. The cargo hold may have additional missiles in storage.

2. **Depth Charge Launchers (2):** A depth charge launcher is located at opposite ends of the ship.

Primary Purpose: Defense and Anti-Sea Monster

Mega-Damage: $2D4 \times 10$ M.D. — explosive canisters.

Rate of Fire: One at a time or volleys of two as often as three times per melee round.

Effective Range: Up to 2000 foot (610 m) depth

Payload: 40 total; 20 depth charges in each launcher.

3. **Additional Weapon Systems can be added:** These can include four to six laser or rail gun turrets, mini-missile launchers, power armor troops, helicopters, and so on.

4. **Power Armor Crew:** Several crew members may use the sting-ray power armor and 1D4 sea star power armor units and/or $1D4 + 1$ TC-R3 or R2 robots are typically part of the ship's resources.

Common Vehicles

About 40% of the conventional looking vehicles in the Tarnow Kingdom are mega-damage structures; motorcycles (100 M.D.C.), automobiles (300 to 650 M.D.C.), jeeps (400 M.D.C.), trucks (500 to 1200 M.D.C. depending on the size and building materials), and small boats (100 to 300 M.D.C.).

Ancient Hand Held Weapons

The Tarnow Crystal can also turn ordinary swords, knives and other metal weapons into mega-damage structures. This means the item is close to unbreakable, stays sharper longer, and can be used against other M.D.C. structures provided the user is strong enough.

Fortifications

Mega-damage walls and bunkers have become a major part of New Tarnow and Port Tarnow's defenses. These defenses can include solid walls of mega-damage iron (about 200 M.D.C. per 10 foot/3 m sq area), concrete with reinforced mega-damage iron, copper or nickel beams and fibers (75 M.D.C. per 10 foot/3 m area), mega-damage plating (50 to 100 M.D.C. per 10 foot/3 m area) and similar.

Experience Tables

Azverkan Knight & Ugakwa Explorer
1 0,000-2,150
2 2,151-4,300
3 4,301-8,600
4 8,601-18,600
5 18,601-26,600
6 26,601-36,600
7 36,601-54,600
8 54,601-75,600
9 75,601-99,600
10 99,601-135,600
11 135,601-185,600
12 185,601-240,600
13 240,601-290,600
14 290,601-343,600
15 343,601-423,600

Mindwerks Cyborg Standard Crazy
1 0,000-2,140
2 2,141-4,280
3 4,281-8,560
4 8,561-17,520
5 17,521-25,520
6 25,521-35,520
7 35,521-50,520
8 50,521-71,000
9 71,001-96,000
10 96,001-131,200
11 131,201-181,300
12 181,301-231,400
13 231,401-281,500
14 281,501-341,600
15 341,601-401,700

Ecto-Traveler & Lycanmorph
1 0,000-2,500
2 2,501-5,000
3 5,001-10,000
4 10,001-20,000
5 20,001-30,000
6 30,001-50,000
7 50,001-80,000
8 80,001-120,000
9 120,001-160,000
10 160,001-190,000
11 190,001-240,000
12 240,001-300,000
13 300,001-370,000
14 370,001-440,000
15 440,001-510,000

Monster Brodkil & Srrynn Cannibal
1 0,000-2,250
2 2,251-4,400
3 4,401-8,800
4 8,801-17,600
5 17,601-24,000
6 25,001-35,000
7 35,001-50,500
8 50,501-72,500
9 72,501-98,500
10 98,501-140,500
11 140,501-200,500
12 200,501-250,500
13 250,501-300,500
14 300,501-400,500
15 400,401-500,000

Null Psyborg, Psi-Bloodhound, & Tri-Wolf
1 0,000-2,100
2 2,101-4,200
3 4,201-8,400
4 8,401-16,800
5 16,801-25,000
6 25,001-35,000
7 35,001-50,000
8 50,001-70,000
9 70,001-95,000
10 95,001-130,000
11 130,001-180,000
12 180,001-234,000
13 234,001-285,000
14 285,001-345,000
15 345,001-410,000

Psynetic Crazy
1 0,000-2,250
2 2,251-4,400
3 4,401-8,800
4 8,801-17,600
5 17,601-24,000
6 25,001-35,000
7 35,001-50,500
8 50,501-72,500
9 72,501-98,500
10 98,501-140,500
11 140,501-200,500
12 200,501-250,500
13 250,501-300,500
14 300,501-400,500
15 400,401-500,000

Simvan & Seeker
1 0,000-1,925
2 1,926-3,850
3 3,851-7,450
4 7,451-15,000
5 15,001-21,500
6 21,501-31,500
7 30,501-41,500
8 41,501-54,000
9 54,001-75,000
10 75,001-105,000
11 105,001-140,000
12 140,001-190,000
13 190,001-240,000
14 240,001-300,000
15 300,001-350,000

Other O.C.C.s & R.C.C.s

Characters from the **Rifts RPG** and **Rifts Worldbooks** like the True Atlantean, druid, temporal raider, knight, crazy, line walker, technowizard, wilderness scout, mind melter, dragon and others can all be used in the European setting. See the appropiate **Rifts RPG books** for the experience tables and additional data about these characters.

The New German Republic

DENMARK

BALTIC SEA

NORTH SEA

RUINS OF HAMBURG

THE NEW GERMAN REPUBLIC

RUINS OF BERLIN

POLAND

HOLAND

MUNSTER

ESSEN

DORTMUND

HAGEN

HANNOVER

DUSSELDORF

KOLN

BONN

RHINE

DRESDEN

BELGIUM

FRANKFURT-AM-MAIN

CZECHOSLOVAKIA

SAARBRUCKEN

HEIDELBERG

FURTH

NURNBERG

DANUBE

FRANCE

NORTH BADEN

BLACK FOREST

BIBERACH

MEMMINGEN

MUNICH

FREIBURG

TREE OF DARKNESS

RAVENSBURG

WANGEN

LAKE CONSTANCE

SWITZERLAND

ZURICH RUINS

AUSTRIA

0   50   100 MILES

0   80   160 km

BAVARIAN ALPS

SWISS ALPS

109

The Nations of Human Kind

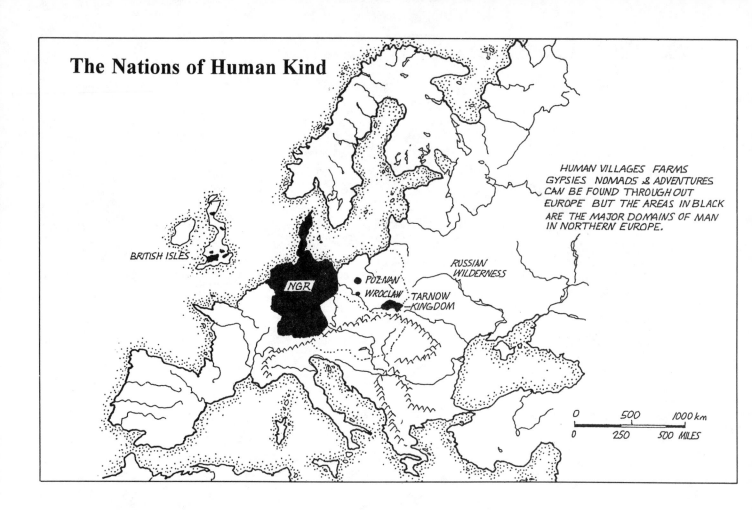

HUMAN VILLAGES FARMS
GYPSIES NOMADS & ADVENTURES
CAN BE FOUND THROUGHOUT
EUROPE BUT THE AREAS IN BLACK
ARE THE MAJOR DOMAINS OF MAN
IN NORTHERN EUROPE.

BRITISH ISLES

NGR

● POZNAN
● WROCLAW

TARNOW
KINGDOM

RUSSIAN
WILDERNESS

0   500   1000 km
0   250   500 MILES

Gargoyle & Brodkil Empires

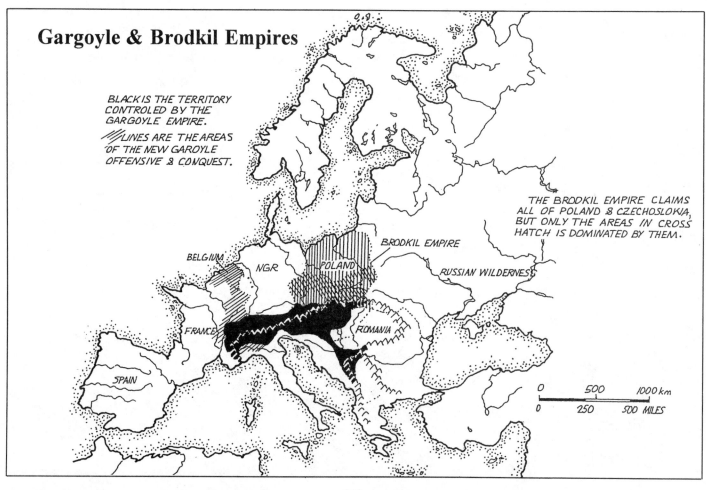

BLACK IS THE TERRITORY
CONTROLED BY THE
GARGOYLE EMPIRE.

/// LINES ARE THE AREAS
OF THE NEW GAROYLE
OFFENSIVE & CONQUEST.

THE BRODKIL EMPIRE CLAIMS
ALL OF POLAND & CZECHOSLOWA,
BUT ONLY THE AREAS IN CROSS
HATCH IS DOMINATED BY THEM.

BELGIUM

NGR

POLAND

BRODKIL EMPIRE

RUSSIAN WILDERNESS

FRANCE

ROMANIA

SPAIN

0   500   1000 km
0   250   500 MILES

Detail Map of Black Forest Region

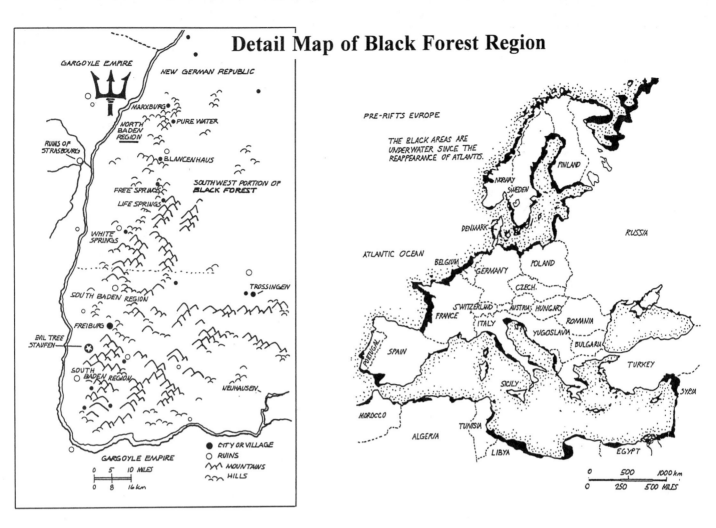

Detail Map of Black Forest Region

GARGOYLE EMPIRE

NEW GERMAN REPUBLIC

MARXBURG

PURE WATER

NORTH BADEN REGION

RUINS OF STRASBOURG

BLANCENHAUS

FREE SPRINGS

SOUTHWEST PORTION OF BLACK FOREST

LIFE SPRINGS

WHITE SPRINGS

SOUTH BADEN REGION

TROSSINGEN

FREIBURG

EVIL TREE STAUFEN

SOUTH BADEN REGION

NEUHAUSEN

GARGOYLE EMPIRE

0   5   10 MILES
0   8   16 km

● CITY OR VILLAGE
○ RUINS
〰 MOUNTAINS
⌃ HILLS

PRE-RIFTS EUROPE

THE BLACK AREAS ARE UNDERWATER SINCE THE REAPPEARANCE OF ATLANTIS.

FINLAND

NORWAY

SWEDEN

DENMARK

RUSSIA

ATLANTIC OCEAN

BELGIUM

GERMANY

POLAND

FRANCE

SWITZERLAND

AUSTRIA   HUNGARY

ITALY

ROMANIA

PORTUGAL

SPAIN

YUGOSLAVIA

BULGARIA

TURKEY

SICILY

SYRIA

MOROCCO

TUNISIA

EGYPT

ALGERIA

LIBYA

0   500   1000 km
0   250   500 MILES

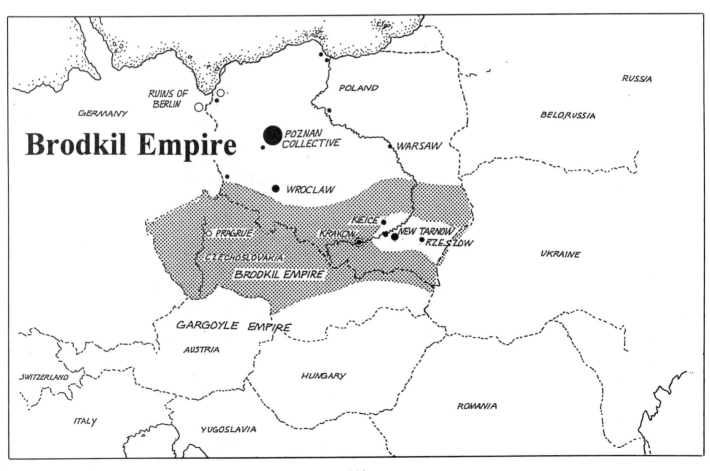

Brodkil Empire

RUINS OF BERLIN

GERMANY

POLAND

RUSSIA

BELORUSSIA

POZNAN COLLECTIVE

WARSAW

WROCLAW

KEICE

PRAGUE

NEW TARNOW

KRAKOW

RZESZOW

CZECHOSLOVAKIA

BRODKIL EMPIRE

UKRAINE

GARGOYLE EMPIRE

AUSTRIA

SWITZERLAND

HUNGARY

ITALY

YUGOSLAVIA

ROMANIA

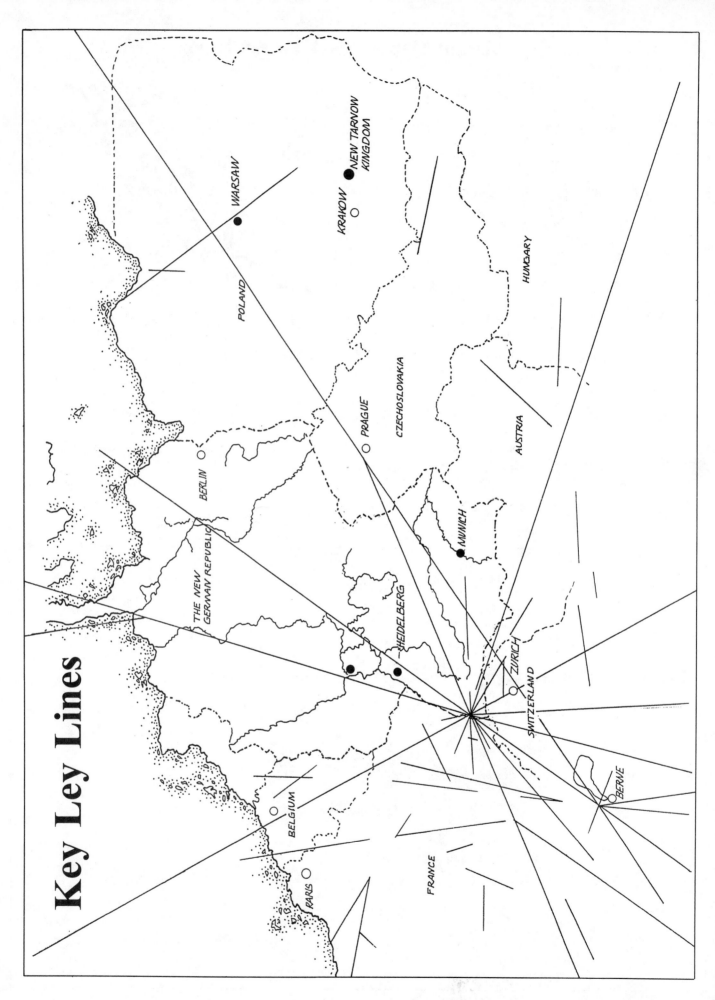

Key Ley Lines

WARSAW

POLAND

KRAKOW

NEW TARNOW
KINGDOM

HUNGARY

PRAGUE

CZECHOSLOVAKIA

AUSTRIA

BERLIN

THE NEW
GERMAN REPUBLIC

MUNICH

HEIDELBERG

ZURICH

SWITZERLAND

BERNE

BELGIUM

FRANCE

PARIS